# Eat Up Slim Down!

## Annual Recipes ✳ 2010

200 Simply Delicious Dishes for Permanent Weight Loss

From the Editors of *Prevention*

RODALE

*In all Rodale cookbooks, our mission is to provide delicious and nutritious recipes. Our recipes also meet the standards of the Rodale Test Kitchen for dependability, ease, practicality, and, most of all, great taste. To give us your comments, call (800) 848-4735.*

This book is intended as a reference volume only, not as a medical manual. The foods discussed and information and recipes presented here are designed to help you make informed decisions about your diet and health. It is not intended as a substitute for any treatment that may have been prescribed by your doctor. Keep in mind that nutitional needs vary from person to person, depending on age, sex, health status, and total diet. If you suspect that you have a medical problem, we urge you to seek competent medical care.

Mention of specific companies, organizations, or authorities in this book does not imply endorsement by the author or publisher, nor does mention of specific companies, organizations, or authorities imply their endorsement of this book, its author, or the publisher.

Internet addresses and telephone numbers were accurate at the time this book went to press.

*Eat Up Slim Down* and *Prevention* are registered trademarks of Rodale Inc.

Portions of this book have been adapted from material that previously appeared in *Prevention* magazine.

Printed in the United States of America
Rodale Inc. makes every effort to use acid-free ⊗, recycled paper ♻.

Cover and interior design by Barbara Reyes
Interior photography credits appear on page 358.
Front cover recipe: Chocolate Lava Cakes, page 280
Back cover recipes: Grilled Pork Tenderloin Tacos with Corn and Black Bean Salsa, page 140; Chocolate Waffle Cookies, page 250; Fancy Fruit Tart, page 294; and Apple Sausage Penne, page 149

ISBN-13 978–1–60529–713–2
ISBN-10 1–60529–713–5

2  4  6  8  10  9  7  5  3  1  hardcover

**We inspire and enable people to improve their lives and the world around them**
For more of our products visit **rodalestore.com** or call 800-848-4735

## SPECIAL THANKS

In grateful appreciation to all the contestants in the many *Prevention* recipe contests, we would like to thank all the readers of *Prevention* magazine and www.prevention.com who were kind enough to share their delicious recipes, clever tips, and inspiring stories of weight loss. We salute you and wish you continued success.

And sincere, heartfelt thanks to the five weight loss winners who shared their stories with us in personal profiles: Melissa Benavides, Karen Brennan, Carol Cuccarese, Ramani Durvasula, and Stacy Zandee.

# Contents

# Contributors

This book includes many of the delicious and creative recipes sent to us by weight loss and health winners across the United States and beyond. The number of recipes we received was so great it was a difficult task to choose which ones appear here. But after a careful selection process and many long hours in our test kitchen, we managed to whittle it down. Here are this year's recipe contributors. We salute their innovative efforts in the kitchen and hope you'll enjoy using their recipes to reach your own weight loss goals.

| NAME AND RESIDENCE | RECIPE | PG |
|---|---|---|
| Kris Adams, Westhampton, New Jersey | Breakfast Bowl-of-Oatmeal Cookies | 60 |
| Geneva Alexander, Riverdale, Illinois | Vegetable Ragout | 225 |
| Michelle Anderson, Eagle, Idaho | Salmon and Mango Wraps | 168 |
| Virginia Anthony, Blowing Rock, North Carolina | Fish en Papillote | 169 |
| | Maple-Rum Strawberries with Vanilla Frozen Yogurt | 306 |
| Pamela Beach, Dearborn, Michigan | Jicama and Carrot Salad | 94 |
| Terry Bedwell, Terre Haute, Indiana | Peanut Butter Pie | 287 |
| Taliena Beer, Brookings, Oregon | Blueberry Yogurt Parfait | 257 |
| Judi Berman-Yamada, Portland, Oregon | Pineapple Cream Cheese Pudding with Blueberries | 67 |
| | Feta-Walnut Stuffed Cucumbers | 100 |
| Mary Bilyeu, Ann Arbor, Michigan | Dijon Chicken Patties with Cider Mashed Sweet Potatoes | 162 |
| | Curried Chickpeas and Rice | 180 |
| Sally Blades, Lutes Mountain, New Brunswick | Caramel Applesauce Pie | 286 |
| Abigail Bradshaw, Meridian, Idaho | Pumpkin Zucchini Spice Bread | 79 |
| Laura Breck, Baltimore, Maryland | Chicken Sausage Minestrone | 112 |
| Yolanda Bridges, Bronx, New York | Strawberry Soy-Fu Smoothie | 82 |
| | Peanutty Treats | 252 |
| Bernadette Cason, Seffner, Florida | Date Breakfast Pudding | 59 |
| Jennifer Chung, Sarasota, Florida | Fancy Fruit Tart | 294 |
| Anne Cilio, Apopka, Florida | Fruit "Sherbet" | 316 |
| Marla Clark, Moriarty, New Mexico | Grilled Steak with Cilantro Pesto | 128 |
| | Navajo Tacos | 133 |
| | Pescado Con Salsa Roja | 191 |
| | Salmon with Red Salsa | 167 |
| | Wheat Berry–Sweet Potato Bake | 201 |
| Linda Cochran, Austell, Georgia | Blender Ice Cream | 259 |

Contributors

# Introduction

**We admit it:** We can't wait to make our selections for each new edition of *Eat Up Slim Down Annual Recipes*. After all, we get to do all of the taste-testing! And every year, our readers seem to outdo themselves with their inspired culinary creations.

The 2010 edition is no exception, with 200 recipes handpicked just for you. Some were sent to us by readers; others are favorites culled from the pages of Prevention. We've counted the calories, carbs, proteins, and fats for you, so you can seamlessly slip these dishes into your eating plan. While they may be "skinny," they don't skimp on taste or satisfaction. This is diet food that your whole family will enjoy!

We've packed the first six chapters of *Eat Up Slim Down* with a sampler of essential weight-loss information and advice. Start with "The Do-It-Yourself Diet," which shows you how to take the best ideas from popular diet philosophies such as low-carb or high-fiber and make them work for you. Learn strategies for navigating restaurant menus and supermarket aisles. Meet the health food imposters; they promise to enhance weight loss and general health, but invariably don't live up to their claims.

If you can't wait to get cooking, you're welcome to skip ahead to Chapter 7, which is where you'll find the recipes. Then tomorrow you can start your day with Pecan French Toast, a Breakfast Berry "Sundae," or a grab-and-go Sweet Potato Muffin. Stave off midday cravings with a Fruit Roll-Up Snack or Roasted Mixed Nuts. Dinner can be a classic comfort food like Chicken and Dumplings or a dish with ethnic flair, like Pescado con Salsa Roja. And let's not forget dessert! You can take your pick of 41 delectable treats, including Heavenly Tiramisu and Cappuccino Cream Dessert.

As you browse the recipes, don't miss "Nutrition News to Use," highlighting key breakthroughs and noteworthy finds from the world of nutrition and weight-loss research. For example, a study from the Washington University School of Medicine points to one day of the week when we're most likely to blow our diets. Can you guess which day it is? (For the answer, turn to page 93!)

For a little extra inspiration, read "It Worked for Me," in which women recount their personal journeys to weight loss and share the secrets of their success. One woman, Ramani Durvasula, came up with the idea of buying the ingredients for her weekday lunches on the weekend. Then on Monday, she carries a bag of groceries to work with her, so she can prepare a healthy lunch each day. The before-and-after photos of Ramani and the rest of our weight-loss winners will motivate you to stay on track toward your weight-loss goals.

We hope that we've piqued your interest—and tempted your taste buds! There's more good stuff waiting; just turn the page.

—*The Editors of Prevention*

# The Do-It-Yourself Diet

**Every new diet** book promises to help you drop pounds fast—if you follow a restrictive eating plan to the letter. But most of us can't stick to these printed plans, according to recent market research. In fact, the most popular—and successful—diet today is the one we make up ourselves.

"The key is to take a few proven weight loss tricks and personalize them," says Lisa Young, PhD, a professor of nutrition at New York University. So rather than adapting your life to fit a set of rules, you adapt the rules to fit your life.

Here's a look at popular diet strategies backed by solid research and smart, practical ways to make them work for you.

## WHAT WORKS | CARBOHYDRATES

It's simple math, really: The average American eats about twice the recommended daily servings of grains (many in the form of refined flour products such as white bread, pasta, and baked goods), plus about 20 teaspoons of sugar a day (mostly from sweetened drinks). Eliminating those nutrient-wimpy simple carbohydrates cuts a big source of empty calories; skipping even just one 20-ounce cola every day saves you 17 teaspoons of sugar, 250 calories—and about 26 pounds over the course of a year!

DO IT YOUR WAY Your body needs carbohydrates for energy; what you should do is eat smaller amounts of healthier ones, says Kathy McManus, RD, director of nutrition at Brigham and Women's Hospital in Boston. Here's how:

> **Choose whole grains** They're an important source of vitamins and fiber. They also help keep your blood sugar steady between meals and your appetite in check.

> **Have one good carb with every meal and snack** You'll get the appropriate five or six servings a day. To control portions, picture your plate as a clock and limit your carbs to the space between noon and 3 pm.

> **Balance the bad carbs** If you do eat refined foods, like white bread, pair them with a food that has protein or healthy fat, like hummus. That will help nix a blood sugar spike-and-crash episode, says Cathy Nonas, RD, an assistant clinical professor at Mount Sinai School of Medicine in New York City.

When you're hungry, you want to eat. Choose foods high in water and fiber and low in calories (think salad and broth-based soup), and you can eat a lot, feel full, and still lose weight. Consuming larger portions of these foods activates stretch receptors in your stomach, which then fire off "full" signals to your brain—but you've filled up without overdoing it on calories.

DO IT YOUR WAY Add heft to every meal by reducing your portion of low-volume foods and folding in high-volume (but low-cal) ones. Fruits and vegetables, which are 80 to 95% water, are good additions, as are air-filled foods, such as puffed cereal instead of flat flakes. Try these simple swaps to fill your belly with more nutrients but far fewer calories:

> **Low volume:** Cheese and crackers
> **High volume:** 6 cups of popcorn sprinkled with Parmesan cheese

# ✳ OUTWIT THESE DIET TRAPS

The best strategies for beating five common weight loss saboteurs

| The Trap: Fancy Dinner Out | The Trap: Over-scheduled Day | The Trap: 4 pm Munchies | The Trap: Party Buffet | The Trap: Late-Night Cravings |
|---|---|---|---|---|
| **The Fix: Boost Protein + Volumize** | **The Fix: Journal + Use Meal Replacements** | **The Fix: Cut Carbs + Volumize + Boost Protein** | **The Fix: Boost Protein + Volumize** | **The Fix: Journal + Volumize** |
| Have a high-protein snack midafternoon (such as almonds and fresh fruit) to take the edge off your hunger. Then order a bowl of broth-based soup or a green salad before the meal. | The night before, plan out your day with a reverse food journal (see "Keep a Food Diary," page 5). Toss a protein bar or an apple in your bag in case plans change or you're starving with no time to buy lunch. | Skip refined carbs in favor of whole grains, such as whole wheat crackers. Bulk up your lunch with extra veggies (grape tomatoes, baby carrots) and protein (lean ham, sunflower seeds, chopped egg). | Fill at least three-quarters of your plate with low-calorie buffet standbys that are rich in fiber, water, or low-fat protein, such as shrimp cocktail, vegetables, lean meats, and fruits. | Jot down what you eat on every trip to the kitchen. If you must munch while watching TV, choose low-cal foods you can eat more of, like air-popped popcorn or a plate of cut-up veggies. |

> **Low volume:** Dried fruit and nut mix
> **High volume:** Fresh fruit, like strawberries or grapes, and ¼ cup of nuts

> **Low volume:** Rice
> **High volume:** Half the amount of rice cooked with a box of frozen veggies

## WHAT WORKS | BOOST PROTEIN

Protein can take about 4 hours to digest, while carbs take only 2; slower digestion means you feel fuller longer. Plus, protein may help jack up your metabolism: In a 2007 study from Purdue University, dieters who took in 30% of their calories from protein preserved more lean body mass while losing weight than those who ate only 18%. The more lean body mass you hold on to, the more calories you burn at rest.

**DO IT YOUR WAY** Forget the cheese and bacon of diets past; instead, add a little protein to every meal and snack, says McManus.

> **Choose healthy sources** That means proteins that have heart-healthy unsaturated fats (like salmon, nuts, and soy), not the cholesterol-boosting saturated kind (like packed into fatty cuts of beef and whole dairy products).

> **Stick to proper serving sizes** Three ounces of lean meat looks like a deck of cards, the same amount of fish is the size of a checkbook, and an ounce of cheese is the equivalent of four dice.

> **Add protein to your favorites** Combine shrimp or ground turkey with spaghetti and sauce; stir 1 ounce of walnuts into oatmeal; spread almond butter on toast before the jam.

## WHAT WORKS | REPLACE MEALS WITH BARS & SHAKES

These products make portion control a snap. "It's calorie cutting without a calculator," says Nonas. An analysis of studies from Columbia University found that women who had one to two liquid meal replacements daily lost an extra 2 pounds per month compared with other dieters who took in the same number of calories.

**DO IT YOUR WAY** Think of a bar or shake as your go-to food when you're in a pinch. Whether you use them as

# ✱ LOW-CAL LETDOWN

Are 100-calorie snack packs a part of your stay-slim repertoire? Turns out, the preportioned treats may sabotage your diet. When researchers from the Netherlands gave TV-watching students either two large bags of potato chips or several portion-controlled ones, those with the smaller bags ate twice as many chips. The scientists say people tend to eat more than one minibag as a snack. If you find yourself reaching for a second 100-calorie bag, leave the empty pack in plain sight—previous research shows that people consume less food when they can see evidence of what they've already eaten.

a meal or as a snack, look for at least 3 grams of fiber, 10 grams of protein, and 3 grams or less of saturated fat, and follow these healthy eating guidelines:

> **As a meal** Most bars and shakes have about 220 calories, so pair with either a small salad with low-fat dressing or a piece of fruit to help fill you up.

> **As a snack** Between meals, 220 calories is too much. If you have a bar late in the afternoon, for example, cut dinner by half to keep your calorie counts in check.

## WHAT WORKS : KEEP A FOOD DIARY

Journaling helps expose bad habits that may otherwise fly under the radar, so you can change them. "When you write down what you eat, you eat less," says Anne Fletcher, RD, author of *Thin for Life.* A study from Kaiser Permanente Center for Health Research showed that keeping a food diary was a better predictor of weight loss than even exercise!

DO IT YOUR WAY Beat journal boredom—and the guilt that comes with committing that chocolate chip cookie to paper—by planning your ideal eating day: Essentially, keep a "reverse" food journal where you map out your menu ahead of time and try to stick to it. Be sure to track your victories, too: Buy gold star stickers and put one in your planner for every serving of veggies. "The positive reinforcement builds confidence and motivation, and that's key to success," says McManus.

# ✳ TEST YOUR TRANS FAT SMARTS

A survey of 1,000 adults found that although trans fat awareness increased to 92% in 2007—from 84% in 2006—nearly half of respondents couldn't name even one source of these fats. Labeling laws have prompted companies to remove trans fats from products, but they still crop up in familiar fare. (Look for partially hydrogenated oil in ingredient lists, as an item can claim to have no trans fat if it contains under 0.5 grams.) Try our quiz and see how you do.

Could This Contain Trans Fats?
1. French fry
YES    NO
2. Doughnut
YES    NO
3. Stick margarine
YES    NO
4. Cookie
YES    NO
5. Vegetable shortening
YES    NO
6. Cracker
YES    NO
7. Soft tub margarine
YES    NO
8. Pastry
YES    NO
9. Potato chip
YES    NO
10. Candy
YES    NO

**ANSWERS:** All may contain artificial trans fats.

**Nabisco Grahams** Original

This product contains 6g of whole grain per serving. Nutritionists recommend consuming 48g of whole grain per day.

## Nutrition Facts

Serving Size 8 crackers (31g)
[1 serving = 2 full cracker sheets]
Servings Per Container about 13

| Amount Per Serving | |
| --- | --- |
| **Calories** 130 | Calories from Fat 25 |

| | %Daily Value * |
| --- | --- |
| **Total Fat** 3g | 5% |
| Saturated Fat 0.5g | 3% |
| Trans Fat 0g | |
| Polyunsaturated Fat 1.5g | |
| Monounsaturated Fat 0.5g | |
| **Cholesterol** 0mg | 0% |
| **Sodium** 190mg | 8% |
| **Potassium** 75mg | 2% |
| **Total Carbohydrate** 24g | 8% |
| Dietary Fiber 1g | 4% |
| Sugars 7g | |
| **Protein** 2g | |

| | | | |
| --- | --- | --- | --- |
| Vitamin A 0% | • | Vitamin C 0% | |
| Calcium 2% | • | Iron 6% | |

*Percent Daily Values are based on a 2,000 calorie diet. Your daily values may be higher or lower depending on your calorie needs:

| | | Calories: 2,000 | 2,500 |
| --- | --- | --- | --- |
| Total Fat | Less than | 65g | 80g |
| Sat Fat | Less than | 20g | 25g |
| Cholesterol | Less than | 300mg | 300mg |
| Sodium | Less than | 2,400mg | 2,400mg |
| Potassium | | 3,500mg | 3,500mg |
| Total Carbohydrate | | 300g | 375g |
| Dietary Fiber | | 25g | 30g |

INGREDIENTS: ENRICHED FLOUR (WHEAT FLOUR, NIACIN, REDUCED IRON, THIAMINE MONONITRATE (VITAMIN B1) RIBOFLAVIN (VITAMIN B2), FOLIC ACID), GRAHAM FLOUR (WHOLE GRAIN WHEAT FLOUR), SUGAR, SOYBEAN OIL, MOLASSES PRESERVED WITH SULFUR DIOXIDE, HIGH FRUCTOSE CORN SYRUP, PARTIALLY HYDROGENATED COTTONSEED OIL, LEAVENING (BAKING SODA AND/OR CALCIUM PHOSPHATE), SALT, SOY LECITHIN (EMULSIFIER).
CONTAINS: WHEAT, SULFITES, SOY.
KRAFT FOODS GLOBAL, INC.
NORTHFIELD, IL 60093-2753 USA

(KRAFT)    Kraft Foods

visit us at: nabiscoworld.com
1-800-622-4726
please have package available

# ✳ OUTSMART YOUR CRAVINGS

One minute you're innocently going about your day—the next, you're in the clutches of desire. Your object of lust: a cupcake with buttercream icing. Before you know it, you're licking frosting off your fingers. What just happened? You were clobbered by a craving. In a recent study from Tufts University, 91% of women said they experienced strong cravings. And willpower isn't the answer. These urges are fueled by feel-good brain chemicals such as dopamine that are released when you eat these types of foods, creating a rush of euphoria that your brain seeks over and over. What you need is a plan that stops this natural cycle—and helps prevent unwanted weight gain. The next time you're hit with an insatiable urge for a double-chocolate brownie, ask yourself these four questions to get to the root of the craving, then follow our expert tips tailored to tame your trigger.

**1. Am I stressed out?** When you're under pressure, your body releases the hormone cortisol, which signals your brain to seek out rewards. Comfort foods loaded with sugar and fat basically "apply the brakes" to the stress system by blunting this hormone, explains researcher Norman Pecoraro, PhD, who studies the physiology of stress at the University of California, San Francisco. When you reach for food in response to negative feelings such as anger or sadness (like potato chips after a fight with your spouse), you inadvertently create a powerful connection in your brain. Remember Pavlov's dog? It's classic brain conditioning. "The food gets coded in your memory center as a solution to an unpleasant experience or emotion," says Cynthia Bulik, PhD, author of *Runaway Eating* and director of the Eating Disorders Program at the University of North Carolina Chapel Hill. Face that same

problem again, and your brain will likely tell you, "Get the Cheetos!"
**Smart tip Choose the best distraction** "What you're really craving is to feel better," says Linda Spangle, RN, a weight loss coach in Broomfield, CO, and author of *100 Days of Weight Loss*. You've heard the trick about phoning a friend or exercising instead of eating. But "taking a solo walk won't help if you're feeling lonely," says Laurie Mintz, PhD, a professor of counseling psychology at the University of Missouri. Instead, identify your current emotion (bored, anxious, mad) by filling in these blanks: "I feel ____ because of ____." Then find an activity that releases it. If you're stressed, channeling nervous energy into a workout can help; if you're upset over a problem at the office, call a friend for advice.

**2. Have I been eating less than usual?** If you're eating fewer than

1,000 calories a day or restricting an entire food group (like carbs), you're putting your body in prime craving mode. Even just 3 days of strict dieting decreases levels of the appetite-reducing hormone leptin by 22%. Experts note that "restrained eaters"—dieters who severely limit calories or certain foods—aren't necessarily thinner than regular eaters; they're actually about 1 to 2 BMI points higher, or the equivalent of 10 to 20 pounds, as their self-imposed food rules often backfire. According to research from the University of Toronto, restrained eaters are more likely to experience cravings and to overeat the "forbidden" food when given the chance. In a study from the journal *Appetite*, women who were asked to cut carbs for 3 days reported stronger cravings and ate 44% more calories from carb-rich foods on day 4. "Making certain foods off-limits can lead to obsessing and bingeing," notes Kathy McManus, RD, director of nutrition at Brigham and Women's Hospital in Boston.

**Smart tip Don't "eat around" cravings** Trying to quell a craving with a low-cal imitation won't satisfy your brain's memory center, says Marcia Levin Pelchat, PhD, a researcher at Monell Chemical Senses Center in Philadelphia. For example, if you're craving a milkshake, yogurt won't cut it—especially if you've been depriving yourself. You may even take in more calories than if you'd just had a reasonable portion of what you wanted in the first place. Munching five crackers, a handful of popcorn, and a bag of pretzels, all in the name of trying to squash a craving for potato chips, will net you about 250 more calories than if you'd eaten a single-serving bag.

**3. Am I getting enough sleep?** In a University of Chicago study, a few sleepless nights were enough to drop levels of the hormone leptin (which signals satiety) by 18% and boost levels of ghrelin, an appetite trigger, by about 30%. Those two changes alone caused appetite to kick into overdrive, and cravings for starchy foods like cookies, potato chips, and bread jumped 45%.

**Smart tip Have some caffeine** It can help you get through the day without any high-calorie pick-me-ups. It won't solve your bigger issue of chronic sleep loss, but it's a good short-term fix.

**Smart tip Portion out a serving** You probably don't have the energy to fight it, so try this trick: Before you dig in, dole out a small amount of the food you want (on a plate) and put the rest away.

**4. Am I a creature of habit?** Seemingly innocent routines, such as eating cheese popcorn while watching TV, create powerful associations. "The brain loves routine," says Bob Maurer, PhD, author of *One Small Step Can Change Your Life*. The thought of letting go of a pattern can cause a fear response in an area of the brain called the amygdala. "Once the food hits your lips, the fear response shuts off," he says.

**Smart tip Eliminate sensory cues** Smells, sights, and sounds all act as triggers. Watch TV in your basement or bedroom so you're far away from the kitchen and the snacks.

**Smart tip Shift your focus** Australian researchers found that distracting your brain really does work. Beat a craving by diverting your attention to something visual not related to food, like e-mail.

Try this!
> Share a treat (and its calories) with a friend.

# ✳ WEIGHT LOSS UNIVERSITY

Learn the secrets behind four cutting-edge academic weight loss programs On the very campuses where students order in late-night pizza, specialized centers on the front lines of diet, exercise, and behavioral research help thousands of people drop pounds safely and effectively every year. Here, the philosophy behind four of the leading university-based weight loss programs, plus key tips that you can use to reach your own goal.

Duke University
Diet & Fitness Center
Durham, NC

## Weight Loss Philosophy
### Abandon the Strict Diet Mindset
Chronic dieters often have a "been there, done that" mentality. The first task for participants of the Duke Diet & Fitness Center program is to leave that thinking behind. For 4 weeks, dieters live near campus and meet with specialists to gain new insights about weight loss. The key—and where Duke's program differs from many diets—small, sustainable changes. Exercise specialists tailor activities to fit each person's lifestyle. Dieters learn healthful cooking techniques, go on grocery store tours, and attend "mindful eating classes."

In a 2005 study, 80% of the center's graduates reported improved quality of life, including better stamina, self-confidence, and mobility. The center's research finds that participants lose, on average, up to 5% of their body weight during the first month and 10% in the first year.

## Lessons Learned
> **Move more.** Stand up while chatting on the phone; talk to coworkers face-to-face instead of by e-mail; stretch during TV commercials.
> **Monitor your meals.** Before you sit down, make a conscious decision about how much you're going to have instead of eating until you're full.
> **Fill up on fiber.** Swap your old standbys with their whole grain equivalents—the fiber slows digestion, which keeps you fuller longer. Try multigrain or whole wheat pasta or bread.

## Real-Life Results
Susan Ray,
48, Virginia Beach, VA
**Pounds lost:** 85
**Height:** 5' 4½"
**Weight now:** 140 pounds
"At the Duke Diet & Fitness Center, I found the root cause behind my habits—I was burying my emotions in food. Once I realized that, I started taking steps toward weight loss. The nutritionists offered creative ways to include more produce in my diet. Food can be enjoyable and healthful if you use it to nourish your body instead of to bury your emotions."

University of Alabama
EatRight Program
Birmingham, AL

## Weight Loss Philosophy
### Liberate Yourself from Food
In the EatRight Optifast program, participants with 50 pounds or more to lose replace daily meals and snacks with Optifast shakes for 12 weeks. The physicians who developed EatRight believe that the extreme change frees chronic dieters from unhealthy patterns so they can consider how they've been eating—and why. Supervision is imperative before and during the program because meal-replacement diets can cause rapid weight loss and put stress on the body. After the initial 12 weeks, dieters transition back to food for 6 weeks, and then start the

EatRight Lifestyle program, a 12-week plan that favors low-calorie, high-volume foods.

In the journal *Obesity* UAB reported that 75% of graduates maintained a loss of, on average, 4 to 5% of their starting weight for longer than 2 years.

### Lessons Learned
**> Break poor eating patterns**. Replace the meal you're most likely to overeat with a healthful, preportioned frozen dinner.

**> Think sneakers, not snacks.** If you always take an afternoon cookie break, try going for a walk instead. You may learn that what you really crave is a break from your workday.

**> Fill up on soup**. Minestrone, chicken noodle, and split pea soups are EatRight foods—sip a cup before your meal to fill up on fewer calories.

### Real-Life Results
Karen Matthews,
54, Montgomery, AL
**Pounds lost:** 100
**Height:** 5' 8"
**Weight now:** 172 pounds
"The EatRight program forced me to think about why I ate when I wasn't hungry—I'd overdose on sweets when I felt sad. I learned strategies to manage my feelings. I used to vacuum when I was upset, but now I take a walk. I dropped 100 pounds and 100 points off my cholesterol in

9 months. A clean house is nice, but being thin is better!"

## University of Colorado
## Colorado Weigh, Denver, CO

**Weight Loss Philosophy**
**Portions, Exercise, and a Good Attitude** Experts at Colorado Weigh use bioelectrical impedance to measure the number of calories their participants need every day, then create individual eating plans based in part on that number. At weekly group meetings with dietitians, participants learn how to keep portions in check, and how to replace self-defeating thoughts with positive ones. Dieters are encouraged to wear pedometers and track how many steps they walk daily. This motivates them to move more, even if it means simply taking the stairs instead of the elevator. A study in the *Journal of Physical Activity and Health* found that after the first 16 weeks, participants lost about 6% of their body weight, which jumped to about 11% in the next 12 weeks.

### Lessons Learned
**> Patrol your portions.**

**> Find out your true calorie needs**. One diet does not fit all.

**> Buddy up!** Find a friend who's also trying to lose weight and exchange motivation.

**> Be a pedometer pro.** This easy-to-use gadget clocks your steps. Aim for 10,000 daily.

### Real-Life Results
Lupe Reyther,
34, Denver, CO
**Pounds lost:** 42
**Height:** 5' 4"
**Weight now:** 140 pounds
"I joined Colorado Weigh with several work colleagues. I quickly began losing 1 to 2 pounds each week. I wore a pedometer and scheduled breaks in my day to walk. Or I'd use exercise bands while I helped my daughter with her homework. When it got tough, I remembered that being healthy enough to see her grow up is worth every bit of effort!"

## University of Vermont
## Vtrim, Burlington, VT

**Weight Loss Philosophy**
**No Weight Loss Goals Necessary**
A diet program that requires you to give up the drive to lose weight seems contradictory. But the creators of Vtrim say it's better to make health your goal, then—one at a time—adjust the habits that stand in your way. For example, "I'm going to exercise 4 days a week" replaces the desire to be a size 6. Pounds come off as a side effect. Participants use food journals to keep track of every morsel of food they eat, from morning coffee to supermarket samples. At the end of each week, they meet with nutrition specialists to look for patterns in their diets and identify simple ways to cut calories.

Studies published in *Obesity*

*and Annals of Behavioral Medicine* reported that Vtrim participants can expect to lose about 20 pounds after 6 months. A year later, they'll have kept off two-thirds of the weight they lost.

### Lessons Learned

**> Identify your weak spot.** Does a spoonful of ice cream always turn into a pint? Allow yourself one serving—go out for a small cone, or buy a portion-controlled treat at the grocery store.

**> Set nonweight goals.** Aim to exercise every other day, or eat 5 cups of produce daily.

**> Review your diet each week.** Jot down everything you eat for a week, look for easy ways to shave calories (like switching to low-fat yogurt), and use those changes the next week.

### Real-Life Results
Nancy Rabinowitz,
56, Burlington, VT
**Pounds lost**: 42
**Height**: 5' 8½"
**Weight now**: 145 pounds
"Everything changed when I started Vtrim. I gave up added sugar for 4 months, which meant no sweets—my trigger foods. When I incorporated them into my diet again, I had less of an urge to overeat. Journaling kept me honest. If I wanted a steak, fine; I just had to write it down and not overdo other foods. The journals serve as a record of how far I've come."

# ✱ 10 SIMPLE RULES FOR WEIGHT LOSS

When it comes to losing weight, tried-and-true strategies work, period. Obese adults who were given a pamphlet with 10 basic rules were motivated enough to lose 4 pounds in 8 weeks. Follow them all, and you could shave off up to 900 calories a day, study authors say—enough to lose nearly 15 pounds in the same amount of time.

1. Eat your meals on a regular schedule.
2. Choose low-fat foods.
3. Wear a pedometer and walk 10,000 steps a day.
4. Pack healthy snacks.
5. Check the fat and sugar content on food labels.
6. Portion wisely and skip seconds (except vegetables).
7. Stand for 10 minutes every hour.
8. Avoid sugary drinks.
9. Turn off the television while you eat.
10. Eat at least five servings of fruits and veggies daily.

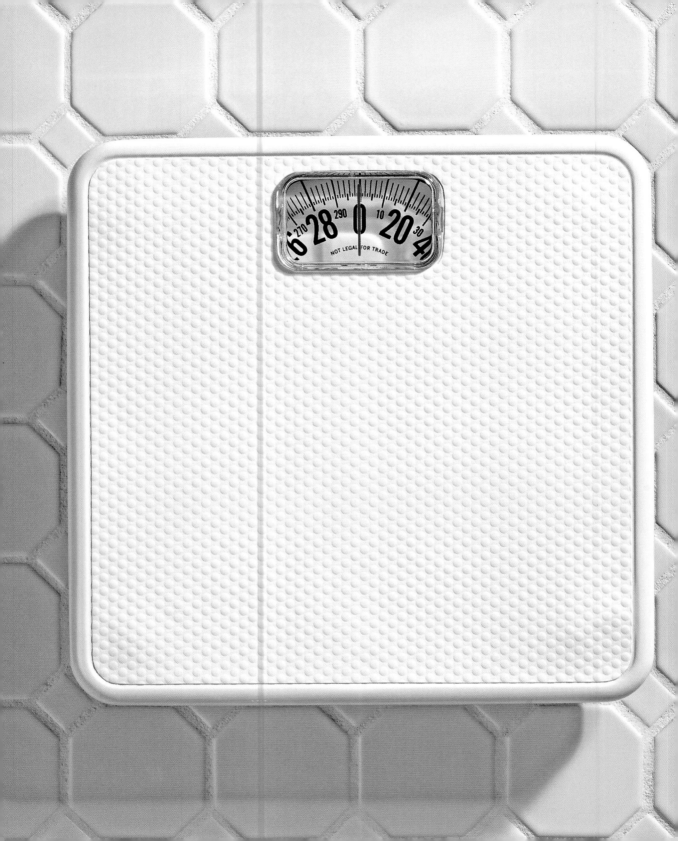

# Weight Loss for Healthy Eaters

**You snack on fruit**, check calorie counts, and start most days with a walk or swim. So when you step on that scale and the needle stays put, you wonder what the heck you're doing wrong. Even with such healthy habits, sometimes a seemingly inconsequential snack choice or a larger (but common) food myth can keep pounds in place. Take heart: A simple, slight adjustment in how you eat and think can help you reach your weight loss goal.

## HEALTHY HABIT | YOU COUNT CALORIES

The key to weight loss: Take in fewer calories than your body needs to maintain your current weight and you will drop pounds. But only 11% of Americans correctly estimate their ideal daily calorie requirements, according to a recent survey. The rest of us tend to overestimate, says Bonnie Taub-Dix, RD, a spokesperson for the American Dietetic Association, and that's what keeps you from losing weight. Let's say you assume that a target of 2,000 calories per day will allow you to get to your weight goal, but it really takes 1,800: Those extra 200 are enough to keep an additional 20 pounds on your frame.

DO IT BETTER Determine the right number of calories you need each day—and stick to it

> **Get your max intake** Go to prevention.com/caloriecalculator and plug in the weight you want to be (as well as your height, age, and activity level) to get your daily calorie allowance.

> **Divvy it up** Set limits on your meals and snacks. If 1,800 calories is your max, split it into three 500-calorie meals and one 300-calorie snack.

> **Create a custom meal** If your favorite frozen entrée has 500 calories, that's all you get. Find one for 300, however, and you can have some fresh fruit and a small salad with it.

## HEALTHY HABIT | YOU'RE CONSISTENTLY ACTIVE

Spend a few hours running errands and it feels like you've worked off some serious weight. But even between the aisle laps at the mall, hauling around shopping bags, and loading and unloading the car, you burned only about 400 calories—that's about one-tenth of a pound.

DO IT BETTER Rev your routine

Short bursts of intense activity burn more calories—and up to 36% more fat, according to a recent study published in the *Journal of Applied Physiology.* Strolling around the mall or the park for an hour works off about 150 calories; pick up the pace 1 minute out of every 5 to burn over one-third more calories (try a similar method if you bike). Swimmers can switch from freestyle or breaststroke to a more challenging crawl every few laps, or just go a little faster. Even small steps make a difference: Skip the elevator and carry your groceries up the stairs

to burn 128 more calories, or instead of hitting an automatic car wash, do it yourself and zap 204 calories.

| HEALTHY HABIT | YOU CHOOSE NUTRITIOUS FOODS |
|---|---|

What you put on your plate is important, but healthy eating is also about being mindful of how much you consume. For example, your husband has pancakes with butter and syrup for breakfast, your son grabs a doughnut, and you opt for a cup of oatmeal with a handful of walnuts, a sliced banana, and a large glass of organic blueberry juice. You may win on nutrients, but when it comes to calories you're dead last: That healthy-sounding

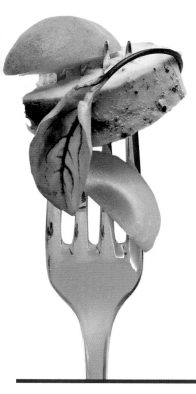

# ✳ BUFFET SECRETS OF THE NATURALLY SLIM

Serve-yourself smorgasbords with their all-you-can-eat allure are typically diet duds. But new research shows that there are fundamental differences between how overweight and healthy-weight people approach a spread. These findings—based on behaviors at a Chinese food buffet—can help you stay on track when you're faced with the urge to graze.

**Look before you eat:**

71% of normal-weight diners—versus 33% of obese people—browsed the food selections before serving themselves.

**Sit in a booth:**

38% of normal-weight diners sat in a booth instead of at a table (making it less convenient to get out), compared with 16% of obese diners.

**Pick the right chair:**

73% of normal-weight diners sat facing away from the buffet, versus 58% of obese people.

**Chew each bite**

15 times: This was the average for normal-weight people. Obese diners chewed 12 times.

meal adds up to almost 700, more than a third of your allotment for the day.

DO IT BETTER Keep portions of even healthy foods in check

The best way to know if you're eating too much is to write it down. "Even if you note it on a napkin and then throw it away, that's okay. Just the act of writing makes you more aware," says Taub-Dix. Portion control cues help, too: a baseball-size serving for chopped veggies and fruits; a golf ball for nuts and shredded cheese; a fist for rice and pasta; and a deck of cards for lean meats. Also, swap higher-calorie healthy foods for high-fiber, lower-cal varieties like these:

> **Fruit** A ½-cup serving of strawberries has 23 calories, while a medium banana has more than 100. An orange has almost half the calories of a glass of orange juice. More low-cal picks include melon and blueberries.

> **Vegetables** Per 1 cup, raw spinach has 7 calories and boiled eggplant contains 35 calories; mashed sweet potato, however, has 249.

> **Whole grains** Two full cups of air-popped popcorn (a whole grain) has about the same number of calories as three little whole wheat crackers.

| HEALTHY HABIT | YOU ORDER THE HEALTHIEST SOUNDING ITEM ON THE MENU |
| --- | --- |

Choose the turkey sandwich over pizza and you think you're being good, but again, looks can be deceiving. A turkey sandwich at Panera Bread comes on focaccia with cheese and mayo and delivers 960 calories. Two slices of pepperoni pan pizza from Pizza Hut total 560 calories. Put your sandwich in a spinach wrap instead of regular bread? It's the same difference, says Tara Gidus,

# ✳ BE A MENU GENIUS

People actually do make better food choices when they can read nutrition information on menus, according to a new study published in the *American Journal of Public Health*. Patrons at the fast-food chain Subway who read calorie counts purchased 52 fewer calories than customers who didn't see the numbers. Make that choice (or a similar one) every day and you could lose 5½ pounds over the course of a year.

See if you can match these virtuous-sounding foods . . .
1. Subway foot-long tuna sub
2. Panera Bread fresh tomato and mozzarella salad
3. Jamba Juice banana berry (original size)
4. Starbucks no-sugar-added banana nut coffee cake
5. Wendy's chicken BLT salad

. . . to their shocking calorie counts:
a. 470 calories
b. 790 calories
c. 1,060 calories
d. 890 calories
e. 450 calories

**ANSWERS:** 1c, 2d, 3e, 4a, 5b

RD, a spokesperson for the ADA. "My clients think they get more nutrients and save on calories with 'healthy bread,' but often that's not the case."

**DO IT BETTER** Look up fast-food nutrition facts before deciding what order

Many restaurants offer nutrition information, from Taco Bell to Subway. See if your favorite eatery has nutrition facts online or in the store—you may be surprised at what you see. We were when we checked out Baskin Robbins: A medium strawberry-banana smoothie has 80 more calories than a strawberry milk shake!

| HEALTHY HABIT | YOU SATISFY CRAVINGS WITH "DIET" TREATS |
| --- | --- |

When you want something sweet, all those fat-free, sugar-free options seem like a smart idea. But researchers at Cornell University found that overweight people who choose low-fat versions of snack foods rather than the regular kinds consume on average twice as many calories. "The terms fat-free or sugar-free can create a green light effect, triggering people to eat more," says Cynthia Sass, MPH, RD. But many fat-free foods have about the same number of calories (or more) as their full-fat counterparts. Case in point: One variety of oatmeal-raisin cookie has 107 calories and 9 g of sugar, and the fat-free version of the same brand has 106 calories plus 14 g of sugar.

**DO IT BETTER** Go for reasonable amounts of the real thing and savor every bite!

If you adore ice cream, have a small scoop of premium. "You won't stick to a diet that doesn't include your favorites," says David Grotto, RD, a spokesperson for the ADA. Bottom line: Life's too short for forbidden foods.

# ✱ 4 WAYS TO STOP STRESS EATING

Can't resist snacks at the office? Blame your boss. According to researchers at Emory University, when alpha female monkeys ordered around less dominant pack members, the inferior animals ate significantly more (and gained more weight) over a 2-month period than those in charge. The submissive monkeys had higher levels of cortisol, the stress hormone linked with dangerous belly fat. Here are four ways to prevent stress eating at work:

1. E-mail yourself every time you eat. Include circumstances and note how you were feeling. Review the messages every Friday and look for patterns.

2. **Phone a friend.** Instead of turning to food, call a buddy and tell her how you're feeling. Your conversation might dissuade you from heading to the kitchen.

3. **Sip green or black tea** before you reach for a snack. The drink contains theanine, an amino acid that increases levels of relaxing chemicals in the brain.

4. Join an Internet support community. Log on when a craving strikes. Try the emotional-eating forum on the Prevention Web site (prevention.com/foodtriggers).

# ✳ EAT OUT WITH EASE

From the time we were kids, we've been taught that dining out is fun. And let's face it—it really is fun. You get a multitude of delectable choices, tasty meals, desserts, cocktails and wines, time to spend with friends or family, and good conversation. But a night eating at a restaurant can be detrimental to your weight loss efforts. "When you eat out, you have no idea of the hidden oils, added carbohydrates, or quality of the nutrients you are eating, so you are behind the eight ball right away," says Francine Kaufman, MD, head of the Center for Diabetes, Endocrinology, and Metabolism at Children's Hospital Los Angeles. Plus, the portion sizes at restaurants are out of control. But you can still enjoy the occasional evening out at a bistro or a weekend diner brunch. If you plan ahead and choose wisely, you won't sacrifice your health by eating out.

**Take a course in food 101.** If you don't know the basics of nutrition, figuring out the most sensible choices on a menu can be as difficult as taking a calculus test without studying. The first thing you should do when starting a weight loss plan is to take a crash course in healthy eating. "Go to a weight loss group, an online program, follow a plan in a book, or sit down with a nutritionist; once you know about food, you can even eat at McDonald's or Burger King because you will know to order a salad or a BK Broiler," says Donna Rice, RN, CDE, past president of the American Association of Diabetes Educators. "It is all about the decisions you make you are a product of what you eat."

**Choose only one carbohydrate.** From the moment you sit down at a restaurant, you'll be tempted by simple carbohydrates—a full basket of bread and butter, oversize sides of rice and potatoes, heaping plates of pasta, and so many desserts they require a separate menu. To avoid blowing all your efforts, limit yourself to just one carb, advises Cheryl Marco, RD, CDE, a registered dietitian in the weight management program at Thomas Jefferson University in Philadelphia. If you're partial to bread, have it, but skip the rice, potato, and dessert. "If you love sweets, then have a protein [chicken, lean meat, or fish], double up on your vegetables, and save your carbohydrates for dessert—create a balance," she says.

**Buy one, get one free.** "Many meals at restaurants are 1,600 calories or more in and of themselves, and that doesn't include a beverage or dessert," says Alan Marcus, MD, a private practitioner in Laguna Hills, CA, who specializes in diabetes management and endocrinology. Turn your meal into dinner and lunch for the next day. Ask the server to wrap up half of your meal immediately, so you can't polish off your plate.

**Beware of buffets.** "Studies have shown that when people go to buffets, they eat more than they would if they were sitting down and being served," says Barry J. Goldstein, MD, PhD, director of the division of endocrinology, diabetes, and metabolic diseases at Jefferson Medical College of Thomas Jefferson University. If you do find yourself faced with an endless array of options, start by piling your plate with salad so there's very little space left for other foods. Filling up on low-calorie greens will make you less likely to overeat. A good rule of thumb: Fill half your plate with greens or vegetables, a quarter with protein, and a quarter with carbohydrates.

**Dress for success.** If you top your salad with a vinegar-based dressing, you'll be in even better shape. "Having some kind of acid, such as vinegar, with a meal slows gastric emptying and lowers the glycemic index," says Ralph Felder, MD, PhD, section chief for cardiovascular nutrition in the cardiology fellowship program at Banner Good Samaritan Medical Center in Phoenix and author of *The Bonus Years Diet.* Order or place dressing on the side so you can control how much goes on your greens.

**White out your omelet.** "If you love eggs, egg whites are a great option, and most restaurants will make egg white omelets," says Edwidge Jourdain Thomas, DrNP, assistant professor of clinical nursing at Columbia University. Not only are egg whites low in carbohydrates and cholesterol, they are high in protein and can easily be mixed with other flavorful, nutrient-rich fillers. "If you can't get past the idea of white eggs, ask the restaurant for a three-egg

omelet—one whole egg and the rest whites," she says.

**Keep the water pitcher close by.** Not only will drinking lots of water at a restaurant keep you hydrated—which is important for weight loss—it will make you full faster. "Sensors in your body let your brain know that you are full and tell you to stop eating," Thomas says. "Water helps activate those sensors."

**Say no to predinner cocktails.** "Alcohol is not your friend, calorie-wise, when you are watching your weight, and it lowers your inhibitions so you eat more," Thomas says. "If you are on medication, alcohol will compete with your liver as far as metabolism is concerned." If you want to have a drink with dinner, keep it to an absolute minimum—one if you're a woman, two if you're a man.

# ✳ COOK LIKE YOUR LIFE DEPENDED ON IT

Piling your shopping cart high with healthful staples like veggies, fish, and lean meat? Great! Now, take it to the next level. It's what you do with those fantastic foods once you bring them home that transforms them into real nutritional superstars. Take the tomato: Eat it cooked instead of raw and you'll get as much as 171% more of the cancer-fighting compound lycopene. "Even one little change in the kitchen can result in a huge health payoff," says Robin Plotkin, RD, a Dallas-based nutritionist. Follow these simple rules for cooking smarter and amp up the disease-fighting power of every meal.

## Bake tomatoes

> For: Younger skin (and cancer protection). Compared with fresh tomatoes, cooked tomatoes (and products like pasta sauce) contain more lycopene, a powerful antioxidant. Research suggests lycopene may guard the skin against damage from the sun's UV rays. Baking tomatoes makes them healthier and more versatile, adding a flavorful twist to sandwiches, salads, and pastas.

> How: Wash and dry 30 cherry or grape tomatoes and place in a small baking dish. Drizzle with 1 tablespoon olive oil. Bake at 450°F for 15 minutes.

## Roast omega-3-rich fish

> For: A slimmer waistline. Roasting a fatty fish, such as salmon, with a bit of olive oil doesn't increase its fat content, according to a study published in the *Journal of Agriculture and Food Chemistry*. When researchers fried the fish, it absorbed the olive oil, increasing fat content by about 10% (and adding unnecessary calories).

> How: Drizzle a baking dish with olive oil. Select fresh fish fillets, approximately ⅓ pound per person. Roast the fillets skin-side down in a dish in a 450°F oven for 10 minutes per inch of thickness, or until a meat thermometer reaches an internal temperature of 145°F. Properly prepared fish will flake easily with a fork

(overcooking makes it dry). Remove from the oven; serve immediately.

## Crush garlic

> For: Healthier arteries. Crushing garlic cloves—and letting them stand for up to 30 minutes before heating them—activates and preserves the garlic's heart-protecting compounds, according to a 2007 study from Argentina. Cooking uncrushed garlic for as little as 6 minutes can completely suppress its protective strength.

> How: Wash and peel the outer papery skins of a clove of garlic and trim ends. To crush: Place the clove on a cutting board and lay the flat side of a wide knife against it, pressing down firmly. For easier use in recipes, finely chop the clove, starting at one side. Crush again: Press the flat side of the knife against the chopped garlic firmly, then finely chop again. Let it rest for 30 minutes at room temperature. Scrape the crushed and chopped pieces and juice from the cutting board into recipe.

## Steam broccoli

> For: Reduced cancer risk. Steaming broccoli increases its content of glucosinolates, compounds that fight cancer; other cooking techniques, like frying, reduce them, according to new research from Parma, Italy.

> How: Clean and trim 1 pound of broccoli, cutting into florets. Bring 1 inch of water to a boil in a saucepan. Place the florets in a metal colander over boiling water. Cover and reduce the heat to medium. Cook for 6 to 7 minutes or until tender (or you can microwave on high in a covered but vented dish for that time).

## Slow-cook meat

> For: Preventing inflammation linked to diabetes and heart disease. When meats are cooked in liquid at moderate heat, they develop fewer cell-damaging compounds known as AGEs (advanced glycation end products) than when they are broiled or grilled. Researchers say that switching to "wet" cooking methods can reduce AGE intake by as much as 50%.

> How: Trim any visible fat from 1 pound of sectioned beef, pork, or poultry. Place the meat in a slow cooker. Add 1 cup of liquid (like broth). Add vegetables and seasoning. Cover and cook on high for 1 hour. Reduce the heat to low and cook for 2 to 8 hours longer (depending on the thickness and type of meat) or until the meat reaches an internal temperature of 145°F for beef, 160°F for pork, and 165°F for poultry.

# Fat-Burning Myths— Busted

**Google the word** *metabolism* and you'll find nearly 45 million results—advice on how to "speed-up," "ignite," "kick-start," and "boost" your body's fat-burning capacity. Truth is, there are probably more myths about metabolism than there are about the Loch Ness Monster and Bigfoot combined.

The reality: Your body does burn 2 to 5% fewer calories with each decade after age 40, and women tend to put on about a pound a year as a result, but these changes are not inevitable, says Matt Hickey, PhD, director of the Human Performance Clinical Research Lab at Colorado State University. Simple tweaks to your daily routine can up your calorie burn and compensate for the deficit, keeping you from succumbing to age-related weight gain. Take our quiz and learn the truth about harnessing your metabolism to keep off unwanted pounds.

## YOUR BODY BURNS MORE CALORIES DIGESTING ICE-COLD BEVERAGES AND FOODS (T/F)

**TRUE.** But before you give yourself an ice-cream head-ache, there's more. "The small difference in calories probably won't make a significant dent in your diet," explains Madelyn Fernstrom, PhD, CNS, founder and director of the UPMC Weight Management Center in Pittsburgh.

On the bright side, different studies have suggested that five or six ice-cold glasses of water could help you burn about 10 extra calories a day—equaling about 1 pound of nearly effortless weight loss each year.

TIP Although the metabolism-boosting effects are small, it can't hurt to pour no-cal drinks—water, tea, coffee—on the rocks to maximize your calorie-burning potential.

## DRINKING THE RIGHT AMOUNT OF WATER CAN HELP YOU BURN MORE CALORIES (T/F)

**TRUE.** All of your body's chemical reactions, including your metabolism, depend on water. If you are de-hydrated, you may be burning up to 2% fewer calories, according to researchers at the University of Utah who monitored the metabolic rates of 10 adults as they drank varying amounts of water per day. In the study, people who drank either eight or twelve 8-ounce glasses of water a day had higher metabolic rates than those who had only four glasses.

TIP If your urine is darker than light straw in color, you may not be drinking enough fluid to fuel your metabo-lism. Try sipping one glass before each meal and snack to help you stay hydrated.

## DIETING DROPS YOUR RESTING METABOLIC RATE, MAKING IT HARDER TO KEEP WEIGHT OFF (T/F)

**TRUE.** For every pound you lose, your resting metabolism drops by about 2 to 10 calories a day. Lose 10 pounds, and you now have to eat 20 to 100 fewer calories to maintain your trimmer physique, not factoring in exercise. However, you can prevent your metabolic rate from slipping while you get slim. One way is to lose fat but maintain muscle. You can do this by reducing calories and increasing aerobic and resistance exercise, says Hickey. Crash diets (fewer than 1,000 calories a day) may result in a higher percentage of muscle loss.

TIP Lose weight by cutting 250 calories a day and burning 250 calories per day through exercise. That will help you retain—or even gain—muscle while you lose a greater percentage of body fat.

## HOT FOODS WILL FIRE UP METABOLISM (T/F)

**TRUE.** Capsaicin, the bioactive compound that makes chile peppers exude heat, can turn your metabolism up a notch while also enhancing satiety and reducing hunger. Studies show that eating about 1 tablespoon of chopped red or green chile pepper—which is equal to 30 milligrams of capsaicin—resulted in up to a temporary 23% boost in metabolism. In another study, 0.9 gram of red pepper was given in capsule form or naturally in tomato juice before each meal. The researchers noted that the individuals reduced their total calorie intake by 10 or 16%, respectively, for 2 days after and still reported being full.

TIP Sprinkle red-pepper flakes onto pasta dishes and into chilies and stews; fresh chile peppers work well in salsas and can add a fiery flavor to many of your other dishes.

## EATING MORE PROTEIN WILL REV UP YOUR METABOLISM (T/F)

**TRUE.** Protein provides a metabolic advantage compared with fat or carbohydrates because your body uses more energy to process it. Studies show that you may burn up to twice as many calories digesting protein as carbohydrates. In a typical diet, 14% of calories come from protein. Double that (and reduce carbs to make up for the extra calories), and you can burn an additional 150 to 200 calories a day, explains Donald Layman, PhD, a professor of nutrition at the University of Illinois.

TIP To reap protein's rewards, strive for between 10 and 20 grams at each of your meals, says Hickey. Try an 8-ounce cup of low-fat plain yogurt with breakfast (about 13 grams), a ½-cup serving of hummus with lunch (about 10 grams), and a 3-ounce salmon fillet for dinner (about 17 grams).

## EATING A GRAPEFRUIT BEFORE EVERY MEAL SPEEDS METABOLISM (T/F)

**FALSE.** Grapefruit won't work miracles for your metabolism, but it can help you lose weight. Half a grapefruit before meals helped individuals lose about 4 pounds in 12 weeks, according to a study published in the Journal of Medicinal Food. The reason: Its fiber and water fill you up on fewer calories, so you eat less at your next meal.

TIP Try a juicy piece of fresh fruit—such as half a grapefruit or a tangerine—before your main course.

## LIFTING WEIGHTS BOOSTS YOUR METABOLISM MORE THAN A CARDIO WORKOUT (T/F)

**TRUE.** When you strength-train enough to add 3 pounds of muscle, you increase your calorie burn by 6 to 8%—meaning that you burn about 100 extra calories every day. Aerobic exercise, on the other hand, doesn't significantly increase your body's lean muscle mass. "The best way to gain muscle mass is to do resistance training," notes Ryan D. Andrews, RD, a certified strength-training specialist in Colorado.

TIP "You want to focus on exercises that recruit the largest muscles and use two-part movements, because they will help you build more lean mass," Andrews says. His favorites include squats, push-ups, and any exercise that combines upper- and lower-body movements. For a metabolism-boosting strength-training workout, visit prevention.com/burnfat.

## CELERY IS A "NEGATIVE CALORIE FOOD" BECAUSE DIGESTING IT USES UP MORE CALORIES THAN IT PROVIDES (T/F)

**FALSE.** The thermic effect of food does cause your body to burn up calories as it processes meals, snacks, and beverages. But this process accounts for anywhere from 0 to 30% of the calories you eat (protein, for example, takes more calories to digest than fat or carbohydrates; see page 86). A medium-size rib of celery has only about 6 calories; its TEF is approximately half a calorie. In reality, "negative calorie foods" are nothing more than wishful thinking.

# ✱ THE FORMULA FOR SMART SNACKING

Tummy rumbling between lunch and dinner? Follow this slimming tip from nutritionist Cynthia Sass, MPH, RD. The rule: Eat up to 100 calories per hour for each hour between the snack and your next meal. For example, if it's 4 pm and dinner isn't until 6, limit yourself to no more than 200 calories. Choose a high-fiber carb, such as fruit, as your base, then add healthy protein or fat to help you stay satisfied longer.

If your next meal is in . . .

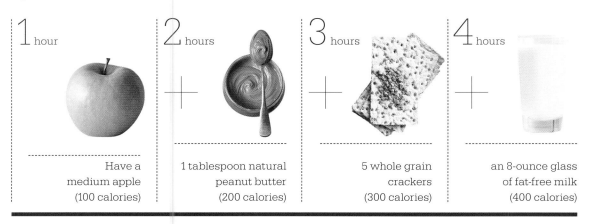

| 1 hour | 2 hours | 3 hours | 4 hours |
|---|---|---|---|
| Have a medium apple (100 calories) | 1 tablespoon natural peanut butter (200 calories) | 5 whole grain crackers (300 calories) | an 8-ounce glass of fat-free milk (400 calories) |

TIP Include celery as a low-cal but filling addition to salads and stir-fries. It is healthful: Celery has phthalides, compounds that can help reduce blood pressure.

## TEA REVS YOUR NATURAL CALORIE BURN (T/F)

**TRUE.** Catechins found in green and oolong teas can boost the body's fat-burning fire. One study of Japa-nese women compared the effects of drinking green tea, oolong tea, or water on various days. Just one large cup of oolong tea increased calorie burning by up to 10%, a boost that peaked 1½ hours later. Green tea raised metabolism by 4% for 1½ hours.

Other studies show that drinking two to four cups of green or oolong daily (about 375 to 675 milligrams of catechins) may translate into an extra 50 calories burned each day—about 5 pounds' worth in a year.

TIP Try a cup of green or oolong tea in place of your morning coffee for a dose of caffeine that will wake up your metabolism as well. Instead of milk or sweetener, add a squeeze of lemon, which may help your body absorb more catechins.

## PMS CRAVINGS ARE RELATED TO THE BOOST IN METABOLISM BEFORE YOUR PERIOD (T/F)

**TRUE.** If there is a silver lining to PMS, it's that our resting metabolic rate may increase during the part of the menstrual cycle known as the luteal phase (the day after ovulation to the first day of your period). The metabolic boost we get from being "hormonal" can equal as much as 300 calories a day—which is why our appetite increases during this phase.

TIP Keep a journal of what you eat the week before and the weeks after your period. Try to maintain your eating pattern over the course of the month so that you can take advantage of this hormone-driven calorie burn. If you give in to cravings, make sure that you keep portions in check.

# ✳ 4 MORE REASONS TO LOSE WEIGHT

The health benefits of achieving a healthy weight are well known—decreased risks of heart disease, diabetes, and some cancers—but excess weight may also be at the root of other common ailments. Lose those pounds and reap these four quality-of-life rewards:

**1. Fewer headaches.** Obese adults had up to a 40% higher likelihood of severe headaches or migraines than did healthy-weight people in a recent CDC study.

**2. Improved oral health.** As many as 52% of overweight and obese adults have gum disease, compared with 14% of normal-weight adults, reports a recent study in the *Journal of Clinical Periodontology.*

**3. Longer and deeper sleep.** Overweight adults sleep less and wake more than normal-weight counterparts, say researchers at Penn State.

**4. Brighter outlook.** Overweight and obese women were up to 31% more likely to have depression than normal-weight women, according to a recent *International Journal of Obesity* study of more than 177,000 adults.

# ✱ IS YOUR DIET MAKING YOU GAIN WEIGHT?

If you're trying to slim down, you've probably amassed a menu full of calorie-cutting tips and tricks. So it may come as a shock to learn that many of the ones you've sworn by are actually keeping you fat. "In their quest to lose weight, many women unknowingly sabotage themselves," says Elisa Zied, RD, an American Dietetic Association spokesperson. Here, five well-intentioned approaches to weight loss that can go awry, and the expert and research-proven ways to drop pounds for good.

## 1. You save your calories to splurge on a big dinner

Yes, cutting total calories leads to weight loss. But bank most of those calories for the end of the day and your hunger hormones will go haywire, making you eat more. Middle-aged men and women who ate their daily number of calories in one supersize supper produced more ghrelin, a hormone that causes hunger, than when they ate the same number of calories in three square meals, found researchers at the National Institute on Aging.

**Smarter move: Front-load your calories.** Overeating at night keeps you from being hungry in the morning, setting off a vicious cycle in which you're never interested in breakfast but always starving by dinner. The key is to rebalance your day so you don't set yourself up for an evening binge. To get your appetite back in the morning, cut your evening meal in half. Then eat a breakfast of about 450 calories such as a scrambled egg with low-fat cheese on a whole wheat English muffin with an 8-ounce glass of juice. Once your appetite adjusts, don't go more than 5 hours without another meal of roughly the same size.

## 2. You graze instead of eating regularly scheduled meals

Trouble is, eating in this manner may contribute to weight gain, according to a 2005 *American Journal of Clinical Nutrition* study. When researchers asked women to eat at regular, fixed times or to break their usual amount of food into unscheduled meals throughout the day, they made a startling discovery: The women actually burned more calories in the 3 hours after eating the regular meals than they did after the unplanned meals. They produced less insulin, too, potentially lowering their odds of insulin resistance, which is linked to weight gain and obesity. What's more, grazing instead of planning ahead can set you up to eat mindlessly, says Zied.

Smarter move: Figure out how many times a day you need to eat—everybody is different—and then stick to a schedule. "It's not great to feel starved, but it is okay to feel slightly hungry," says Zied.

## 3. You assume calories from healthy, natural foods are low

People consistently underestimate the calories in nutritious items such as yogurt, fish, and baked chicken, found researchers at Bowling Green State University who quizzed students on calorie counts. "Just because a food is healthy doesn't mean you can eat big portions," says D. Milton Stokes, MPH, RD, owner of One Source Nutrition in Stamford, CT.

**Smarter move: Count all calories.** Once you learn that $1/2$ cup of cereal can have as much as 200 calories or that there are about 220 calories in that "single-serving" bottle of OJ, you'll be more prudent about how much you consume.

## 4. You set short-term weight loss goals

The National Weight Control Registry estimates that only 20% of dieters successfully keep off lost weight for more than a year. That's because after we reach our goal, we let old eating habits creep back in. But people who win at weight loss consistently eat the same way even after they've slimmed down. In fact, the NWCR found that dieters who maintain their healthy eating habits every single day are 1½ times more likely to maintain their weight loss than those who relax their diets on the weekends.

**Smarter move: Think of healthy eating as a work in progress, not as a "diet" with a beginning and an end.** The key: making small changes you can maintain so they become long-term habits. Start by creating a list of problem areas in your diet, then tackle them one at a time. Once you've made that a habit, pat yourself on the back and move on to your next goal.

## 5. Your splurge foods are "low-fat" and "sugar-free"

Research suggests that when a food is described as a diet food, we're subconsciously primed to eat more—even if it's actually as caloric as regular food. When Cornell University researchers offered the same M&M's candies labeled either regular or low-fat to visitors at a university open house, visitors ate 28% more of the "low-fat" snacks. While less fat does not necessarily mean fewer calories, people make the assumption that it does, setting them up to overeat, say scientists.

**Smarter move: First, check food labels: So-called diet foods frequently don't save you calories.** Take low-fat chocolate chip cookies—because they've been infused with extra carbs to add flavor, you save only 3 calories per cookie. Once you have that reality check, follow the golden rule for any food: Keep close tabs on portions. Limit yourself to two small cookies, for example, or trade in a bowl of frozen yogurt for a kid's-size scoop; measure out condiments such as low-fat sour cream or low-fat ranch dressing. And remember—if you prefer the flavor of full-fat foods, you'll still lose weight if you watch your portion sizes.

# Fill Up on Fiber

**Are you ready** for a weight loss solution that helps you slim down by giving you more to eat—not less? Satisfy your stomach and increase your weight loss success with high-fiber foods. Here, essential fiber facts to get you started.

Fiber helps in two ways. First, it slows the entrance of sugar into the bloodstream, keeping blood sugar levels steady and reducing the need for the pancreas to make insulin. Research shows that high-fiber foods can reduce post-meal blood sugar levels up to 28 percent and fasting insulin levels roughly 11 percent.

Second, when bacteria ferment fiber in the colon, they release acids that enter the bloodstream and sensitize cells to insulin. When cells are more sensitive to this hormone, they sop up blood sugar better. In one study, 17 overweight or obese people who ate 31 grams of fiber a day—the amount in three servings of high-fiber cereal or two servings of barley—improved insulin sensitivity by about 8 percent.

To get the most out of a high-fiber diet, look for foods that are low on the glycemic index (GI). Low GI foods include legumes, bran, and cereals. These foods digest slowly and do not raise blood sugar as fast as high GI foods.

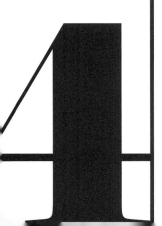

## CHOOSE THE RIGHT FOODS

Chances are, when you think of finding a food that is "fiber-rich," you probably expect to bite into something that tastes like a cardboard box. In reality, the world of fiber includes a wealth of sinfully delicious foods such as dark chocolate, guacamole, corn on the cob, popcorn, raspberries, baked potatoes, bean and beef chilies, and even pizza.

Sound good? Fiber can be so tasty you'd never know that it's great for your waistline and your health. Fiber is found in plant foods—vegetables, fruits, grains, beans and legumes, and nuts and seeds. There are two different kinds of fiber and each helps your body in its own unique way.

> **Soluble fiber = slow.** Soluble fiber got its name because it dissolves in water. It has been shown to slow digestion, slow blood sugar absorption, reduce blood sugar–related cravings and fatigue, increase a sense of full-ness after eating, reduce cholesterol, and soften stool so it's easier to pass. Foods that contain soluble fiber include oats, peas, beans, apples, citrus, carrots, and barley.

> **Insoluble fiber = incredible size.** Insoluble fiber puffs up when it's mixed with water, triggering a sense of fullness. It keeps you regular and reduces constipation-related bloating. Foods that contain insoluble fiber are fruit (with skins), bran, nuts, and vegetables.

## YOUR DAILY VEGETABLE SERVING GOAL  3+

Low in calories and rich in nutrients, vegetables provide a vital combination of fiber and water that helps you feel full. Consider three daily servings your minimum, and strive for closer to seven. Reap rewards from every bite:

> **Skip peeling whenever possible.** Raw bell peppers have more fiber than the skinless roasted type.

> **Go whole.** Eat vegetables in their most whole form. Cup for cup, fresh corn kernels will offer more fiber than an equivalent amount of corn muffins.

Branch out beyond salads. Don't rely on lettuce and salad greens to supply all of your fiber: You'd have to eat 6 pounds of lettuce to get 30 grams of fiber in a day.

> **Eat raw vegetables.** Vegetables in their natural state require more chewing than cooked ones, which makes for slower eating, so you fill up on fewer calories.

## YOUR DAILY FRUIT SERVING GOAL

Like vegetables, fruits are loaded with plenty of fiber and water to fill up your stomach so you know when to stop eating. Also, because fruit provides a wealth of antioxidants, it is critical for fighting diseases associated with excess weight. A study at the University of Navarra in Pamplona, Spain, found that women who lost weight on a diet composed of 15 percent fruit (compared with a diet of only 5 percent fruit) reduced blood markers for free radical activity, dropping their overall risk of heart disease. The most colorful fruits tend to be richest in antioxidants. Think oranges, watermelon, blueberries, and lemons. Get the most fiber from your daily fruit servings:

> **Favor whole fruit over fruit products.** As with vegetables, don't forget to eat the skin of fruits like pears, which is where most of the fiber resides.

> **Eat fresh or frozen fruit over canned.** Most canned varieties have been skinned.

> **Choose fruit over fruit juice.** A cup of apple juice, for example, contains only 0.2 grams of fiber, whereas the whole apple offers you 5 grams.

> **Don't pass over the pith.** When eating citrus fruits like oranges, eat the white pith. It contains most of the fiber.

## YOUR DAILY WHOLE GRAIN SERVING GOAL

When grains are refined, their fiber-rich outer layer is removed. And because there's not much fiber left to slow digestion, your body reacts as if you've just eaten sugar when you eat processed grains. Blood sugar levels rise rapidly, requiring the pancreas to overproduce insulin. This triggers fatigue, hunger, cravings, and fat storage.

It's easy to get confused when choosing whole grains. To pump up the fiber count, some manufacturers are adding high amounts of processed fiber from wheat bran, corn bran, lentils, or peas to their prepared foods, such as breakfast cereals, bread, and pasta. Although these additives increase the fiber grams per serving, they don't offer the same complete package as true whole grains. Maximize your whole grain choices:

> **Stock up on whole grain pasta.** This healthy take on comfort food has come a long way in recent years. Choose whole grain over added-fiber products.

> **Sneak oatmeal into everything.** Oats contain a special type of fiber called beta-glucan that has antimicrobial and antioxidant properties. It boosts immunity, speeds wound healing, and may improve the effectiveness of antibiotics.

> **Switch to whole grain bread.** Choose breads with the word "whole" within the first few ingredients on the label.

> **Start the day with a high-fiber cereal.** A serving of bran cereal offers double or even triple the amount of fiber in supplements. Mix one of these cereals with berries and you can get 15 to 20 grams of fiber—in just one meal.

> **Read labels carefully.** Make sure the list of ingredients specifies "whole" in front of the type of grain. Oats and quinoa are an exception, as they are always whole. Look for the Whole Grains Council stamp that says "100 percent whole grains" on foods, which means all grains in the product are whole.

## YOUR WEEKLY BEANS/ LEGUMES CUP GOAL | 3

Because beans contain both soluble and insoluble fiber, they are particularly effective at keeping a lid on hunger and cravings. They are also an excellent source of vitamins, minerals, and protein. Increase your consumption of beans:

> **Start with a spread.** Mash any type of bean with oil and water to make a sandwich spread or dip for veggies.

> **Make them your secret ingredient.** Beans are easy add-ins for salads, soups, or rice dishes.

> **Add to snacks.** Order nachos with beans instead of just cheese.

## YOUR WEEKLY NUTS & SEEDS SERVING GOAL | 4-5

Nuts and seeds provide a delicious way to meet your fiber quota. Don't worry about the high amounts of fat they contain—it's been shown to be good for your heart. Eat more nuts:

> **Top off any meal.** Sprinkle peanuts on your morning oatmeal or dress up desserts with chopped walnuts.

> **Munch between meals.** Stash individual servings of nuts or seeds in your desk or glove compartment.

> **Mix it up.** You don't have to be outside to enjoy a great trail mix. Combine several different kinds of nuts and seeds for an on-the-go breakfast or snack.

# ✳ FIBER UP WITH EACH (TASTY) BITE

**Coffee** Researchers in Madrid reported that coffee bean fiber does make its way from beans to brew. Coffee is also a rich source of antioxidant compounds called phenolics, which have been shown to be beneficial in controlling blood sugar.

**The fiber in your brew (grams per cup):**
Instant coffee: 1.8
Espresso: 1.5
Filtered coffee: 1.1

**Chocolate** Chocolate comes from the fibrous cocoa plant. In a study done in Madrid, rats that consumed cocoa fiber had lower levels of total and LDL ("bad") cholesterol. Get a double dose of fiber by pairing chocolate with nuts or berries.

**Get your fill of fiber (grams per serving):**
Chocolate candy: >2
Chocolate-coated coffee beans: 3

**Spices** Two teaspoons of any spice will get you between 1 and 2 grams of fiber closer to your goal. Some spices are also known to ease the flatulence and bloating associated with high-fiber diets.

**Best for digestion:**
Fennel
**Also good:** Cardamom, cayenne, cumin, and turmeric

# ✳ GET CEREAL SMART

Here's an eye-opening fact about breakfast: People who skip it are 4½ times as likely to be obese as those who always eat it. Here's another: A new Harvard health study found that those who consumed whole grain cereal seven or more times per week had the lowest incidence of heart failure. Still not excited? Yet another study from the University of Minnesota reported that the risk of all coronary events was reduced by 10% for each 10 grams of grain fiber consumed per day. And because cereal is one of the best sources of these lifesaving whole grains, that means a single daily serving has the potential to slash your risk of heart disease, the number one killer of women. A higher whole grain intake is also linked to lower rates of breast cancer, type 2 diabetes, high blood pressure, and stroke. And then there's this: Cereal is fast and convenient and comes in a gazillion varieties. But that's also its potential downfall. If you don't know what to look for, you could end up with a bowl full of empty calories instead of a nutritional powerhouse. To make sure you're getting the most bang for your cereal buck, follow these tips:

**1. Be a fiber fiend.** Look for the words "high fiber" on the box; that ensures at least 5 grams per serving. But don't stop there. Check the label; in some brands, the benefits of fiber are overshadowed by the addition of refined grains, added sugar, or cholesterol-raising fats.

**2. Go "whole" hog.** Where that fiber comes from matters, too, so check the ingredient list to find out exactly what those flakes or squares are made from. Millet, amaranth, quinoa, and oats are always whole grain, but if you don't see whole in front of wheat, corn, barley, and rice, these grains have been refined.

**3. Watch for hidden sugar.** The "total sugars" listing doesn't distinguish between added and naturally occurring sugars. There's no need to avoid the natural sugars found in nutrient-rich whole grains and fruits. But added sugars tack on extra calories without vitamins or minerals and can wreak havoc on your blood sugar and energy levels. The best way to tell is to scan the ingredients again. The following terms represent added sugars: brown sugar, corn sweetener, corn syrup, dextrose, fructose, high fructose corn syrup, invert sugar, maltose, malt syrup, molasses, sugar, and sucrose. Skip cereals that list any of these within the first three ingredients (which are listed by weight).

**4. Avoid sugar alcohols or artificial sweeteners.** They're sometimes added to boost sweetness without calories. I'm not a fan of anything artificial, and sugar alcohols can bloat your belly, so I recommend avoiding them. Steer clear of cereals containing sucralose, aspartame, sorbitol, mannitol, xylitol, maltitol, maltitol syrup, lactitol, and erythritol. Instead, add natural sweetness by topping your cereal with fresh fruit.

Fill Up on Fiber

# Secrets of the Cart-Smart

**You enter the grocery** store with the best of intentions: to buy healthy foods for yourself and your family. But then autopilot kicks in and you buy the same things over and over even when you suspect (or know) you could be making better choices. It's time to get cart-smart!

Read on for 10 shopping strategies that will teach you how to track down the most nutritious foods, what temptations and distractions to avoid, how not to get caught in the impulse-buying trap, and most important, how to complete your healthy shopping mission. Plus, you'll meet three real women who transformed their carts—and their diets.

# 1 COME PREPARED

Savvy shopping starts before you leave the house, says Kelly Brownell, PhD, director of Yale University's Rudd Center for Food Policy and Obesity, and his pre-trip advice is simple: "Make a list, and only stray from it if the item is a healthy one." He also recommends shopping after you've eaten and, if possible, when you're in a calm, stable mood. Hunger and stress make you more susceptible to—you guessed it—temptation. And try to go without the kids, says Lisa Sasson, RD, a clinical associate professor of nutrition at New York University. Sasson, who's shopped with and without them, believes that your health goals can be met more easily if you leave little ones at home where they can't pester you for candy. Handled correctly, however, Brownell points out, shopping with kids can be a positive experience. The key is to turn the outing into an educational activity. "Charge the

kids with finding the most healthful choices," he suggests. "Take them to the fruit section and say, 'You can pick anything you want.'" It can be a fun game where everybody wins.

# 2 HIT THE WALLS

Even before you walk through the store's sliding doors, Sasson says, you should start strategizing. "The first thing to do is shop the perimeter," she explains. "That's where the whole-foods action is." Nowadays, that also means walking through a bakery piping out dangerously enticing, fresh-from-the-oven smells. Sasson explains that supermarket design has changed, and not necessarily in a healthy shopper's favor. Until recently, fruits and vegetables were the first thing you saw when you entered a store. Today, most supermarkets have in-store bakeries, and some are near the entrance, meaning you have to run the gauntlet of cakes, muffins, and doughnuts just to grab that bag of spinach. "Smells, especially cinnamon, will get many shoppers to buy baked goods," warns Kevin Kelley, founding partner of Shook Kelley, a marketing firm that consults with national grocery chains. So hold your nose if you have to.

## 3 BEWARE OF SEEMINGLY INNOCENT FOODS

The produce section definitely wins the supermarket beauty contest. It has pyramids of gleaming fruits, big leafy greens, stacks of bright red berries—but then there's a cream cheese dip loaded with fat and calories. What's that doing there? "They're trying to tempt you by offering a healthful food with an unhealthful one, as if there's innocence by association," Sasson says. "I'm seeing this more often, and I tell my clients, 'Buy the fruits and vegetables, but skip the dip and candy coating—you don't need them.'"

Kelley agrees with Sasson that healthy-unhealthy adjacencies in supermarkets are a trend. Marketers call it "vignetting." Like the boutique that wants to sell you a scarf with your sweater or a handbag with your shoes, the supermarket wants to sell you the processed cheese with your trans-free crackers.

## 4 THERE'S NO SUCH THING AS A FREE LUNCH

When you spot a smiling employee handing out samples of the rich, fatty-looking dips you just saw in the produce section, keep on walking. "If you don't want a food in your house, don't sample it," Sasson says. Once you've tasted it, you're much more likely to buy it. (Kelley adds that most supermarkets "sample" poor-selling products as a way to get them into your cart and out the door.) A similar principle applies to coupons. "Don't clip a coupon if it's not for a healthy food," says Sasson. In other words, if you can get a discount on the soy milk or granola you'd buy anyway, great. But the chance to get three bags of leftover Christmas candy for the price of one is no health bargain, no matter how much money you save.

## 5 RETHINK FRESH FOODS

Healthy shoppers need to know how to make sure they're buying the freshest foods. "Time your fish buying according to your market's schedule," Sasson says. "Try not to shop for fish on Sundays; there aren't many deliveries over the weekend. Ask your supermarket manager when fish comes in, and shop that day or the next. Then cook it the same day." Fish labeled "fresh," notes Kelley, only means

# ✳ COOL OFF WITH FLAXSEED

A daily dose of fiber-rich flaxseed may cut uncomfortable hot flashes in half. Scientists at the Mayo Clinic studied 21 postmenopausal women who had at least 14 hot flashes each week; none were taking hormone therapy. When the women sprinkled 4 tablespoons of crushed flaxseed daily into yogurt, cereal, juice, or water, after 6 weeks the severity and number of their hot flashes dropped by 50%. The researchers suggest starting at a half dose of flaxseed—about 2 tablespoons—because the added fiber can cause abdominal discomfort.

that the fish hasn't been frozen. But freezing is usually your best bet for food-safety reasons. Frozen fish doesn't go bad, and commercial freezing techniques minimize textural damage. The deli is a different story. "When you're buying deli meat, choose fresh over the processed versions, which are more likely to be high in salt, sugar, and preservatives. Your butcher will know the difference." Sasson says to steer clear of the white deli salads made with lots of high-calorie, high-fat mayonnaise, such as macaroni and potato salads and coleslaw. Better nutritional options include carrot salad, hummus, and coleslaw made with vinegar.

## 6 | BE A CHEESE WHIZ

Most markets have two cheese sections: one with domestic cheeses such as American and sliced pepper jack, and a second, usually near the deli, with a wider variety of imported and fancy cheeses with hard-to-pronounce names. This is where Sasson recommends shopping. The reason: "You'll find a lot of more flavorful choices—blue, Parmesan, Camembert. A little of these varieties goes a long way, so you use much less, and that means fewer calories and fat." Sasson learned this while doing supermarket comparisons in Europe, where many people eat cheese every day and don't get as fat as Americans do.

## 7 | CHOOSE SELECT MEATS

At the meat counter, Sasson advises not to buy based on the government grades of prime and choice; they indicate marbling—a polite way of saying "lots of fat." A better

# ✻ SHOP SMART TIPS

Follow these easy dos & don'ts to make the healthiest choices at the store

**Dos**

> Make a shopping list before you leave the house.

> Ask for fresh rather than processed foods at the deli counter and find out what day the fish is delivered.

> Opt for European cheeses; they are usually more flavorful.

> Buy select cut meats, which are the leanest and most affordable.

> Look high and low on shelves. The high-fiber, low-sugar cereals are often sitting above and below the high-sugar cereals lined up at your waist level.

> Utilize the self-checkout aisle. Last-minute impulse buys often happen while you're waiting in line.

**Don'ts**

> Beware of unhealthy foods lurking in the produce section.

> Skip the samples. All they'll do is add calories and tempt you to buy a product you don't need.

> Quit browsing. Just get in and get out (in other words, shop like a man).

> Pass on the beverage aisle. Most of what's on the shelves will just add unwanted calories and sugar.

> Think twice about organics. Organic doesn't always mean healthy. Organic cake is still cake.

> Ignore the smells from the bakery section (usually in the front) and head straight to the produce aisle.

idea: Choose select cuts, which are the leanest, most healthful, and most affordable meats you can find.

Most meat is packaged in family-size cuts. Portion control is key to weight control, so supersize beef doesn't help. The fix: Ask the butcher to package the exact amount you need. Buying less doesn't guarantee you'll eat less, but it sure makes it easier. "And beware of perishables like dairy, produce, and meat on sale. They're often at the end of their life," warns Sasson. Be sure to always check the expiration date—if the date stamped on the package is the same as the day you're buying it, you may want to skip it.

# 8  SKIP THE BEVERAGE AISLE

"There's nothing there you want or need," Sasson warns, advising shoppers to nix the smoothies, juice, sodas, and sports drinks, and the sugar they all contain. "Kids grow up associating satisfying their thirst with a sweet drink, and that's one of the culprits in pediatric obesity," which leads to adult obesity. Sasson says that, with increasing frequency, high-calorie drinks aren't limited to the beverage aisle. More than 10% of the calories Americans consume come from a combination of soft drinks and juice, and food companies are making it easier to guzzle your calories. In many stores, there are sugary yogurt drinks in with the plain yogurt; high-calorie smoothies in with the juices; sugar-packed iced teas alongside the unsweetened ones; flavored, sweetened milks in with the dairy; and sugary coffee drinks in with the coffee. You'll often even find sodas in coolers by the checkout to tempt you as you're leaving.

# 9  LOOK HIGH AND LOW FOR HEALTH FOOD

The cereal aisle can be an overwhelming place. When did Chocolate Mud & Bugs hit the market? And Cinnamon Marshmallow Scooby-Doo? There's a reason these high-sugar, practically fiber-free products stand out.

Sasson notes that all those cereals are lined up at our waist level, which corresponds to where the average kid's line of vision is centered. We almost have to get out the binoculars to spot the reduced-sugar or no-sugar-added cereals, such as Grape-Nuts or Uncle Sam Cereal, relegated to the nosebleed shelves.

In any store, some products are right in your face and others are much harder to find. Many of those easy-to-spot products are paying to be there; a portion of supermarket profits comes from so-called placement fees, money that many manufacturers pay grocers for premium positioning. But what's in your face shouldn't necessarily go into your cart. "Heavily promoted items are more likely to be unhealthy," asserts Brownell. So look high, low, and around corners for alternatives—it's worth the extra time.

And watch out for those tempting breakfast cereal-to-go bars marketed mainly to women. "All are high in sugar and rarely have more than 2 g of fiber per serving," says Sasson. In other words, these bars aren't health bargains.

# 10  CHECK YOURSELF OUT

When you're waiting in line to pay for your groceries, you immediately spot the racks of candy in your path. They're there for a reason. Research shows that many customers succumb to last-minute purchases while they're in line—and, no surprise, there is no Brussels sprouts display here. So bury yourself in a magazine instead. Or try an alternative: the self-checkout station, where fewer customers make those last-minute, indulgent food buys. Use it and minutes later you'll be driving away with a carful of healthy whole foods—and a very clear conscience.

Go Power
Shopping

# Go Power Shopping

**Your grocery cart** is filled with good-for-you basics such as fresh produce, whole grains, and heart-smart oils. Now take your shopping list to the next level with even healthier picks. "Eating a wide range of nutrient-dense foods gives you access to more vitamins, minerals, and other disease-fighting antioxidants," says Dave Grotto, RD, author of *101 Foods That Could Save Your Life!* Plus, having the same stuff day in and day out—even if it's great for you—qualifies as a rut, meaning you're missing out on new flavors, which help keep healthy eating fun. Our aisle-by-aisle guide to the good, better, and best supermarket superstars will help you make smart picks based on preference, availability, and budget. Upgrade your shopping list with these weight-busting, disease-fighting, energy-revving foods.

## AT THE MEAT COUNTER

### > **Good** Lean beef

**WHY** It's high in protein but lower in calories and saturated fat than other cuts of beef—and still brimming with B vitamins, which help your body turn food into energy. Cuts that have the words "loin" or "round" in their names (like tenderloin or top round steak) are lower-fat choices. When buying ground beef, look for one that's at least 92% lean. (Beef labeled 80% lean doesn't mean it has only 20% calories from fat. It's 20% fat by weight and has closer to 70% calories from fat—about 20 grams per 3½-ounce serving!)

### > **Better** Organic beef

**WHY** The cattle were raised without hormones or antibiotics, substances that some people worry may contribute to consumers' reproductive disorders and antibiotic resistance. Organic beef also makes a more environmentally friendly burger, since it comes from cows fed only organic feed (which was grown without chemical pesticides). Just be sure the label says the word "organic," because natural beef isn't the same.

### > **Best** Grass-fed beef

**WHY** It's pricier than regular beef, but the health perks make it worth the splurge. Compared with grain-fed beef, grass-fed packs twice the concentration of vitamin E, an antioxidant that protects cells from damage that can lead to chronic diseases. It's also high in the compound CLA, fatty acids that researchers link with weight loss. Plus, it's rich in heart-healthy omega-3 fatty acids, rivaling some fish. According to researchers from the University of California Cooperative Extension Service, feeding grass to cattle boosts the omega-3 content of beef by 60%. Because this type of beef tends to be lower in overall fat, it can be tough—so marinate it, and use a meat thermometer to avoid overcooking.

## IN THE EGG SECTION

### > **Good** Packaged egg whites

**WHY** They're a low-calorie protein powerhouse, with no

cholesterol or fat. In recipes, substitute the equivalent of two egg whites for each whole egg. Added bonus: Any egg-based dish makes an affordable alternative to pricier meat-based ones.

> **Better** Whole eggs

WHY The yolk is home to tons of nutrients, including choline, which is linked to lower rates of breast cancer. (One yolk has more than 25% of your daily needs.) It's also rich in antioxidants that may help prevent macular degeneration and cataracts. Worried about the fat and cholesterol? Though people with heart disease should limit egg yolks to two a week, a recent study didn't find a connection between eating up to six eggs per week and increased rates of heart attack or stroke in healthy people.

> **Best** Omega-3-fortified eggs

WHY They have all the nutrients of regular eggs, plus up to 300 milligrams or so of the heart-protective fatty acids in each one. Many experts recommend 1,000 milligrams of DHA and EPA a day; however, because most people don't eat enough fish to meet this goal, these eggs offer another way to add omega-3s to your diet.

## IN THE DAIRY CASE

> **Good** Fat-free milk

WHY It contains only traces of fat, while even 2% milk packs 3 grams of the artery-plugging saturated kind in every 8-ounce glass. Each cup of fat-free also supplies 76 milligrams more calcium than the same amount of whole milk does.

> **Better** Skim Plus

Why: It's as good for you as fat-free milk, with a richer taste. Skim Plus (also called skim deluxe or supreme) is fortified with extra milk protein, making it thicker, creamier tasting, and easier to transition to from whole or 2%.

> **Best** Organic fat-free milk

WHY A recent study from the United Kingdom found that organically raised cows produce milk with higher levels of antioxidants and fatty acids such as CLAs and omega-3s—thanks to all the grass and clover they consume. You'll pay more for organic milk, but because it's often ultrapasteurized (heated at higher temps and labeled UHT), it may last longer in your fridge.

## ON THE BUTTER SHELF

> **Good** Trans-free margarine

WHY It's a wiser pick than butter because it doesn't contain any cholesterol and has much less saturated fat. It also doesn't pack the dangerous trans fats that many margarines do—the kind of fats that boost bad cholesterol and lower the good kind. Some are even fortified with bone-building calcium or heart-healthy omega-3 fatty acids.

> **Better** Light trans-free margarine

WHY Your toast and baked potatoes will still get a buttery kick. But even if you use a whole tablespoon, you'll

# ✳ ANTIOXIDANTS BY THE BUNCH

Grab some grapes! According to a recent study, they may help prevent colon cancer, the third most common type in the United States. When patients with colon tumors consumed 80 milligrams of grape powder daily (the equivalent of three servings of grapes), biopsies showed a significant decrease in cancer activity, according to researchers at the University of California, Irvine. Supplements of resveratrol—the component in red grapes thought to have cancer-fighting power—didn't produce the same effect.

# ✱ HEALTH FOOD IMPOSTORS

Even if you haven't bought full-fat mayo or sugary soda since blue eye shadow was in style (the first time), you may be getting duped into less-than-stellar food choices at the supermarket. The culprit? The "health halo." "From a distance, some foods seem like healthful choices because of the way they're packaged or labeled," says Janel Ovrut, MS, RD, a Boston-based dietitian. "But just because a product's marketing gives it an aura of health doesn't necessarily mean it's good for you." Check out these six notorious health food impostors, plus smarter swaps that up the nutritional ante and still give you the flavor you crave.

**Impostor: Baked potato chips**
Yes, they're lower in fat. But they're still high in calories and low in nutrients, with little fiber to fill you up.
**Smarter sub: Popcorn** You'll get the salt and crunch of chips plus fiber, and around 65% fewer calories per cup. Look for oil-free microwave popcorn or brands that are air-popped or popped in healthful oils such as olive or canola.

**Impostor: Gummy fruit snacks**
Although these products may contain some juice, they're |usually nothing more than candy infused with vitamins. They also contain high fructose corn syrup, which is linked with obesity, and heart-unhealthy partially hydrogenated oils.
**Smarter sub: Fresh or dried fruit** Both are packed with filling fiber and cancer-fighting antioxidants, which you'll miss if you opt for gummy snacks.

**Impostor: Light ice cream**
Light ice cream can have fewer calories than regular, but there's no guarantee. What's more, some light brands can lack the rich taste you crave, so you're less satisfied and may be inclined to eat more than one serving.
**Smarter sub: Dairy-free ice cream** Soy and coconut milk ice creams may save you a few calories, and they have a creamy, satisfying texture.

**Impostor: "Calorie-free" spray margarine**
Even though some spray margarines claim to be "calorie-free," labeling laws allow products with fewer than 5 calories per serving to claim to have zero calories. So, while one spritz may be inconsequential, the whole bottle could have as many as 900 calories.
**Smarter sub: Spray-it-yourself olive oil** In this case, a bit of real fat is more healthful and flavorful—and within a reasonable calorie range if you watch your portions. Investing in an olive oil mister ensures you don't put on too much.

**Impostor: Nonfat salad dressing**
Fat-free salad dressings are often packed with sugar—so your dressing may be loaded with calories. Ironically, a salad without fat is not living up to its potential. "You need a little fat to absorb vitamins A, D, E, and K and other nutrients," says Katherine Tallmadge, RD, spokesperson for the American Dietetic Association.
**Smarter sub: Oil-based salad dressings** You'll get good-for-you fats instead of the saturated fat found in some creamy dressings. Look for ingredients like olive oil, vinegar, and herbs.

**Impostor: 100-calorie snack packs**
You might want to skip these if you're trying to lose weight. A recent study showed that people may eat more food and calories if the portions are presented in small sizes and packages. With smaller serving sizes, study participants didn't feel the need to regulate their intake, so they ate more than one portion before feeling satisfied.
**Smarter sub:** A small serving of almonds. Their healthy monounsaturated fat, fiber, and protein will tide you over until your next meal.

take in as few as 45 calories and 5 grams of fat.

> **Best** Margarines with added plant stanols/sterols

WHY You'll pay more for this margarine, but it's a powerful cholesterol fighter, thanks to plant stanols/sterols, which naturally reduce the amount of LDL cholesterol the body can absorb. In a study in the American Journal of Cardiology, eating 25 grams of margarine a day enriched with plant stanols/sterols lowered LDL cholesterol by 8% in 4 weeks.

## IN THE YOGURT SECTION

> **Good** Low-fat flavored yogurt

WHY Cup for cup, yogurt has about 70 milligrams more calcium than milk, plus enough protein to make it a satisfying snack. It's rich in beneficial bacteria that can ward off tummy troubles and yeast infections. Look for Lactobacillus (*L. acidophilus*) and/or Bifidobacterium (*B. bifidum*) in the ingredients.

> **Better** Low-fat plain yogurt

WHY Despite the health benefits, some flavored varieties have a ton of added sweetener, such as sugar or high fructose corn syrup. For a healthier treat, pick plain and swirl in a spoonful of all-fruit spread. (You can also drizzle in honey for a bonus shot of antioxidants.)

> **Best** Greek yogurt

WHY "I love recommending Greek yogurt to clients," says Lara E. Metz, RD, a New York City nutritionist. "It has just as much calcium as regular yogurt and twice the protein—but it's richer and creamier." Be sure to choose the 0% fat variety to minimize calories.

## AT THE FISH COUNTER

> **Good** Tilapia

WHY It's an affordable pick and a dieter's dream. Each 3-ounce serving contains only 110 calories and 2.5 grams of fat—but a whopping 22 grams of fill-you-up protein. According to the FDA, tilapia has the lowest mercury level

of all fish. Although other fish have more heart-smart omega-3 fatty acids, tilapia is still a healthy choice at dinnertime.

### > **Better** Halibut
**WHY** It boasts more heart-healthy omega-3s per serving than tilapia. In fact, a 5-ounce fillet packs your entire day's needs of EPA and DHA, fatty acids that can increase "good" HDL cholesterol and may also help prevent cognitive decline related to aging.

### > **Best** Salmon
**WHY** Salmon's one of the best sources of omega-3s you can find. Research has found that a healthy diet including fatty fish like salmon is linked to lower risk of heart disease, stroke, and diabetes. Wild has a slight edge over farm-raised because it may be lower in contaminants such as PCBs and dioxins—but both versions are equally nutritious. "Just remove the skin after cook-

ing, because that's where most of the contaminants are found," says Grotto.

## IN THE PRODUCE SECTION

### > **Good** Romaine
**WHY** Rich in vitamins A and K, crunchy romaine makes a respectable base for any salad. Romaine also boasts more than eight times the vitamin C of iceberg lettuce.

### > **Better** Watercress
**WHY** This peppery leaf not only adds a kick to salads but also adds a small dose of calcium. A study from the University of Ulster in the United Kingdom found that eating watercress daily is linked with reduced cellular DNA damage that may lead to cancer. If you find the flavor too strong, toss it with milder lettuces (say,

bib or red leaf) or layer it with tomato on your turkey sandwich.

> **Best** Spinach

**WHY** Spinach is rich in iron, which helps deliver oxygen to your cells to keep you alert and energized. And research from the Massachusetts Eye and Ear Infirmary links eating antioxidant-rich spinach with a lower risk of age-related macular degeneration.

## IN THE SNACK AISLE

> **Good** Popcorn

**WHY** It's a stealth whole grain, packing 3 grams of fiber and an entire serving of whole grains in each 3-cup, 90-calorie, air-popped bowl. That's why people who snack on it get two more servings of whole grains and 22% more fiber every day than people who don't, according to a recent study in the *Journal of the American Dietetic Association.*

> **Better** Peanuts

**WHY** With as much protein as ½ cup of black beans, a handful of peanuts also contains 7 grams of heart-healthy monounsaturated fat. Women who ate peanuts and peanut butter at least five times a week had up to 27% less risk of developing type 2 diabetes, possibly because the healthy fats increase insulin sensitivity, according to a study from the Harvard School of Public Health. Because they're easy to overeat, measure out your 1-ounce, 160-calorie portion (a small handful—about 40 nuts).

> **Best** Almonds

**WHY** "They're one of the most nutritious nuts around," says David Katz, MD, director of the Yale Prevention Research Center. Almonds are also the go-to snack when you're trying to drop weight. In one study, women who ate almonds had higher levels of cholecystokinin, a hunger-suppressing hormone, circulating in their systems. Another study found that a heart-healthy diet including almonds lowered LDL cholesterol as much as a statin drug did.

## IN THE CONDIMENTS AISLE

> **Good** Low-fat creamy salad dressing

**WHY** If you prefer creamy dressings (such as ranch or blue cheese), these are a perfect way to add flavor to your favorite greens without drowning them in extra calories or fat.

> **Better** Full-fat oil-based dressing

**WHY** The fats in oils like canola and olive are healthier for you. They're a good source of vitamin E and help your body soak up all the vitamins in veggies. In one study, people absorbed more carotenoids from a salad with full-fat dressing than with reduced-fat dressing. (Those eating fat-free dressing absorbed just traces.) The calories add up fast, so measure out a 2-tablespoon portion.

> **Best**   Olive oil and flavored vinegar

**WHY** With a do-it-yourself dressing, you don't have to worry about the quality of the ingredients. Mix 2 teaspoons of olive oil (or canola or flaxseed—they all contain higher amounts of heart-healthy monounsaturated fat) with flavored vinegar such as raspberry, then toss in any herbs you like.

49

# Recipes That Slim & Satisfy

**Let's get cooking!** Here are more than 200 family-pleasing recipes, many from readers who have successfully lost weight and kept it off. Looking for a classic with a twist? Try the Chicken Sausage Minestrone, Grilled Steak with Cilantro Pesto, or Banana Bread Cake. Whip up the Navajo Tacos, Chicken Tikka Kabobs with Coconut "Cream," or Caramel Applesauce Pie when in the mood for something new and exciting. Turn the pages to find a delicious, satisfying recipe for any occasion.

# breakfasts

—Carmen McKiernan, Orlando, Florida

# Granola with Nuts

½ cup honey

¼ cup canola oil

1 tablespoon almond extract

1 tablespoon ground cinnamon

1 tablespoon ground nutmeg

3 cups rolled oats

1 cup raw almonds

1 cup unsalted dry-roasted peanuts

½ cup unsalted mixed nuts

½ teaspoon salt

**PREHEAT** the oven to 300°F. Line a large rimmed baking sheet with parchment paper.

**WHISK** together the honey, oil, almond extract, cinnamon, and nutmeg in a large bowl. Add the oats, almonds, peanuts, mixed nuts, and salt; toss to coat well.

**SPREAD** evenly on the baking sheet. Bake for 25 to 30 minutes, stirring the mixture every 10 minutes to prevent burning, until browned and dry.

**COOL** on a rack for 15 minutes.

Total time: 1 hour ✱ Makes 6 cups

Per ½ cup: 346 calories, 10 g protein, 33 g carbohydrate, 21 g fat, 2 g saturated fat, 99 mg sodium, 6 g fiber

This granola tastes great and is a lot healthier than most other snack foods. Serve it alone, as cereal, or on top of yogurt.

**—Carmen**

—Renay Ivens, Fairfax, Vermont

# Banana Bran Oats

1 cup fat-free milk

1 cup water

2 tablespoons butter or trans-free margarine

¼ cup sugar-free maple syrup

1 cup oat bran

½ cup unprocessed bran

2 medium bananas, cut into bite-size pieces

½ cup fat-free hazelnut creamer

¼ cup bran buds cereal

**BRING** the milk, water, butter, and syrup to a boil in a medium saucepan over medium heat. Remove from the heat and slowly stir in the oat bran and unprocessed bran, stirring constantly to prevent lumps. Cook, stirring, for 3 to 5 minutes or until cooked through.

**REMOVE** from the heat and stir in the bananas. Cover and let stand for 2 minutes or until thickened and set. Spoon into 4 bowls. Drizzle each with 2 tablespoons creamer and sprinkle with 1 tablespoon bran buds. Serve immediately.

Total time: 25 minutes ✻ Makes 4 servings

Per serving: 268 calories, 8 g protein, 54 g carbohydrate, 8 g fat, 4 g saturated fat, 96 mg sodium, 11 g fiber

This hearty dish is a great way to start the day—especially on cold mornings. Change up the flavors by substituting berries for the banana and vanilla creamer for the hazelnut.

**NUTRITION NEWS TO USE**

Three: That's the minimum number of food groups you should eat in the morning to boost your brain health. Students scored higher on mental-functioning tests with each food group added to their morning meal, according to Australian nutritionists who tracked 800 teens. A wide range of nutrients may improve how the brain works, the researchers say. **Our ideal morning mix = whole grains + produce + dairy:** ✻ Whole grain cereal with fat-free milk and a small sliced banana ✻ Fat-free Greek-style yogurt with sliced fruit and a handful of rolled oats ✻ Whole grain toast with low-fat cheese and tomato slices

# Sweet Ricotta Cheese Crepes with Fruit

½ cup golden raisins

¼ cup rum or orange juice

Crepes

1¼ cups fat-free milk

1 large egg

⅔ cup whole grain pastry flour

Filling

1 container (15 ounces) part-skim ricotta cheese

1 large egg yolk

¾ teaspoon Splenda or other granular sugar substitute

½ cup toasted, finely chopped almonds, divided

Custard

1 large egg

1 cup fat-free milk

¾ teaspoon Splenda or other granular sugar substitute

Topping

½ cup all-fruit black raspberry spreadable fruit

½ cup fat-free sour cream

**PREHEAT** the oven to 375°F. Coat a 13" × 9" baking dish with cooking spray. Soak the raisins in the rum in a small bowl. Set aside.

To Make the Crepes:

**WHISK** together the milk, egg, and flour in a medium bowl just until smooth. Coat an 8" nonstick skillet with cooking spray and heat over medium heat. Pour a scant ¼ cup batter into the pan and quickly swirl the pan to completely coat the bottom. Cook for 30 seconds or until the edges are golden and the middle is solid. Carefully loosen and flip with a spatula or your fingers. Cook for 10 seconds or until solid. Invert onto a plate. Repeat to make 8 crepes.

To Make the Filling:

**DRAIN** the raisins, reserving the rum. Combine the raisins, ricotta cheese, egg yolk, sugar substitute, and ¼ cup of the almonds in a medium bowl. Beat with an electric mixer until smooth and fluffy.

To Make the Custard:

**WHISK** together the egg, milk, and sugar substitute in a small bowl until smooth.

To Make the Topping:

**STIR** together the spreadable fruit and the reserved rum in a small bowl.

To Assemble the Crepes:

**PLACE** ¼ cup of the filling on the lower half of each crepe. Roll the crepe and place in the prepared baking dish, seam side down. Repeat. Pour the custard over the crepes. Bake for 20 minutes or until the custard is set and the edges are just starting to crisp. Let stand 5 minutes. Spoon the topping over the crepes and top each with 1 tablespoon of the sour cream. Sprinkle with ½ tablespoon of the remaining almonds.

---

Total time: 35 minutes  ✱  Makes 8 servings

Per serving: 301 calories, 14 g protein, 36 g carbohydrate, 9 g fat, 3 g saturated fat, 138 mg sodium, 3 g fiber

You don't have to dine in Paris to enjoy these tasty crepes. Using a small nonstick pan makes preparing the crepes a breeze.

# Oatmeal with Ricotta, Fruit, and Nuts

2 cups apple cider

2 cups water

2 cups rolled oats

⅛ teaspoon salt

½ teaspoon ground cinnamon

¼ cup ricotta cheese

1 large peach or plum, chopped

2 tablespoons sunflower seeds or chopped toasted almonds

**COMBINE** the cider, water, oats, and salt in a medium saucepan. Bring to a boil over medium heat. Reduce the heat to low. Cook, uncovered, stirring occasionally, for 3 to 5 minutes or until thick and creamy.

**SPOON** the oatmeal into 6 bowls and sprinkle with the cinnamon. Top with the ricotta, peach, and sunflower seeds. Serve hot.

Total time: 10 minutes  ✱  Makes 6 servings

Per serving: 187 calories, 7 g protein, 31 g carbohydrate, 4 g fat, 1 g saturated fat, 67 mg sodium, 3 g fiber

✱

For more chewy oatmeal, bring the cider, water, and salt to a boil, then stir in the oats. For sweeter oatmeal, drizzle each serving with 1 to 2 teaspoons low-calorie maple syrup.

Oats are even healthier than the FDA originally thought a decade ago when it approved the health claim linking them with a reduced risk of heart disease, according to new research. They can also cut your risk of high blood pressure and type 2 diabetes. To reap the benefits, eat ½ cup daily—preferably unsweetened.

✱ TURKEY MEATBALLS Mix 1½ lb ground lean turkey with ¾ c quick-cooking oats, ½ c chopped onion, ½ c tomato sauce, and 1 egg. Roll into 1" balls and bake in shallow pan at 400°F about 20 minutes. Simmer in 1½ to 2 c tomato sauce and serve.

✱ PARMESAN-CRUSTED TILAPIA Coat 1 tilapia or salmon fillet with 1 Tbsp olive oil. Roll in mixture of ¼ c quick-cooking oats, 1 Tbsp grated Parmesan cheese, and ¼ tsp ground nutmeg. Bake at 350°F for 10 minutes per inch of thickness.

✱ BLUEBERRY-CHOCOLATE PARFAIT Place ¼ c frozen wild blueberries in small ovenproof dessert dish. Cover with ½ c cooked oatmeal and top with 30 dark chocolate chips. Microwave on high for about 30 seconds.

[ **SUPERFOOD SPOTLIGHT: OATS** ]

# Date Breakfast Pudding

- 1 cup quick-cooking rolled oats
- 1 tablespoon Splenda or other granular sugar substitute
- ¼ cup chopped dates
- ½ teaspoon butter or trans-free margarine
- ½ teaspoon ground cinnamon
- 3 cups water

**COAT** a 1½- to 2-quart slow cooker with cooking spray. Add the oats, Splenda, dates, butter, and cinnamon. Stir in the water. Cover and cook on low for 4 to 6 hours.

---

Total time: 4 hours ✱ Makes 4 servings

Per serving: 121 calories, 3 g protein, 23 g carbohydrate, 2 g fat, 0 g saturated fat, 2 mg sodium, 3 g fiber

This is delicious as is for breakfast or spoon into individual dessert dishes and top with a small dollop of whipped topping for a satisfying dessert. Enjoy warm or chilled. For breakfast, I often make it at night before going to bed.

**—Bernadette**

—Kris Adams, Westhampton, New Jersey

# Breakfast Bowl-of-Oatmeal Cookies

1 cup rolled oats

⅓ cup no-carb protein powder

½ teaspoon ground cinnamon

¼ cup packed brown sugar
   Pinch of salt (optional)

½ cup raisins

1 tablespoon trans-free
   margarine, softened

¼ teaspoon vanilla extract

1 large egg, lightly beaten

2 tablespoons 1% milk

**PREHEAT** the oven to 400°F. Coat a baking sheet with cooking spray.

**STIR** together the oats, protein powder, cinnamon, brown sugar, salt, raisins, and margarine in a medium bowl. Stir in the vanilla and egg. Add the milk and stir with a large spoon until the mixture sticks together to form a dough. Add more milk, a tablespoon at a time, if necessary, until the dough is just sticky.

**SCOOP** 2 tablespoons of the dough and roll by hand into a ball. Place on the baking sheet and press flat to ¼" thick. Repeat, making 8 large cookies.

**BAKE** for 10 to 12 minutes or until the cookies are dry and lightly browned. Cool on a rack for 5 minutes before removing from the baking sheet.

---

Total time: 25 minutes　✱　Makes 8 cookies

Per cookie: 144 calories, 8 g protein, 22 g carbohydrate, 3 g fat, 1 g saturated fat, 33 mg sodium, 2 g fiber

I wanted a way to have a daily bowl of oatmeal that was portable. You can make these in the morning and snack on them in the car or at your desk, and they're quite filling.
　　　　　　　　　　　　　　　　　　　　　　　　　　　　　　　　**—Kris**

# Sausage, Egg, and Vegetable Casserole

1 pound sweet Italian sausage, casing removed and meat cut into 1" pieces

1½ teaspoons olive oil

½ small head escarole, chopped

2 medium zucchini, halved and thinly sliced

1 red bell pepper, chopped

1 small red onion, halved and thinly sliced

¼ teaspoon salt

¼ teaspoon black pepper, divided

7 large eggs, at room temperature

½ cup 2% milk, at room temperature

¼ cup grated Parmesan cheese

**PREHEAT** the oven to 350°F. Coat an 8"× 8" baking dish with cooking spray.

**COOK** the sausage in a large nonstick skillet over medium-high heat until half-cooked, 6 to 8 minutes, stirring occasionally. Spread over the bottom of the prepared baking dish. Discard the fat in the skillet.

**HEAT** the oil in the same skillet over medium heat. Cook the escarole, zucchini, bell pepper, onion, salt, and ⅛ teaspoon of the black pepper for 8 to 10 minutes, stirring occasionally, until the vegetables are tender and the liquid evaporates. Let cool for 10 minutes. Spread over the sausage.

**WHISK** together the eggs, milk, cheese, and remaining ⅛ teaspoon black pepper in a large bowl. Pour over the vegetables. Bake for 40 to 45 minutes or until the eggs are set. Cut into squares to serve.

Total time: 1 hour 15 minutes  ✳  Makes 6 servings

Per serving: 281 calories, 23 g protein, 7 g carbohydrate, 18 g fat, 6 g saturated fat, 695 mg sodium, 2 g fiber

✳

This delicious breakfast dish is quite versatile. Change it up by substituting kale, broccoli rabe, or broccoli for the escarole. Or replace the pork sausage with chicken or turkey sausage.

## NUTRITION NEWS TO USE

Enjoying a cup of chamomile tea is more than a restful nighttime ritual—the herb may help rein in blood sugar fluctuations and prevent the ravages of type 2 diabetes, according to a recent study. When researchers fed chamomile tea to rats with diabetes, the animals had significant decreases in blood sugar and lower levels of compounds that can cause diabetes complications. While more research is needed, those with diabetes may reap the same benefits from sipping chamomile daily, say the scientists.

# Creamy Scrambled Eggs
# with Sausage and Scallions

- 6 ounces breakfast turkey sausage patties or links, cut into bite-size pieces
- 8 large eggs
- 3 scallions, thinly sliced
- ¼ teaspoon salt
- ¼ teaspoon black pepper
- 6 drops hot-pepper sauce
- 2 teaspoons butter

**WARM** a large nonstick skillet over medium heat. Add the sausage and cook for 8 to 10 minutes or until heated through.

**WHISK** together the eggs in a medium bowl. Stir in the scallions, salt, black pepper, and pepper sauce.

**MELT** the butter in the skillet with the sausage over medium-low heat. Pour in the eggs. Cook, stirring frequently, for 6 to 8 minutes, until the eggs are set but still soft and creamy.

Total time: 30 minutes   ✱   Makes 4 servings

Per serving: 230 calories, 21 g protein, 2 g carbohydrate, 15 g fat, 5 g saturated fat, 557 mg sodium, 0 g fiber

Perfect for leftovers; store any remaining eggs in a covered container in the refrigerator for up to 2 days. Serve warm or at room temperature. Reheat the eggs in foil at 350°F for 5 minutes.

**SUPERFOOD SPOTLIGHT: KEFIR**

A probiotic long before *probiotic* was a buzzword, kefir is a tangy fermented milk drink that is packed with healthy bacteria. It costs less per serving than individually packaged probiotic drinks on the market.

**TRY:** Sipping it like you would a smoothie; it comes in flavors such as raspberry and pomegranate.

**BUY:** Lifeway Kefir; lifeway.net for stores

—Diane Nemitz, Ludington, Michigan

# Strawberry-Banana Pancakes

Topping

- 1 **cup strawberries, sliced**
- 1 **banana, sliced**
- 4 **tablespoons sugar-free maple syrup**

Pancakes

- 1 **cup fat-free or 1% low-fat cottage cheese**
- 4 **large eggs**
- 1 **very ripe banana**
- ½ **cup all-purpose flour**
- ¼ **cup whole wheat flour**
- 4 **tablespoons butter or trans-free margarine, melted**

¼–½ **cup 1% milk**

To Make the Topping:
**STIR** together the strawberries, banana, and syrup in a medium bowl. Set aside.

To Make the Pancakes:
**BLEND** the cottage cheese, eggs, and banana in a blender just until smooth. Place in a large bowl. Stir in the flour and butter. Add enough milk to make a thin batter.

**COAT** a nonstick griddle or skillet with cooking spray. Drop the batter by 3 tablespoons onto the griddle for each pancake, to make a total of 16. Flip the pancakes when bubbles appear on top. Cook for 1 minute or until browned.

**DIVIDE** the pancakes among 4 plates. Spoon the topping over the pancakes.

Total time: 25 minutes ✳ Makes 4 servings

Per serving: 376 calories, 17 g protein, 40 g carbohydrate, 17 g fat, 9 g saturated fat, 333 mg sodium, 4 g fiber

Breakfasts

I really don't like the usual kind of banana pancakes with slices of the fruit cooked in, but I love the flavor of bananas, so I came up with the idea of incorporating them in my favorite cottage cheese pancakes. I substituted whole wheat flour for some of the white flour for extra fiber. **—Diane**

—Judi Berman-Yamada, Portland, Oregon

# Pineapple Cream Cheese Pudding with Blueberries

- ½ cup slivered almonds
- 1 can (8 ounces) crushed pineapple packed in juice, well drained
- 2 large eggs
- 1 package (12 ounces) light firm or extra-firm tofu, drained
- 3 ounces reduced-fat cream cheese
- ⅓ cup granular fructose
- 1 tablespoon vanilla extract
- ½ teaspoon almond extract
- ¼ teaspoon salt
- 2 tablespoons whole wheat pastry flour
- Ground nutmeg or ground cinnamon
- 2 cups blueberries or other berries

**PREHEAT** the oven to 350°F. Coat a 9" × 9" glass baking dish with cooking spray. Scatter the almonds evenly over the bottom of the dish.

**PROCESS** the pineapple, eggs, tofu, and cream cheese in a blender or food processor until smooth. Scrape down the sides of the container.

**ADD** the fructose, vanilla, almond extract, salt, and flour. Pulse until well blended. The mixture will be thick and smooth.

**POUR** into the baking dish; sprinkle the top with nutmeg.

**BAKE** for 30 to 40 minutes or until a knife inserted in the center comes out clean. Cool slightly. Cut into 8 rectangles and place each on a plate with ¼ cup blueberries.

----

Total time: 50 minutes ✱ Makes 8 servings

Per serving: 171 calories, 7 g protein, 22 g carbohydrate, 6 g fat, 2 g saturated fat, 84 mg sodium, 2 g fiber

I am an early retiree who was very stressed in my career and got out of shape sitting at a desk. So, we moved from the country to the city. I got healthy, started hiking, walking, and taking aerobic classes, and I lost 40 pounds. This recipe helped.　**—Judi**

# Pecan French Toast

2 large eggs

½ cup pecans, finely chopped

4 slices whole grain cinnamon-raisin bread, diagonally sliced

¾ cup sugar-free maple syrup or 4 teaspoons strawberry jam

1 cup strawberries, sliced

**WHISK** together the eggs in a 13" × 9" glass baking dish. Stir in the pecans. Soak the bread in the egg mixture for 3 minutes, turning once, until liquid is absorbed.

**COAT** a large nonstick skillet with cooking spray. Add the bread slices, in batches if necessary, and cook for 4 minutes, turning once, until browned.

**PLACE** on 2 plates and top with the syrup or jam and strawberries.

-----

Total time: 15 minutes ✳ Makes 2 servings

Per serving: 590 calories, 14 g protein, 65 g carbohydrate, 35 g fat, 6 g saturated fat, 353 mg sodium, 6 g fiber

✳

Cinnamon bread adds a unique flavor to this French toast studded with pecans. If you can't find whole grain cinnamon-raisin bread, add ¼ teaspoon cinnamon to the eggs and use whole wheat or whole grain bread.

## NUTRITION NEWS TO USE

Trying to whittle your waistline? You might want to rethink your morning meal. Recent research found that men and women who ate two eggs for breakfast as part of a low-calorie diet lost 65% more weight and had a 61% greater reduction in BMI than their counterparts who started the day with an equal-calorie bagel breakfast. Eggs, a high-quality protein, kept people more satisfied until their next meal, which helped them stick to and succeed on a reduced-calorie diet. To keep fat down, try scrambling an egg yolk (around 210 miligrams cholesterol) with two egg whites for a high-protein, fat conscious breakfast.

—Peter Halferty, Corpus Christi, Texas

# Sunday Morning Brunch Waffles

2 cups strawberries, sliced

1 cup raspberries

1 cup blueberries or blackberries

1 package (4-serving size) fat-free, sugar-free instant vanilla pudding

2¼ cups cold 1% milk

1 tablespoon grated lemon zest

2 tablespoons lemon juice

1 cup thawed light frozen whipped topping

8 small Belgian or regular frozen waffles, toasted

**COMBINE** the strawberries, raspberries, and blueberries in a small bowl. Set aside.

**WHISK** together the pudding, milk, lemon zest, and lemon juice for 2 minutes or until well blended. Gently stir in the whipped topping.

**PLACE** ¼ cup of the pudding mixture on each of 8 plates. Top each with a waffle. Spoon fruit over each and drizzle with the remaining pudding.

---

Total time: 15 minutes ✱ Makes 8 servings

Per serving: 277 calories, 8 g protein, 43 g carbohydrate, 9 g fat, 3 g saturated fat, 562 mg sodium, 4 g fiber

Perfect for a large gathering, this recipe serves eight. To serve less, prepare the pudding using only what you'll need and store in the refrigerator for up to 3 days. Adjust the fruit and berries as well.

# Sweet Potato Muffins

1 can (29 ounces) yams, drained

1 cup whole grain pastry flour

1 cup cake flour

½ cup finely chopped walnuts

½ cup bran flakes

¼ cup Splenda or other granular sugar substitute

1 tablespoon baking powder

1 teaspoon salt

¼ teaspoon ground cinnamon

¼ teaspoon ground ginger

2 large eggs

¾ cup 1% milk

4 tablespoons trans-free margarine, melted

**PREHEAT** the oven to 350°F. Line 20 muffin cups with paper liners or coat with cooking spray.

**MASH** the yams to measure 2 cups.

**COMBINE** the flours, walnuts, bran flakes, Splenda, baking powder, salt, cinnamon, and ginger in a large bowl.

**WHISK** together the eggs, milk, and margarine in a medium bowl. Whisk in the yams. Stir into the flour mixture just until blended.

**FILL** the muffin cups two-thirds full with the mixture. Bake for 25 to 30 minutes or until a toothpick inserted in the center comes out clean.

**REMOVE** to a rack to cool.

---

Total time: 40 minutes  ✻  Makes 20 muffins

Per muffin: 143 calories, 3 g protein, 23 g carbohydrate, 5 g fat, 1 g saturated fat, 336 mg sodium, 2 g fiber

Here's a great way to incorporate more beta-carotene into your diet. Although they're called "yams" in the can, they are actually a type of sweet potato. (True yams have a much paler color and aren't sweet.) When buying raw sweet potatoes, reach for the darkest orange ones to get the most beta-carotene.

## NUTRITION NEWS TO USE

Women who drink 2 to 3 cups of regular coffee daily have a 25% lower risk of death from cardiovascular disease than nondrinkers, according to researchers who tracked the habits of more than 100,000 adults. Coffee drinkers also had a 30% lower risk of death from causes other than cancer or cardiovascular disease than coffee skippers. Researchers say the protective effect may come from something other than caffeine, because decaf drinkers also had lower death rates (though not as low as those of caffeine drinkers). Our advice: Use fat-free milk and minimal sweetener to add flavor—some coffee drinks can pack 300-plus calories!

—Frances Burcar, Davison, Michigan

# Banana-Nut Muffins

2 cups low-fat biscuit baking mix

1 packet (1 ounce) instant oatmeal

1 package (4-serving size) cook-and-serve sugar-free vanilla pudding

⅓ cup Splenda brown sugar blend

½ cup chopped walnuts

2 medium bananas

2 large eggs

⅔ cup fat-free milk

1 teaspoon vanilla extract

½ teaspoon banana extract (optional)

**PREHEAT** the oven to 350°F. Line a muffin pan with paper liners or coat with cooking spray. Combine the baking mix, oatmeal, pudding, Splenda, and walnuts in a large bowl.

**MASH** the bananas with a fork in a medium bowl. Stir in the eggs, milk, vanilla, and banana extract until well blended. Stir into the dry ingredients just until blended.

**FILL** the muffin cups two-thirds full with the mixture. Bake for 25 minutes or until a toothpick inserted in the center comes out clean. Remove to a rack to cool.

Total time: 35 minutes  ✳  Makes 12 muffins

Per muffin: 157 calories, 4 g protein, 23 g carbohydrate, 5 g fat, 1 g saturated fat, 279 mg sodium, 1 g fiber

✱

Low-fat baking mix and vanilla pudding mix are a surprising base for these flavorful muffins. Studded with oatmeal and walnuts, the muffins make a quick, hearty, and healthy meal. They are great with a glass of fat-free milk.

## NUTRITION NEWS TO USE

To lower your blood pressure, don't just eat less sodium—you should also increase your potassium intake, as it speeds up the body's sodium excretion, say researchers at the Hypertension Institute of Nashville. Lead author Mark Houston, MD, says most Americans consume more sodium than potassium, but it should be the other way around. Some popular potassium-rich foods to help fix this: baked potatoes, tomato paste, lima beans, yogurt, cantaloupe, and bananas.

# Applesauce Spice Muffins

2 **cups whole wheat pastry flour**

1½ **teaspoons baking soda**

1 **teaspoon ground cinnamon**

1 **teaspoon salt**

¾ **teaspoon ground nutmeg**

½ **teaspoon ground cloves**

¼ **teaspoon baking powder**

¾ **cup (1½ sticks) trans-free margarine, softened**

1 **cup Splenda sugar blend**

2 **large eggs**

2 **cups unsweetened applesauce**

¾ **cup raisins (optional)**

**PREHEAT** the oven to 350°F. Line 2 muffin pans with paper liners or coat with cooking spray.

**COMBINE** the flour, baking soda, cinnamon, salt, nutmeg, cloves, and baking powder in a large bowl.

**BEAT** the margarine and Splenda in a large bowl with an electric mixer on medium speed. Add the eggs, one at a time, beating well after each addition.

**ADD** the flour mixture alternating with the applesauce, beating on low speed after each addition. Stir in the raisins.

**FILL** the muffin cups two-thirds full with the mixture. Bake for 25 to 35 minutes or until a toothpick inserted in the center comes out clean. Remove to a rack to cool.

---

Total time: 40 minutes  ✳  Makes 24 muffins

Per muffin: 97 calories, 2 g protein, 9 g carbohydrate, 6 g fat, 2 g saturated fat, 250 mg sodium, 1 g fiber

73

Breakfasts

This is a healthy low-sugar recipe that I have finally perfected through some trial and error.

**—Debi**

—Dorthy Steffan, Sequim, Washington

# Raspberry Muffins

2 cups bran flakes cereal

¾ cup whole wheat flour

½ cup graham flour

1 tablespoon baking powder

1 teaspoon ground cinnamon

½ teaspoon salt

½ cup fat-free egg substitute

½ cup fat-free milk

3 tablespoons light olive oil

3 tablespoons honey

1 teaspoon lemon juice

2 medium peaches, peeled, pitted, and chopped

½ cup raspberries

**PREHEAT** the oven to 400°F. Line a muffin pan with paper liners or coat with cooking spray.

**COMBINE** the cereal, flours, baking powder, cinnamon, and salt in a large bowl.

**WHISK** together the egg substitute, milk, oil, honey, and lemon juice in a small bowl. Stir into the flour mixture just until blended. Gently stir in the peaches and raspberries.

**FILL** muffin cups two-thirds full with mixture. Bake for 22 to 25 minutes or until a toothpick inserted in the center comes out clean. Remove to a rack to cool.

---

Total time: 50 minutes ❋ Makes 12 muffins

Per muffin: 138 calories, 3 g protein, 25 g carbohydrate, 4 g fat, 1 g saturated fat, 296 mg sodium, 3 g fiber

❋

Chopped peaches add a sweet surprise to raspberry muffins. For a change of pace, use blueberries instead of the raspberries and fresh apricots rather than peaches.

# Fall Harvest Muffins

1¾ cups whole grain pastry flour

1½ teaspoons ground cinnamon

1 teaspoon baking powder

½ teaspoon baking soda

½ teaspoon salt

2 large eggs

¾ cup canned solid-pack pumpkin

¼ cup unsweetened applesauce

4 tablespoons trans-free margarine, softened

¾ cup packed brown sugar

½ cup coarsely chopped walnuts

½ cup dried cranberries

**PREHEAT** the oven to 350°F. Line a muffin pan with paper liners or coat with cooking spray.

**COMBINE** the flour, cinnamon, baking powder, baking soda, and salt in a large bowl.

**WHISK** together the eggs, pumpkin, applesauce, margarine, and sugar. Stir into the flour mixture just until blended. Fold in the walnuts and cranberries.

**FILL** the muffin cups two-thirds full with the mixture. Bake for 22 to 25 minutes or until a toothpick inserted in the center comes out clean. Remove to a rack to cool.

Total time: 40 minutes ✱ Makes 12 muffins

Per muffin: 205 calories, 4 g protein, 31 g carbohydrate, 8 g fat, 2 g saturated fat, 254 mg sodium, 3 g fiber

## [ WHAT'S REALLY IN YOUR . . . REDUCED-FAT PEANUT BUTTER? ]

**Peanuts:** Packed with protein, fiber, healthy fats, and a host of other nutrients, peanuts—if eaten regularly—are linked with lower weight and decreased risk of diabetes.

**Corn syrup solids:** This concentrated form of corn syrup (code for sugar) is the second ingredient on the list, after peanuts. It gives this spread its sweet flavor but doesn't add much aside from calories.

**Soy protein:** Enhances texture, helps prevent the product from separating, and improves flavor and moisture retention. It also adds protein, which peanut butter already has in abundance.

**Fully hydrogenated vegetable oils:** Although they do not contain trans fats, these oils are a source of artery-clogging saturated fat.

**Mono- and diglycerides:** Emulsifiers that are added to foods to meld ingredients that don't normally mix together (think oil and water). While they're thought to be safe, there's no way to tell if they're derived from plants or animals—so vegetarians, beware.

**Better Buy:** Smucker's Natural Peanut Butter. For an additional 20 calories and 4 grams of fat per serving, you get only whole foods on the ingredients list: peanuts and salt.

—Brenda Hiddleston, Mississauga, Ontario

# Orange-Berry Muffins

1 whole medium navel orange, roughly chopped

⅓ cup trans-free margarine

1 large egg

½ cup fat-free milk

1¾ cups whole grain pastry flour

½ cup Splenda or other granular sugar substitute

1 teaspoon baking soda

½ teaspoon baking powder

¼ teaspoon salt

1 cup fresh or frozen blueberries

**PREHEAT** the oven to 375°F. Line 15 muffin cups with paper liners or coat with cooking spray.

**PLACE** the orange pieces, margarine, egg, and milk in a blender or food processor. Blend until the orange is finely chopped.

**COMBINE** the flour, Splenda, baking soda, baking powder, and salt in a large bowl. Stir in the orange mixture just until blended. Fold in the blueberries.

**FILL** the muffin cups two-thirds full with the mixture. Bake for 22 to 25 minutes or until a toothpick inserted in the center comes out clean. Remove to a rack to cool.

Total time: 35 minutes ✳ Makes 15 muffins

Per muffin: 95 calories, 2 g protein, 12 g carbohydrate, 4 g fat, 1 g saturated fat, 193 mg sodium, 2 g fiber

Breakfasts

I love this recipe because it is a family favorite and has been handed down from an aunt to my mom and now to me. It was originally made with butter, whipping cream, and white sugar, but I have changed it to reduce the fat and sugar. **—Brenda**

—Abigail Bradshaw, Meridian, Idaho

# Pumpkin Zucchini Spice Bread

- 1½ cups whole grain pastry flour
- 1½ cups all-purpose flour
- 2 teaspoons ground cinnamon
- ½ teaspoon ground nutmeg
- ¼ teaspoon ground cloves
- ½ teaspoon salt
- 2 teaspoons baking powder
- 1 teaspoon baking soda
- 3 large eggs
- 1 cup canned solid-pack pumpkin
- 1 cup packed brown sugar or ½ cup honey
- ½ cup (1 stick) trans-free margarine, softened
- 1 tablespoon vanilla extract
- 2 cups shredded zucchini
- ½ cup finely chopped pecans

**PREHEAT** the oven to 350°F. Coat a 9" × 5" loaf pan with cooking spray.

**COMBINE** the flours, cinnamon, nutmeg, cloves, salt, baking powder, and baking soda in a large bowl.

**WHISK** together the eggs, pumpkin, brown sugar, margarine, and vanilla in a medium bowl until light and fluffy. Stir in the zucchini. Stir into the flour mixture just until blended. Fold in the pecans.

**POUR** into the prepared pan. Bake for 60 to 70 minutes or until a toothpick inserted in the center comes out clean. Cool on a rack for 10 minutes. Remove from the pan and cool completely.

-----

Total time: 1 hour 25 minutes   ✳   Makes 16 servings

Per serving: 228 calories, 4 g protein, 32 g carbohydrate, 9 g fat, 2 g saturated fat, 303 mg sodium, 3 g fiber

Cinnamon, a pronounced flavor in this bread, not only tastes great but is also good for you. Studies have found that cinnamon may help control blood sugar levels.

**[ NUTRITION NEWS TO USE**
At least 11 popular breakfast cereals contain 12 grams of sugar or more— roughly the same amount as a frosted doughnut. **]**

# Breakfast Berry "Sundaes"

2 cups fat-free plain yogurt

½ teaspoon vanilla extract

2 teaspoons toasted wheat germ (optional)

½ teaspoon ground cinnamon

3 tablespoons dried cranberries or cherries

3 tablespoons granola or muesli

2 cups blueberries

3 tablespoons toasted pecans, chopped

**MIX** the yogurt and vanilla in a medium bowl. Divide the yogurt among 4 bowls, reserving ¼ cup. Sprinkle with the wheat germ and cinnamon.

**SCATTER** the cranberries, granola, and blueberries over each serving. Top each serving with 1 tablespoon of the remaining yogurt. Sprinkle with the pecans.

Total time: 10 minutes ❋ Makes 6 servings

Per serving: 208 calories, 7 g protein, 26 g carbohydrate, 10 g fat, 3 g saturated fat, 59 mg sodium, 4 g fiber

Give Greek yogurt a try in this and other dishes. It's available fat free and is a thicker version of yogurt, making it seem more like a full-fat product.

## NUTRITION NEWS TO USE

Grab some wild blueberries when you stock up on frozen foods. Researchers at Cornell University tested 25 fruits for antioxidant activity and found that tangy-sweet wild blueberries (which are smaller than their cultivated cousins) packed the most absorbable antioxidants. Their levels exceeded those of nutrient-rich pomegranates and grapes. Buy: Frozen brands like Dole and Wyman & Sons. Try: Tossing them into salads or mixing with ½ cup of low-fat ricotta and a drizzle of honey.

—Melissa Rorie, Hyattsville, Maryland

# Mixed Fruit Breakfast Smoothie

¾ **cup soy milk**

¼ **cup low-fat ricotta cheese**

½ **cup frozen cranberries**

⅓ **cup frozen mixed fruit**

**PLACE** the soy milk, ricotta, cranberries, and fruit in a blender or food processor. Process for 1 minute or until pureed and well blended.

Total time: 2 minutes ✱ Makes 1 serving

Per serving: 209 calories, 14 g protein, 24 g carbohydrate, 6 g fat, 2 g saturated fat, 156 mg sodium, 6 g fiber

This smoothie is all-natural, tastes great, and is only about 200 calories. I actually put it in a bowl and sprinkle ½ cup of Fiber One on top and eat it like I would ice cream.
—**Melissa**

# Strawberry Soy-Fu Smoothie

1 package (14 ounces) firm tofu, drained and cut into quarters

3 cups fresh or frozen strawberries

½ cup low-fat vanilla soy milk

¼ cup honey

1 orange, juiced

**PLACE** the tofu, strawberries, soy milk, honey, and orange juice in a blender. Process until smooth.

Total time: 5 minutes ✱ Makes 6 servings

Per serving: 148 calories, 8 g protein, 21 g carbohydrate, 5 g fat, 1 g saturated fat, 17 mg sodium, 2 g fiber

Typically you would use silken tofu for drinks; however, I like very thick smoothies so I use firm tofu and blend a bit longer. Feel free to substitute cherries, blueberries, raspberries, or blackberries when they are in season.

**—Yolanda**

[ it worked for me ]

# 70 lbs lost!

## ❋ KAREN BRENNAN

**A heartfelt plea from her daughter was the push Karen Brennan needed to embrace exercise and start eating smart**

### My Story

You might say I was born to be heavy—the biggest baby out of three siblings. Early on, I was compulsive about food. If my mom baked a cake at night, I'd sneak downstairs in the morning to lick off the frosting. As an adult, my weight yo-yoed, until I became a mother and decided it was time to get healthy. I joined Weight Watchers and started swimming and measuring meals. By my 30th birthday, I weighed 145 pounds and felt ready to take on anything.

### The Fall of Supermom

With all my new energy and dreams of being the mom who saved the world, I launched a recycling business. My family hauled 22 tons of recyclables out of our neighborhood—but then I herniated a disk. That was the end of my wonderful new beginning. I was in far too much pain to work out. The setback was disheartening, but instead of dealing with my sadness, I threw my energy into taking care of my kids. Between Girl Scouts and soccer, snacks were always around and my habit reared its ugly head

## VITAL STATS

Pounds Lost: 70

Age: 50

Height: 5'6"

Weight Then: 205

Weight Now: 135 pounds

Health Bonus: "I Beat a
Lifelong Weight Problem"

again. I entered a 15-year cycle of eating, gaining weight, feeling depressed, and eating more.

## Child Support

By the time my daughter returned from her first year at college, I had reached 205 pounds, my heaviest weight yet. One day she leaned over and whispered, "Mom, I want you to take care of yourself." Before, when my husband suggested I join a gym, it felt hurtful, but it was different coming from my child. Soon after, I signed up.

Starting out was tough. When you're heavy, people act like you're invisible. There were days I wanted to quit—but I would think about my family and keep going. I slowly strengthened my back, and eventually, my three visits a week became six.

I began to change my diet, too. One year later, I had lost 70 pounds. Now I'm 50 years old and feel more confident than ever. And these days, as a certified fitness trainer, I'm the one providing encouragement. I prefer to work with very heavy clients in a studio or in their homes to make the process less scary. My flyer has pictures of me then and now, and I always tell clients, "If I could do it, so can you!"

## My Top Tips

✻ Don't eliminate favorites . . . just cut back on them. I'd enjoy bread and pasta in moderation—but to control my tendency to overeat, I wouldn't eat them past 3 pm.

✻ Eat often . . . to help maintain your energy levels. Just keep portion sizes small.

✻ Just exercise . . . even if you don't feel like it. You can't sit around and do nothing an d expect the pounds to roll off!

✻ Use a sound track . . . to pump up your workout. When I didn't want to be at the gym, hip-hop and old rock 'n' roll could get me in the mood.

✻ Make some new friends . . . who support your active lifestyle. I've found a wonderful group of buddies at the gym who help keep me on track.

✻ Remember . . . the benefits. I used to have heel spurs that were unbearable because of the extra weight I was carrying on my frame. Now I can walk anywhere I want without pain!

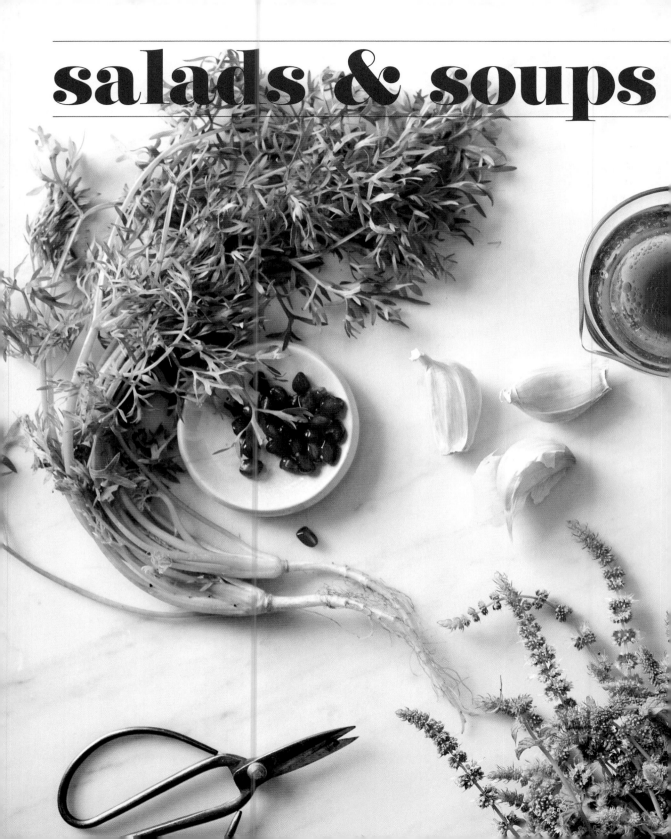

# salads & soups

# Avocado Salad

4  very thin slices red onion, separated into rings

2  oranges

2  avocados

3  tablespoons olive oil

2  tablespoons chopped fresh mint leaves

1  tablespoon lemon juice

¼  teaspoon salt

**SOAK** the onion in a small bowl of ice water to crisp. Peel the oranges with a knife, removing all of the white pith. Cut crosswise into thin circles.

**PIT,** peel, and slice the avocados and place in a medium bowl. Drain the onion well and add to the bowl along with the oranges, oil, mint, lemon juice, and salt. Gently toss to coat.

Total time: 15 minutes  ✱  Makes 4 servings

Per serving: 286 calories, 3 g protein, 18 g carbohydrate, 25 g fat, 4 g saturated fat, 153 mg sodium, 9 g fiber

Beautifully balanced flavors make this salad a taste bonanza. Tart-sweet oranges, piquant red onion, and refreshing mint complement the rich avocados perfectly.

Avocados are bursting with heart-healthy, disease-fighting MUFAS (monounsaturated fatty acids). Numerous studies show that a diet rich in MUFAs is linked to a reduction in LDL cholesterol, the kind that clogs up arteries, and a boost in HDL, the kind that sweeps cholesterol out of the arteries and clears it from the body. They can also lower the risk of heart disease and improve insulin levels. And exciting new research shows that MUFAs can actually help you lose weight, specifically around your middle.

✱ A RIPE AVOCADO is just slightly pliant when gently pressed.

✱ RIPEN at room temperature—faster if you put them in a closed paper bag to capture the ethylene gas (which promotes ripening) given off by the fruit.

✱ TO PREVENT BROWNING of a cut avocado, spread the surface with lemon juice, lime juice, or vinegar.

✱ REFRIGERATE cut avocados in plastic wrap pressed directly onto the cut surface. To eat, scrape off any discoloration; the flavor won't be affected.

✱ TO CHOOSE: Lush California Haas packs a wallop of healthy monounsaturated fat. A Florida avocado has less flavor and less fat.

✱ TO HALVE: Cut avocado in two lengthwise around its pit. Twist halves in opposite directions to separate them and then pull apart.

✱ TO PIT: First, thrust the blade of a sharp paring knife into the pit. Then twist the knife gently to loosen the pit and lift it out.

✱ TO PEEL: Pull the skin off the flesh in strips with your fingers. When the fruit is very ripe, you can often remove the skin in one piece.

[ EAT MORE AVOCADOS! ]

# Beet-Avocado-Pear "Carpaccio"

16 ounces red or golden beets

2 cups arugula leaves

1 tablespoon toasted walnut oil

1 medium avocado, pitted, peeled, and thinly sliced lengthwise

1 tablespoon cider vinegar

Salt

2 medium pears, thinly sliced

1 tablespoon lemon juice

¼ cup crumbled Roquefort or Gorgonzola cheese

¼ cup walnuts, lightly toasted and finely chopped

**PREHEAT** the oven to 400°F. Trim the beet stems to about 1". Wash the beets well. Don't pierce the skin or they'll bleed.

**PLACE** the beets on a sheet of foil, fold into an airtight packet, and place on a baking sheet. Bake the beets for 1 hour or until tender. When cool enough to handle, remove the skins and thinly slice the beets. Cover and chill until ready to prepare the salad.

**SCATTER** the arugula on 6 small plates. Place the beets on the arugula and drizzle with the oil. Top with the avocado and immediately drizzle with vinegar to keep from discoloring. Season with salt.

**LAY** the pear slices on the plates and sprinkle the entire salad with the lemon juice. Top with the cheese and walnuts.

---

Total time: 1 hour 20 minutes  ✱  Makes 6 servings

Per serving: 191 calories, 4 g protein, 20 g carbohydrate, 12 g fat, 2 g saturated fat, 149 mg sodium, 6 g fiber

Arugula is an excellent bone builder, supplying vitamin K, calcium, and magnesium. If you find its flavor too strong, try sweet-tasting baby arugula. If you roast the beets ahead, this salad can be ready in minutes.

**NUTRITION NEWS YOU CAN USE**

Add olive oil, nuts, or avocado to veggie-packed salads. They will increase your absorption of the disease-fighting compounds called carotenoids—including lutein and zeaxanthin, which help protect against cataracts and macular degeneration.

# Beet and Arugula Salad
# with Sunflower Seed Vinaigrette

3 medium beets

3 tablespoons olive oil

1 tablespoon red wine vinegar

3 tablespoons unsalted
  sunflower seeds, toasted

¼ teaspoon salt

⅛ teaspoon black pepper

6 cups arugula leaves

2 ounces goat cheese, crumbled

**HEAT** the oven to 400°F. Trim the beet stems to about 1". Wash the beets well. Don't pierce the skin or they'll bleed.

**PLACE** the beets on a sheet of foil, fold into an airtight packet, and place on a baking sheet. Bake the beets for 1 hour or until tender. When cool enough to handle, remove the skins and cut the beets into ½" cubes. Cover and chill until ready to prepare the salad.

**WHISK** together the oil, vinegar, sunflower seeds, salt, and pepper in a large bowl. Add the arugula, tossing gently to coat. Place on 6 small plates. Top with the beets and sprinkle with the cheese.

Total time: 1 hour 15 minutes  ✱  Makes 6 servings

Per serving: 146 calories, 4 g protein, 6 g carbohydrate, 12 g fat, 3 g saturated fat, 86 mg sodium, 2 g fiber

Salads and Soups

✱

Naturally sweet beets are lower in calories than they taste. Use red or yellow beets or, for a colorful dish, a mix of both.

# Peachy Red Cabbage Salad

½ cup cider vinegar

¼ cup red wine

¼ cup Splenda or other granular
  sugar substitute

2 tablespoons olive oil

  Salt and black pepper

1 medium head red cabbage,
  coarsely chopped

½ large onion, chopped

2 peaches, peeled, pitted, and
  chopped

**WHISK** together the vinegar, wine, Splenda, and oil in a large bowl. Season with salt and pepper, as desired. Add the cabbage, onion, and peaches; toss to coat well.

Total time: 10 minutes  ✱  Makes 8 servings

Per serving: 98 calories, 2 g protein, 16 g carbohydrate, 4 g fat, 1 g saturated fat, 75 mg sodium, 3 g fiber

Fresh summer peaches add sweetness to this tangy dressing tossed with red cabbage.

**SUPERFOOD SPOTLIGHT: CELERIAC**

Grown just for its tasty root (its stems and leaves are usually tossed), this ugly duckling cousin of the celery plant makes a delicious low-cal potato sub. Celeriac, or celery root, tastes like a cross between celery and parsley. One cup (raw) has 66 calories and 10% of your daily requirement of blood pressure–lowering potassium and nearly three-quarters of your daily vitamin K requirement.

✱ A small vegetable that is firm, with as few roots as possible.

✱ Shred into salads, chop and roast in a bit of olive oil, or boil cubes until tender and puree (on their own or mix into mashed potatoes or turnips). Trim or peel the outer roots and crevices, which can harbor dirt.

—Karen Ginn, Montgomery, Illinois

# Delicious Coleslaw

1  cup low-fat sour cream

2  tablespoons white wine vinegar

1  teaspoon chopped fresh dill

¼  teaspoon salt

¼  teaspoon black pepper

½  medium green cabbage, finely sliced

1  carrot, shredded

½  cup pineapple chunks

**MIX** the sour cream, vinegar, dill, salt, and pepper in a large bowl. Add the cabbage, carrot, and pineapple. Toss to mix well.

Total time: 15 minutes  ✳  Makes 4 servings

Per serving: 140 calories, 5 g protein, 15 g carbohydrate, 8 g fat, 5 g saturated fat, 213 mg sodium, 3 g fiber

## QUICK TIP: FOOD'S COLD-COMFORT ZONE

Keep a basic thermometer in your refrigerator and make sure it doesn't rise above 40°F, suggest Tennessee State University researchers. Cold stifles bacterial growth, preventing spoilage. Yet only 10% of fridge owners keep a thermometer inside (the "coldness dial" doesn't cut it). Install one, check it daily, and store perishables such as dairy products on the top shelf (the coldest area) and away from the fridge door. Nearly 40% of doors topped 40°F for 24 hours straight, even when left closed.

# Asian Cucumber Salad

3 tablespoons rice wine vinegar

2 teaspoons packed dark brown sugar

1 tablespoon lime juice

1 tablespoon grated fresh ginger

½ small Thai chile pepper, finely chopped, or ¼ teaspoon red-pepper flakes

1 tablespoon toasted sesame oil

1 large cucumber, peeled and very thinly sliced

¼ cup loosely packed, roughly chopped fresh basil leaves

¼ cup loosely packed, roughly chopped fresh mint leaves

**PLACE** the vinegar and sugar in a small saucepan and bring to a boil over medium-high heat. Immediately reduce the heat to a steady simmer and cook for 5 minutes or until reduced to about 1½ table-spoons. Pour into a serving bowl and let cool for about 10 minutes.

**STIR** in the lime juice, ginger, pepper, and oil.

**ADD** the cucumber, basil, and mint and toss until well coated. Serve immediately.

Total time: 20 minutes  ✽  Makes 4 servings

Per serving: 52 calories, 1 g protein, 5 g carbohydrate, 4 g fat, 1 g saturated fat, 5 mg sodium, 1 g fiber

The mix of basil and mint is divine, but if you have only one herb, don't let that keep you from enjoying this delicious salad. Simply use double the amount of basil or 1½ times the quantity of mint suggested.

## NUTRITION NEWS TO USE

Be wary of what you eat on Saturday—your waistline could end up with a case of the Mondays in the weeks ahead, say Washington University School of Medicine researchers. Using food diaries, exercise monitors, and a series of weigh-ins, they tracked 48 adults (ages 50 to 60) and found that partici-pants consumed more calories on Saturday than on any other day of the week. Over a year, say the researchers, the extra noshing would add up to 9 more pounds.

# Jicama and Carrot Salad

2 limes, juiced

½ cup chopped cilantro

½ teaspoon sugar or sugar
  substitute

¼ teaspoon salt

¼ teaspoon black pepper

1 medium jicama, julienned

3 carrots, julienned

**WHISK** together the lime juice, cilantro, sugar, salt, and pepper in a medium bowl. Add the jicama and carrots and toss to coat well.

---

Total time: 20 minutes  ✳  Makes 6 servings

Per serving: 68 calories, 1 g protein, 16 g carbohydrate, 0 g fat, 0 g saturated fat, 122 mg sodium, 7 g fiber

I really enjoy this recipe because of its texture, lively flavor, and few ingredients. I created it long before I saw other jicama salads in the media. My recipe contains no fat and does not need any.  **—Pamela**

# Warm Potato Salad with Tarragon

1½   pounds boiling potatoes

1½   tablespoons white wine vinegar

1   tablespoon Dijon mustard

½   teaspoon salt

¼   cup olive oil

1   tablespoon roughly chopped fresh tarragon

2   scallions, thinly sliced

2   cloves garlic, minced

**PLACE** the potatoes in a medium saucepan. Bring to a boil over high heat. Reduce the heat to medium and cook, covered, for 20 minutes or until tender when pierced with a fork.

**WHISK** together the vinegar, mustard, and salt in a medium bowl. Whisk in the oil, tarragon, scallions, and garlic.

**DRAIN** the potatoes. When cool enough to handle, cut into cubes. Add to the dressing and toss to coat well.

Total time: 30 minutes  ✳  Makes 4 servings

Per serving: 255 calories, 3 g protein, 31 g carbohydrate, 14 g fat, 2 g saturated fat, 534 mg sodium, 3 g fiber

✳

Tarragon, scallions, and garlic add lively flavor to this potato salad. Use dill or basil instead of the tarragon for variety.

**NUTRITION NEWS TO USE**
Nearly 80% of the salt in our diets is hidden in processed foods such as bread and canned soups and veggies. That excess sodium can raise your risk of heart disease. Now big-name companies like Pepperidge Farm, Campbell's, and Del Monte are rolling out new reduced-salt versions of old favorites such as chicken noodle soup and canned sweet peas, slashing sodium content by 25 to 50%. Read labels to make sure you're not getting more than the recommended 2,300 miligrams per day.

# Pasta Salad with Cucumber, Red Pepper, and Feta

- 6 ounces multigrain penne, elbow, or shells pasta
- ½ cup fat-free sour cream
- ½ cup reduced-fat mayonnaise
- ¼ cup crumbled feta cheese
- 3 tablespoons chopped fresh mint leaves
- 3 tablespoons 2% milk
- 1 tablespoon Dijon mustard
- 1 teaspoon lemon juice
- ¼ teaspoon salt
- ¼ teaspoon black pepper
- 1 medium cucumber, chopped
- 1 red bell pepper, chopped

**PREPARE** the pasta according to the package directions. Drain into a colander and rinse under cold water until cool.

**STIR** together the sour cream, mayonnaise, cheese, mint, milk, mustard, lemon juice, salt, and black pepper in a large bowl.

**ADD** the pasta, cucumber, and bell pepper. Toss to coat well.

Total time: 30 minutes ✳ Makes 4 servings

Per serving: 323 calories, 12 g protein, 40 g carbohydrate, 14 g fat, 4 g saturated fat, 591 mg sodium, 4 g fiber

Put this salad together on the morning of your barbecue bash and refrigerate until ready to serve.

# Cantaloupe and Watercress Salad with Pickled Onions

2 tablespoons honey

¼ teaspoon grated lime zest

2 tablespoons lime juice

1 tablespoon olive oil

¼ teaspoon black pepper

⅛ teaspoon salt

½ red onion, chopped

3 cups cantaloupe cubes

2 plums, thinly sliced

1 bunch watercress, tough stems trimmed

2 tablespoons crumbled goat cheese or feta cheese

2 tablespoons sliced almonds or pumpkin seeds

**WHISK** together the honey, lime zest and lime juice, oil, pepper, and salt in a large bowl. Stir in the onion and let stand for 5 minutes.

**ADD** the cantaloupe, plums, and watercress and toss to coat well. Sprinkle with the cheese and almonds. Serve immediately.

Total time: 20 minutes  ✱  Makes 6 servings

Per serving: 104 calories, 2 g protein, 17 g carbohydrate, 5 g fat, 1 g saturated fat, 97 mg sodium, 2 g fiber

Both cantaloupe and plums are succulent, low-calorie treats that are just as tempting as any delicious salad but with a kiss of fiber thrown in for good measure.

# Spring Greens with Chive Vinaigrette

3 tablespoons chopped chives

1½ tablespoons white wine vinegar

½ teaspoon salt

¼ teaspoon black pepper

¼ cup + ½ tablespoon extra virgin olive oil

8 cups lightly packed mixed spring greens, like arugula, mâche, and frisée

**WHISK** together the chives, vinegar, salt, and pepper in a large bowl. Lightly crush the chives. Whisk in the oil.

**ADD** the greens and toss to coat well. Divide the salad among 6 small plates.

Total time: 10 minutes ✳ Makes 6 servings

Per serving: 107 calories, 1 g protein, 2 g carbohydrate, 11 g fat, 2 g saturated fat, 179 mg sodium, 2 g fiber

✳

The first tender lettuces that sprout after a long winter always seem to taste the best, but this vinaigrette is delicious with any greens. Try baby romaine, bibb, or green leaf lettuce in place of the spring greens for a change of pace.

—Judi Berman-Yamada, Portland, Oregon

# Feta-Walnut Stuffed Cucumbers

½ cup walnut halves

¼ cup chopped parsley

½ cup crumbled feta cheese

¼ cup fat-free milk

1 clove garlic, minced

½ teaspoon ground mild paprika

⅛ teaspoon ground red pepper

4 medium cucumbers, peeled, halved lengthwise, and seeded

**COMBINE** the walnuts and parsley in a blender or food processor and pulse until powdery in texture. Add the cheese, milk, garlic, paprika, and cayenne and process until smooth.

**FILL** the cucumbers with the mixture, patting it into place with a fork or spoon. Slice as desired and lightly sprinkle the tops with additional paprika, if desired.

Total time: 20 minutes ✳ Makes 4 servings

Per serving: 164 calories, 6 g protein, 8 g carbohydrate, 13 g fat, 4 g saturated fat, 222 mg sodium, 3 g fiber

✳

Salty feta mixes nicely with the flavor of slightly bitter walnuts, a prime source of omega-3 fats, which may enhance brain function.

# Grilled Chicken with Sweet 'n' Sour Squash Salad

¼ cup olive oil

¼ cup fat-free ranch dressing

¼ cup sugar

½ teaspoon black pepper

⅛ teaspoon salt

4 grilled or roasted boneless, skinless chicken breast halves, cut into thin strips

3 ribs celery, sliced

4 medium zucchini, halved and thinly sliced

1 large red onion, thinly sliced

1 red bell pepper, diced

1 green bell pepper, diced

**WHISK** together the oil, dressing, sugar, black pepper, and salt in a large bowl. Add the chicken, celery, zucchini, onion, and bell peppers. Toss to coat well.

Total time: 20 minutes ✱ Makes 8 servings

Per serving: 196 calories, 15 g protein, 17 g carbohydrate, 8 g fat, 1 g saturated fat, 202 mg sodium, 2 g fiber

✱

This colorful salad is bursting with healthy vegetables bathed in a quick dressing. Serve with whole grain rolls for a quick meal.

## NUTRITION NEWS TO USE

Snacking on celery and green bell peppers may help keep your mind sharp. Luteolin, a plant compound abundant in these two green veggies, can prevent inflammation in the brain linked with aging and diseases such as Alzheimer's and multiple sclerosis, according to researchers at the University of Illinois. The scientists studied the compound's effect on human brain cells in a test tube and on mice, and in both cases found that it decreased inflammation.

Try dipping celery and green bell pepper slices in hummus, or chop and mix with tuna, herbs (like parsley or chives), and a dollop of plain yogurt for a healthy tuna salad.

# Berry Special Chicken Salad

3 tablespoons Splenda or other granular sugar substitute

¼ cup red wine vinegar

2 tablespoons extra virgin olive oil

1 teaspoon poppy seeds

½ teaspoon mustard powder

6 cups rinsed, dried, and torn spinach leaves or 1 bag (6 ounces) baby spinach

2 cups cooked, cubed chicken

2 cups sliced strawberries

1 cup pomegranate seeds

**WHISK** together the sugar substitute, vinegar, oil, poppy seeds, and mustard in a large bowl. Add the spinach, chicken, strawberries, and pomegranate seeds. Toss to combine.

---

Total time: 15 minutes  ✱  Makes 6 servings

Per serving: 183 calories, 14 g protein, 16 g carbohydrate, 7 g fat, 1 g saturated fat, 65 mg sodium, 3 g fiber

This salad comes together in minutes. If you'd like to prepare it ahead of time, combine the dressing and salad ingredients separately and then toss everything together at the last minute.

## NUTRITION NEWS TO USE

What you eat (and don't) may play a major role in your risk of developing type 2 diabetes, according to a new study from researchers at Tulane University and Harvard School of Public Health who tracked the eating habits of more than 71,000 women for 18 years. Here's how to prevent the disease, based on their research.

**Add:** Leafy greens. For every additional serving of spinach, kale, or chard you eat, you may lessen your likelihood by as much as 9%.

**Add:** Whole fruit. For every three servings, you may slash your diabetes risk by up to 18%.

**Avoid:** Juice. Consuming one serving a day may raise your odds by nearly 18%. Some varieties are rich in antioxidants, but if you're at risk of diabetes, consider trading your daily glass of juice for whole fruit.

# Summer Breeze Tropical Fruit Chicken Salad

1 small banana, sliced

½ cup pineapple juice, divided

3 tablespoons balsamic vinegar

½ teaspoon salt

¼ teaspoon black pepper

6 tablespoons olive oil, divided

1 head romaine lettuce, chopped

1 cup chopped fresh pineapple

1 ripe mango, peeled, pitted, and chopped

3 scallions, chopped

1 pound boneless, skinless chicken breast halves, cut into thin strips

2 tablespoons grated coconut

**MIX** the banana and ¼ cup pineapple juice in a small bowl.

**WHISK** the remaining ¼ cup pineapple juice, vinegar, salt, and pepper in another small bowl. Slowly whisk in 4 tablespoons oil until well blended.

**PLACE** the lettuce on a large serving platter. Scatter the banana, pineapple, mango, and scallions over the lettuce.

**HEAT** the remaining 2 tablespoons oil in a large skillet over medium-high heat. Add the chicken and cook, stirring constantly, for 5 minutes or until golden brown and no longer pink. Place over the lettuce and drizzle with the dressing. Top with the coconut.

---

Total time: 15 minutes   ✱   Makes 4 servings

Per serving: 427 calories, 28 g protein, 29 g carbohydrate, 23 g fat, 4 g saturated fat, 380 mg sodium, 4 g fiber

This summer salad takes the boring out of chicken salad and makes it an exciting main dish that is healthy and tasty.

—**Donna**

# Shrimp and Crab Salad
# with Edamame and Tarragon

3 tablespoons mayonnaise

3 tablespoons sour cream

½ teaspoon grated lemon zest

2 tablespoons lemon juice

1¼ pounds chilled cooked shrimp, tails removed

12 ounces Dungeness or blue crabmeat

1½ cups cooked shelled edamame or thawed frozen edamame

2 scallions, finely chopped

1 tablespoon chopped fresh tarragon

**WHISK** together the mayonnaise, sour cream, lemon zest, and lemon juice in a large bowl. Add the shrimp, crab, edamame, scallions, and tarragon. Toss to coat well.

---

Total time: 30 minutes  ✳  Makes 6 servings

Per serving: 265 calories, 37 g protein, 6 g carbohydrate, 10 g fat, 2 g saturated fat, 502 mg sodium, 1 g fiber

✳

You can find cooked, shelled edamame (soybeans) in the refrigerator section of most supermarkets. Buy the seafood already cooked, too. If you like, garnish with lemon wedges.

# Pan-Seared Spicy Scallops Salad

2 tomatoes, chopped

1 mango, peeled, pitted, and chopped

½ small onion, chopped

¼ cup chopped cilantro

2 tablespoons lime juice

1 teaspoon finely chopped jalapeño pepper (wear plastic gloves when handling)

1 tablespoon chili powder

1 teaspoon ground cumin

½ teaspoon salt

¼ teaspoon black pepper

1 pound sea scallops, trimmed

1 tablespoon extra virgin olive oil

8 cups mesclun or mixed greens

**COMBINE** the tomatoes, mango, onion, cilantro, lime juice, and jalapeño in a medium bowl. Set aside.

**COMBINE** the chili powder, cumin, salt, and pepper on a plate. Add the scallops and toss to coat.

**HEAT** the oil in a large nonstick skillet over medium-high heat. Add the scallops and cook, stirring, for 3 minutes or until opaque.

**DIVIDE** the mesclun among 4 plates and top with the tomato mixture. Top with the scallops.

------------------------------------

Total time: 25 minutes ✱ Makes 4 servings

Per serving: 305 calories, 40 g protein, 25 g carbohydrate, 6 g fat, 1 g saturated fat, 762 mg sodium, 5 g fiber

Scallops have a muscle used for opening and closing their shells. This small muscle is very tough and should be removed before cooking. Simply peel the muscle from the scallop and discard.

—Lesley Pew, Lynn, Massachusetts

# Wilted Spinach Salad with Steak and Pasta

½ cup balsamic vinegar

¼ cup olive oil

6 cloves garlic, minced

¾ teaspoon dried basil

¾ teaspoon dried tarragon

¾ teaspoon ground cumin

1½ pounds top round sirloin steak

6 ounces whole grain penne pasta

Salt and black pepper

1 package (10 ounces) spinach, rinsed, dried, and torn into bite-size pieces

1 red onion, cut into thin wedges

½ cup golden raisins

**COAT** a grill rack or broiler pan with cooking spray. Preheat the grill or broiler.

**WHISK** together the vinegar, oil, garlic, basil, tarragon, and cumin in a measuring cup. Transfer ½ cup to a 13" × 9" baking dish and add the steak. Cover and refrigerate for 30 minutes or up to 24 hours. Cover and refrigerate the remaining oil mixture.

**PREPARE** the pasta according to the package directions; drain.

**REMOVE** the steak from the marinade; discard the marinade. Grill or broil the steak for 10 to 14 minutes, turning once, until a thermometer inserted in the center registers 145°F for medium-rare or 160°F for medium. Let stand for 10 minutes before slicing into thin strips. Season with salt and pepper.

**PLACE** the spinach in a large bowl. Toss with the pasta, onion, raisins, and the remaining oil mixture. Divide among 6 plates. Top with the steak.

Total time: 25 minutes + marinating time  **✱**  Makes 6 servings

Per serving: 429 calories, 32 g protein, 44 g carbohydrate, 15 g fat, 3 g saturated fat, 152 mg sodium, 4 g fiber

**✱**

Warm steak and pasta gently wilt the spinach in this salad, mellowing its bitterness. With its zesty red onion and sweet raisins, this meal is bursting with flavors.

# Beefy Onion Soup

2 tablespoons olive oil

8 ounces flank steak, trimmed

3 large onions, thinly sliced

2 teaspoons sugar

2 cloves garlic, minced

2 tablespoons balsamic vinegar

4 cups reduced-sodium beef broth

1 teaspoon Worcestershire sauce

½ cup whole wheat bread crumbs

Chopped chives (optional)

**HEAT** 1 tablespoon of the oil in a large pot over medium-high heat. Add the steak and cook for 4 to 6 minutes, turning once, for medium-rare. Transfer to a cutting board and let stand for 5 minutes. Slice across the grain into thin strips.

**ADD** the remaining oil to the pot and reduce the heat to medium. Add the onions and sugar. Cook, stirring occasionally, for 25 minutes or until golden. Add the garlic and cook for 2 minutes.

**INCREASE** the heat to medium-high, add the vinegar, and bring to a boil. Cook, stirring, for 1 minute or until the vinegar is almost completely evaporated. Add the broth and Worcestershire sauce. Bring to a boil, then reduce the heat to low. Cover and simmer for 15 minutes. Stir in the bread crumbs and cook for 2 to 3 minutes or until slightly thickened.

**DIVIDE** the soup among 4 bowls. Top with the reserved steak slices and garnish with chives.

Total time: 1 hour   **✻**   Makes 4 servings

Per serving: 300 calories, 19 g protein, 27 g carbohydrate, 13 g fat, 3 g saturated fat, 634 mg sodium, 3 g fiber

✱

Flank steak is a lean cut of beef with only 158 calories per 3-ounce serving. It's usually sold whole, which weighs 1 to 1½ pounds, so cut what you need for this recipe, then freeze any remaining. (Wrap tightly in heavy-duty foil or a freezer storage bag and store for up to 6 months.)

# Super Supper Soup

1 can (10 ounces) minestrone soup

1¼ cups water

2 cups frozen cut green beans

1 can (15 ounces) no-salt-added pinto or kidney beans, rinsed and drained

1 can (14.5 ounces) no-salt-added diced tomatoes

½ cup salsa

¼ cup shredded Parmesan cheese

**MIX** the soup, water, green beans, canned beans, tomatoes, and salsa in a medium saucepan. Bring to a simmer over medium heat and cook for 15 minutes. Ladle into 4 bowls and sprinkle each with 1 tablespoon of cheese.

Total time: 20 minutes ✳ Makes 4 servings

Per serving: 194 calories, 11 g protein, 29 g carbohydrate, 4 g fat, 1 g saturated fat, 797 mg sodium, 7 g fiber

With just a few pantry ingredients on hand, you can whip up dinner in minutes. Serve this hearty soup along with a whole grain roll and simple salad. Perfect for nights when you feel too tired to cook!

## NUTRITION NEWS TO USE

**Fact** Air pollution damages not only your airways but also your heart, according to a recent study.

**Solution** Getting daily recommended amounts of vitamins $B_6$ and $B_{12}$, as well as the amino acid methionine, appears to create a protective buffer for the heart and lungs, say *Harvard Heart Letter* researchers. But don't just start taking supplements, they caution—instead, try eating plenty of whole grain cereals, broccoli, avocado, mushrooms, and methionine-rich foods such as eggs and fish.

# Chicken Sausage Minestrone

- 1 tablespoon extra virgin olive oil
- 2 links sweet low-fat Italian chicken or turkey sausage, thinly sliced
- 1 medium zucchini, thinly sliced
- 1 rib celery, diced
- 2 cloves garlic, minced
- 2 cups no-salt-added tomato sauce
- 1 box (10 ounces) frozen chopped spinach, thawed and squeezed dry
- 1 can (15 ounces) no-salt-added cannellini beans, rinsed and drained
- 8 cups (2 quarts) reduced-sodium chicken broth
- 2 cups low-carb elbow pasta
  Grated Parmesan cheese

**HEAT** the oil in a large soup pot over medium-high heat. Add the sausage and cook, stirring, for 4 minutes or until lightly browned. Add the zucchini, celery, and garlic and cook for 4 minutes or until just tender. Add the tomato sauce, spinach, beans, and broth.

**BRING** to a boil over high heat, reduce the heat to medium, and simmer for 10 minutes. Stir in the pasta. Reduce the heat to low and simmer for 15 to 20 minutes or until the pasta is tender. Serve sprinkled with Parmesan.

Total time: 50 minutes  ✳  Makes 6 servings

Per serving: 314 calories, 30 g protein, 34 g carbohydrate, 8 g fat, 2 g saturated fat, 383 mg sodium, 10 g fiber

I love this recipe because it is simple, quick, and healthy. It can be made with whatever vegetables are in season and tastes great with or without the sausage and beans.

—**Laura**

# Cauliflower Soup with Grilled Shrimp

3 teaspoons olive oil, divided

1 red onion, chopped

2 ribs celery, chopped

4 cups cauliflower florets

½ teaspoon ground coriander

2 cans (14.5 ounces each) reduced-sodium chicken broth

2½ cups water

12 ounces large shrimp, peeled and deveined

½ teaspoon salt, divided

¼ teaspoon black pepper, divided

⅓ cup fat-free evaporated milk

**COAT** a grill rack with cooking spray. Preheat the grill to medium-high.

**HEAT** 2 teaspoons of the oil in a large saucepan over medium heat. Add the onion and celery. Cook, stirring occasionally, for 6 minutes or until lightly browned. Stir in the cauliflower and coriander and cook for 2 minutes. Add the broth and water and bring to a boil. Reduce the heat to medium-low. Cover and simmer for 20 minutes or until the cauliflower is tender. Remove from the heat and cool for 5 minutes.

**SEASON** the shrimp with ¼ teaspoon salt, ⅛ teaspoon pepper, and the remaining 1 teaspoon oil. Grill for 5 minutes, turning once, until opaque.

**PUREE** the soup in batches in a blender or food processor. Return to the pan. Stir in the milk and the remaining ¼ teaspoon salt and ⅛ teaspoon pepper. Warm over medium heat until heated through.

**DIVIDE** into 4 bowls and top with the shrimp.

Total time: 55 minutes  ✱  Makes 4 servings

Per serving: 175 calories, 19 g protein, 15 g carbohydrate, 5 g fat, 1 g saturated fat, 487 mg sodium, 5 g fiber

✱

One cup of cauliflower contains nearly two-thirds of a full day's worth of vitamin C, a high intake of which may be linked to a lower risk of rheumatoid arthritis.

# Quick Thai Seafood Soup

1 tablespoon vegetable oil

2 cloves garlic, minced

1 cup sliced button mushrooms

½ red bell pepper, julienned

2 cups reduced-sodium chicken broth

2 cups water

1 cup clam juice

3 scallions, thinly sliced on the diagonal

2 small (2") pieces lemongrass (from bottom of stalk), smashed

1 large carrot, grated

¾ pound haddock or cod fillet, cut into 2" chunks

1 teaspoon grated lime zest

1 lime, juiced

¼ cup cilantro, chopped

1 teaspoon grated fresh ginger

1 teaspoon reduced-sodium soy sauce

½ teaspoon red-pepper flakes

**HEAT** the oil in a large pot over medium heat. Add the garlic and cook, stirring, for 2 minutes. Add the mushrooms and bell pepper and cook, stirring, for 4 minutes or until tender.

**ADD** the broth, water, clam juice, scallions, lemongrass, and carrot. Bring to a boil over high heat. Reduce the heat to low, cover, and simmer for 5 minutes. Add the fish, lime zest, and lime juice and simmer for 5 minutes or until the fish is opaque.

**STIR** in the cilantro, ginger, soy sauce, and pepper flakes. Remove and discard the lemongrass before serving. Ladle into 6 bowls.

Total time: 25 minutes ✳ Makes 6 servings

Per serving: 105 calories, 13 g protein, 5 g carbohydrate, 3 g fat, 0 g saturated fat, 222 mg sodium, 1 g fiber

✳

This simple soup is made with haddock, a mild-tasting seafood that has little saturated fat and is a good source of niacin to help raise "good" HDL cholesterol.

# Madras Split Pea Soup

### Raita

- 8 ounces fat-free plain yogurt
- 1 tablespoon chopped fresh mint or ½ teaspoon dried

### Soup

- 2 tablespoons olive oil
- 1 onion, coarsely chopped
- 3 cloves garlic, minced
- 2½ teaspoons ground cumin
- 1 teaspoon ground coriander
- 1 teaspoon ground ginger
- 1 teaspoon ground turmeric
- ¾ teaspoon black pepper
- 1½ cups green split peas, sorted and rinsed
- 4 cups reduced-sodium chicken broth
- 2 large carrots, sliced
- 1½ cups frozen cut spinach
- ½ teaspoon salt

To Make the Raita:

**COMBINE** the yogurt and mint in a small bowl. Cover and refrigerate until serving time.

To Make the Soup:

**HEAT** the oil in a Dutch oven over medium heat. Add the onion and garlic and cook, stirring, for 5 minutes or until tender. Add the cumin, coriander, ginger, turmeric, and pepper. Cook, stirring, for 1 minute. Stir in the split peas and broth.

**INCREASE** the heat and bring to a boil. Reduce the heat to low, cover, and simmer for 40 minutes or until the peas are very tender.

**ADD** the carrots, spinach, and salt. Cover and cook, stirring occasionally, for 15 minutes or until the carrots are tender.

**LADLE** the soup into 4 bowls and top each with some of the raita.

---

Total time: 1 hour 25 minutes  ✳  Makes 4 servings

Per serving: 426 calories, 26 g protein, 65 g carbohydrate, 7 g fat, 1 g saturated fat, 987 mg sodium, 4 g fiber

✳

Peas turn this recipe into a powerhouse of fiber and complex carbohydrates! This spice-laden soup digests slowly, so you'll be well satisfied for hours.

# Tex-Mex Tomato Soup

1 cup chopped carrots

1 cup chopped celery

¾ cup chopped red bell pepper

2¼ cups water, divided

1 tablespoon olive oil

1 cup chopped onion

¼ teaspoon salt

1 can (28 ounces) no-salt-added diced tomatoes

1 can (15 ounces) no-salt-added black beans, rinsed and drained

½ cup cilantro, chopped

2 tablespoons chipotle pepper sauce

1 lime, juiced

3 corn tortillas (6" diameter), sliced into ¼" strips

Reduced-fat sour cream (optional)

**PLACE** the carrots, celery, and bell pepper in a small microwave-safe bowl. Add ¼ cup water, cover the bowl loosely with plastic wrap, and microwave on high for 5 minutes or until the vegetables are just tender.

**HEAT** the oil in a large saucepan over medium heat. Add the onion and sauté until translucent, about 5 minutes. Add the steamed vegetables and salt. Sauté for 5 minutes or until the vegetables are slightly caramelized.

**ADD** the tomatoes (with juice) and 2 cups water. Add the beans, cilantro, and chipotle sauce and stir to blend. Bring to a simmer. Reduce the heat to low and cook for 25 to 30 minutes. Add the lime juice. Ladle into 6 bowls and top with tortilla strips and a dollop of sour cream.

Total time: 1 hour ✳ Makes 6 servings

Per serving: 138 calories, 5 g protein, 23 g carbohydrate, 3 g fat, 0 g saturated fat, 186 mg sodium, 6 g fiber

✳

Tomatoes are a top source of lycopene. In a large study, researchers found that women with high levels of the antioxidant had a 34% reduced risk of cardiovascular disease, compared with women with lower levels. Those who got plenty of lycopene were also more likely to have higher blood levels of other beneficial carotenoids such as lutein and beta-carotene.

# Creamy Roasted Garlic Soup

1 head garlic, unpeeled

1 tablespoon olive oil

1 onion, chopped

4 cups reduced-sodium chicken broth

2 cups thinly sliced carrots

1 tablespoon chopped fresh rosemary leaves

1 teaspoon dried basil

1½ cups cooked and mashed potatoes

1 large bunch Swiss chard, stemmed and chopped

1 can (15 ounces) cannellini beans, rinsed and drained

**PREHEAT** the oven to 425°F. Slice off the top third of the garlic head and discard. Wrap the garlic in foil and roast for 40 minutes. Let cool. Squeeze the roasted garlic from the papery skin into a small bowl and discard the skin.

**HEAT** the oil in a large saucepan over medium-high heat. Cook the onion, stirring, for 5 minutes or until translucent. Add the broth and about one-third of the garlic. Bring to a boil. Reduce the heat to low, cover, and simmer for 5 minutes.

**PROCESS** the mixture in batches in a blender or food processor until smooth. Return to the pan.

**STIR** in the carrots, rosemary, basil, and the remaining garlic. Cook over medium heat, stirring frequently, for 10 minutes.

**ADD** the potatoes, chard, and beans; cook, stirring, for 5 minutes or until the chard wilts. Ladle into 8 bowls.

----

Total time: 1 hour 30 minutes  ✳  Makes 8 servings

Per serving: 130 calories, 5 g protein, 23 g carbohydrate, 3 g fat, 1 g saturated fat, 500 mg sodium, 4 g fiber

✳

Roasting garlic softens the cloves and mellows its pungent flavor, creating a buttery garlic mash. Try using the garlic instead of butter on baked potatoes or spread it on sandwiches instead of mayo. Here it's blended into a rich potato soup.

# Hearty Bean Soup

1 pound dried navy beans, rinsed

6 cups reduced-sodium chicken broth

4 cups water

2 ribs celery, chopped

1 onion, finely chopped

1 carrot, finely chopped

4 cloves garlic, minced

1 bay leaf

3 tablespoons tomato paste

1½ teaspoons salt

½ teaspoon black pepper

¼ cup chopped parsley

**SOAK** the beans overnight in water that covers them by about 2 inches.

**PLACE** the drained beans in a large pot with the broth, water, celery, onion, carrot, garlic, and bay leaf. Bring to a boil. Reduce the heat to low. Partially cover and simmer for 1 hour or until the beans are almost tender.

**STIR** in the tomato paste and salt and cook for 30 to 45 minutes or until the beans are cooked through.

**REMOVE** and discard the bay leaf. Process about half of the bean mixture in a blender or food processor until smooth. Return to the pot and stir in the pepper and parsley. Ladle into 8 bowls.

Total time: 2 hours + soaking time ✳ Makes 8 servings

Per serving: 213 calories, 14 g protein, 39 g carbohydrate, 1 g fat, 0 g saturated fat, 919 mg sodium, 15 g fiber

Think of this tasty soup as a blank canvas for a plethora of flavor options. To make Italian, stir 3 tablespoons pesto and 1 cup cooked pasta into the finished soup. For a Mexican variation, use black beans and add ½ teaspoon red-pepper flakes and 2 teaspoons cumin with the tomato paste. Or, go chunky and add a chopped carrot, a diced potato, and a shredded head of Savoy cabbage to the vegetables.

—Diane Neibling, Overland Park, Kansas

# Cajun Black Bean Soup

- 2 cans (19 ounces each) black bean soup
- 1 can (14.5 ounces) diced tomatoes and green chiles
- 2 cups cooked instant brown rice
- 3 cups water
- ½ cup fat-free sour cream
- ½ cup shredded reduced-fat Cheddar cheese

**COMBINE** the soup, tomatoes, rice, and water in a large saucepan. Bring to a boil over high heat. Reduce the heat to low, cover, and simmer for 20 minutes.

**DIVIDE** into 4 bowls and top with the sour cream and cheese.

Total time: 30 minutes * Makes 4 servings

Per serving: 232 calories, 13 g protein, 43 g carbohydrate, 3 g fat, 1 g saturated fat, 886 mg sodium, 9 g fiber

*

Turn an ordinary can of soup into a rich and hearty one by adding zesty canned tomatoes and quick-cooking rice. Serve with vegetable sticks and baked corn chips.

—Jeanne Ebing, Seminole, Florida

# Creamy Italian Vegetable Soup

2 cans (15 ounces each) no-salt-added cannellini or great Northern beans, rinsed and drained

1 tablespoon olive oil

1 package (6 ounces) Canadian bacon, chopped

2 carrots, sliced

2 ribs celery, chopped

1 onion, chopped

1 medium zucchini, chopped

2½ cups reduced-sodium chicken broth

1 can (14.5 ounces) no-salt-added Italian stewed tomatoes

1 package (10 ounces) frozen chopped spinach

1 teaspoon dried basil

½ teaspoon black pepper

6 tablespoons grated Romano cheese

**PLACE** 1 cup of the beans in a medium bowl and mash with a fork until smooth.

**HEAT** the oil in a large saucepan over medium-high heat. Cook the bacon, carrots, celery, onion, and zucchini, stirring often, for 5 to 7 minutes or until softened. Add the broth, tomatoes, spinach, basil, pepper, and the whole and mashed beans.

**BRING** to a boil and stir to break up the spinach. Reduce the heat to low, cover, and simmer for 25 to 30 minutes or until the vegetables are tender.

**LADLE** the soup into 6 bowls and sprinkle each with 1 tablespoon of the cheese.

Total time: 55 minutes   ✳   Makes 6 servings

Per serving: 277 calories, 17 g protein, 36 g carbohydrate, 8 g fat, 3 g saturated fat, 585 mg sodium, 13 g fiber

✳

Canadian bacon is really not bacon at all but more like ham. It comes from a pork loin that's smoked like ham. Often sold in packages of thick or thin slices, it's in the refrigerated meats section of your supermarket. The biggest benefit: Canadian bacon is much lower in fat and calories than slab bacon.

# Spiced Lentil Soup

2 cans (14.5 ounces each) reduced-sodium chicken broth

1 can (28 ounces) stewed tomatoes

1 cup lentils, rinsed and drained

2 potatoes, peeled and chopped

2 carrots, peeled and sliced

1 onion, chopped

1 rib celery, chopped

3 cloves garlic, minced

3 bay leaves

3 tablespoons curry powder

1 teaspoon ground cumin

1 teaspoon ground coriander

1 teaspoon black pepper

**COMBINE** the broth, tomatoes, lentils, potatoes, carrots, onion, celery, garlic, bay leaves, curry powder, cumin, coriander, and pepper in a 4- to 6-quart slow cooker. Stir to blend well.

**COVER** and cook on high for 4 to 5 hours or on low for 8 to 10 hours, until the lentils are tender. Discard the bay leaves before serving. Ladle into 4 bowls.

Total time: 5 hours 15 minutes  ✱  Makes 4 servings

Per serving: 260 calories, 14 g protein, 51 g carbohydrate, 2 g fat, 0 g saturated fat, 930 mg sodium, 15 g fiber

Add lentils to your shopping list. Evidence shows that eating these high-fiber legumes may improve control of blood sugar, cholesterol, and triglycerides. Here, they mix with vegetables and spices for a warming meal.

[ it worked for me ]

# 65 lbs lost!

## ❋ RAMANI DURVASULA

**Small changes helped Ramani Durvasula stop stress-eating, take charge of her weight—and lose big**

### My Story

I never struggled with my weight until my mid-twenties, when I put on 50 pounds thanks to the pressures of graduate school. I went on a diet and kept the weight off until my mid-thirties. I had a new job and a new baby, and was feeling insecure about balancing my life as a professor and mother. I turned to the solace of food. Before I knew it, I was nearly 40, and all the moms in my daughter's kindergarten class looked svelte and fabulous—except me.

But reality didn't hit me until the night of a friend's wedding. My mom had just returned from India with a suitcase full of flowing silk gowns—perfect to disguise my robust figure, or so I thought. Surprise: One after another, the delicate dresses ripped at the seams as I forced them over my waist and hips. I couldn't even stuff myself into a sari! Shocked and saddened, I stood in my closet and cried. Later, I ate like it was my last meal. It would be the final time I let myself indulge in an out-of-control binge.

Pounds Lost: 65

Age: 42

Height: 5'5"

Weight Then: 187 pounds

Weight Now: 122 pounds

Health Bonus: "I Got My Body Back!"

## Slimming Down in Secret

I began with a simple formula: Reduce my portions, stop picking off my kids' plates, and eat produce at every meal. I also began walking each day on our treadmill. I told nobody, in case I failed. Four weeks later, I stepped on the scale: I was 7 pounds lighter—and triumphant.

After 2 months, I hit a plateau. I kicked up the treadmill's incline, increasing it more each week until I reached the steepest path. Pounds started rolling off again, but I got bored, so I began walking outdoors in a weighted vest. I'd even put it on whenever I did chores. Presto—I'd turned laundry into weight-bearing exercise!

I lost 65 pounds in a little over a year, and I've kept it off for nearly two. Workouts used to seem like selfish time away from my children. Now I consider exercise as vital as brushing my teeth. There are still days when I want to dig into an extra slice of pizza—and sometimes I do—but generally, I turn to exercise to cope with stress. What amazes me most is that instead of launching a midlife crisis, turning 40 gave me the courage to become healthier than ever.

## My Top Tips

* Grocery shop every weekend. I'd bring a full bag of groceries to the office on Monday so that I would have all the ingredients I needed to make healthy lunches for the rest of the week.

* Lock your kitchen cabinets. Opening them gave me a 30-second pause to consider the kind of food I would eat. I kept the locks on for 6 months, which really helped me cut down on junk food.

* Make the treadmill/TV connection. I built exercise into my schedule by allowing myself to watch TV only when I was on the treadmill. That got me walking at least 4 days a week!

* Set an example. My older daughter tells her dolls, "Okay, girls, it's time to do our exercises!" And when I stop to do my sit-ups, my 4-year-old gets down on the floor and does them with me.

* Relish your newfound energy. Since losing the weight, I've climbed to the summit of two of California's 10,000-foot peaks, including Mt. Baldy.

# main dishes

# Grilled Steak with Cilantro Pesto

### Pesto

- 2 tablespoons pine nuts, toasted
- 2 cloves garlic
- 1 jalapeño pepper, seeded and chopped (wear plastic gloves when handling)
- 1½ cups chopped cilantro
- 1 lime, juiced
- 2 teaspoons olive oil
- ½ cup reduced-fat sour cream
- ¼ teaspoon salt

### Steak

- 1½ pounds top round steak for London broil
- 1 lime, juiced
- 1 tablespoon olive oil
- 2 cloves garlic, minced
- ½ teaspoon salt
- ½ teaspoon black pepper

**To Make the Pesto:**

**PLACE** the pine nuts and garlic in a blender or food processor. Pulse once or twice. Add the jalapeño, cilantro, lime juice, oil, sour cream, and salt and process until well blended; stop and scrape down the sides of the container as needed. Place in a bowl, cover, and refrigerate.

**To Make the Steak:**

**PLACE** the steak on a large platter. Sprinkle both sides with the lime juice, oil, garlic, salt, and pepper. Let stand while the grill heats.

**COAT** a grill rack or broiler pan with cooking spray. Preheat the grill or broiler.

**GRILL** or broil the steak for 12 to 15 minutes, turning once, until an instant-read thermometer inserted in the center registers 145°F for medium-rare or 160°F for medium. Let stand for 10 minutes before slicing.

**SERVE** with the pesto.

---

Total time: 45 minutes   ✳   Makes 6 servings

Per serving: 260 calories, 28 g protein, 6 g carbohydrate, 14 g fat, 4 g saturated fat, 371 mg sodium, 1 g fiber

This is a super, low-carb dish to serve for lunch, dinner, or a patio party. For appetizers, cut the steak into 1" cubes and serve with toothpicks and the pesto.
**—Maria**

# Savory Pot Roast

½ cup all-purpose flour

1 can (14 ounces) reduced-sodium beef broth

3 tablespoons tomato paste

1 teaspoon dried thyme

1 teaspoon salt

1 teaspoon black pepper

2½ pounds boneless beef chuck roast or top sirloin roast

8 ounces baby carrots

4 ribs celery, chopped

1 cup chopped onion

1 pound small new potatoes

**COAT** a 4- to 6-quart slow cooker with cooking spray. Add the flour and gradually pour in the broth, whisking constantly, until smooth. Whisk in the tomato paste, thyme, salt, and pepper.

**ADD** the beef, carrots, celery, onion, and potatoes to cooker. Spoon some of the sauce over the beef.

**COVER** and cook on high for 4 to 4½ hours or on low for 8 hours or until the meat is tender and an instant-read thermometer inserted in the center reads 160°F.

----

Total time: 8 hours  ✱  Makes 6 servings

Per serving: 391 calories, 46 g protein, 26 g carbohydrate, 10 g fat, 4 g saturated fat, 764 mg sodium, 4 g fiber

✱

Come home to the aroma of Grandma's cooking when you start the day by assembling this classic dinner in a slow cooker. Open a bagged salad and dinner is ready in no time!

# Beef Stroganoff

1½ pounds lean beef stew meat

1 pound mushrooms, sliced

1 onion, chopped

1 clove garlic, minced

1 can (10.75 ounces) fat-free cream of mushroom soup

1 cup water

1 teaspoon salt

¼ teaspoon black pepper

1 cup fat-free sour cream

**COAT** a 4- to 6-quart slow cooker with cooking spray. Combine the beef, mushrooms, onion, garlic, soup, water, salt, and pepper in the cooker, stirring until well blended.

**COVER** and cook on low for 6 to 8 hours.

**STIR** in the sour cream. Cover and cook on high for 5 minutes or until heated through.

Total time: 8 hours  ✳  Makes 6 servings

Per serving: 240 calories, 27 g protein, 15 g carbohydrate, 7 g fat, 2.5 g saturated fat, 800 mg sodium, 1 g fiber

This hearty stew is delicious served over hot cooked brown rice or whole wheat couscous.

## NUTRITION NEWS TO USE

Iodine helps maintain sufficient levels of the thyroid hormones that regulate your weight, energy level, and mood, but a new study finds you may not be getting enough. We tend to get our biggest dose of iodine from table salt, but among 88 randomized samples of common iodized salt brands, 47 didn't contain the FDA's recommended iodine concentration, say University of Texas at Arlington scientists.

Adults should get 150 micrograms of iodine daily (220 micrograms if you're pregnant, 290 micrograms if breastfeeding). Before you take any iodine or kelp-based supplement, talk with your doctor first.

You can satisfy your daily needs by eating:
✳ One serving of ocean fish
✳ Two servings of low-fat yogurt
✳ A few forkfuls of seaweed salad, such as kelp or wakame.

# Navajo Tacos

½ onion, chopped

1 pound extra-lean ground beef (95% lean)

1 envelope (1.25 ounces) taco seasoning mix

1 can (16.3 ounces) refrigerated reduced-fat buttermilk biscuits (8 biscuits)

1 cup canned fat-free refried beans

4 cups shredded lettuce

2 large tomatoes, chopped

6 ounces shredded low-fat Mexican cheese blend

½ cup low-fat sour cream

½ cup salsa

1 avocado, seeded, peeled, and chopped

1 cup chopped cilantro

**PREHEAT** the oven to 350°F.

**COAT** a large skillet with cooking spray, add the onion, and cook over medium heat for 5 minutes, stirring frequently, until browned. Add the beef and cook for 5 minutes, stirring, until no longer pink. Stir in the taco seasoning. Cook for 1 minute. Reduce the heat to low; keep warm.

**MEANWHILE,** lightly flour a flat surface and rolling pin. Roll each biscuit to 6" in diameter. Place on 2 ungreased baking sheets. Bake for 10 minutes or until golden brown.

**PLACE** the beans in a microwave-safe bowl and cook on medium for 3 minutes, stirring, until hot.

**TO** assemble, top each biscuit with the beans, beef, lettuce, tomatoes, cheese, sour cream, salsa, avocado, and cilantro.

------

Total time: 35 minutes  ✳  Makes 8 servings

Per serving: 470 calories, 25 g protein, 43 g carbohydrate, 21 g fat, 7 g saturated fat, 1,087 mg sodium, 5 g fiber

133

Main Dishes

This is a reduced-fat version of a traditional New Mexican favorite. In this recipe, the traditional 'fry bread' is replaced with a reduced-fat biscuit that is rolled flat and baked. When I first came up with this recipe, my husband ate them every night for a week! They were that good! This recipe is a great way to get fiber from the beans and lots of fresh veggies in a delicious Southwestern delight. **—Maria**

# Chicago-Style Buffalo Dogs

4 buffalo hot dogs or 97% fat-free beef hot dogs

4 whole wheat hot dog buns

4 teaspoons yellow mustard

¼ cup sweet pickle relish

¼ small onion, chopped

1 tomato, cut into wedges

2 dill pickle spears, halved

4 pepperoncini, halved

⅛ teaspoon celery salt (optional)

**COAT** a grill rack or broiler pan with cooking spray. Preheat the grill or broiler.

**GRILL** the hot dogs for 5 minutes, turning, until brown.

**PLACE** a hot dog in each bun and top with mustard, relish, onion, tomato wedges, pickle, pepperoncini, and celery salt.

-------------------------------------------------

Total time: 15 minutes ✱ Makes 4 servings

Per serving: 221 calories, 12 g protein, 30 g carbohydrate, 8 g fat, 2 g saturated fat, 851 mg sodium, 4 g fiber

✱

This gives new meaning to "a hot dog with the works"!

**WHAT'S REALLY IN YOUR . . . HOT DOG**

**Beef and pork:** Both are high in protein—and in unhealthy saturated fat and cholesterol; the meat could come from pig and cow skeletal muscle and by-products.

**Mechanically separated turkey:** A pastelike substance produced when tissue is removed from bones through a high-pressure sieve. This product is versatile and cheap—and not just for turkey dogs.

**Sodium nitrite:** Helps preserve the red tint of cured meat. Studies have shown that consuming sodium nitrite may increase cancer risk and trigger migraines.

**Corn syrup:** A combo of cornstarch and acids, corn syrup is used as a thickener and sweetener. It contains no nutrients but does add extra calories.

**Extractives of paprika:** As a spice, paprika is a good source of fiber and vitamins A and E. However, the extractive form doesn't offer much aside from color.

**Better Buy:** Applegate Farms Organic Beef Hot Dogs. Made with USDA–certified organic beef and without nitrites and corn syrup, these dogs are lower in saturated fat, calories, and sodium than typical supermarket or ballpark fare.

# Meat Loaf with Mushroom Gravy

Meat Loaf

- 1 ounce dried mushrooms
- 1½ cups boiling water, divided
- ½ cup bulgur
- 1½ pounds extra-lean ground beef (95% lean)
- 2 large egg whites, lightly beaten
- 2 medium onions, finely chopped
- 1 cup soft whole wheat bread crumbs
- ½ cup dry white wine or reduced-sodium beef broth
- 2 cloves garlic, minced
- 1 teaspoon dried thyme
- 1 teaspoon dried oregano
- ¾ teaspoon salt
- ½ teaspoon black pepper
- 1 can (8 ounces) tomato sauce

Gravy

- 2 teaspoons olive oil
- 1 small onion, chopped
- 8 ounces mushrooms, sliced
- 2 cloves garlic, minced
- 1½ cups reduced-sodium beef broth
- ½ cup dry white wine or ½ cup reduced-sodium beef broth
- 1 teaspoon dried thyme
- ¼ teaspoon salt
- 1 tablespoon cornstarch
- 2 tablespoons water

To Make the Meat Loaf:

**SOAK** the mushrooms in 1 cup of the water for 20 minutes. Drain, reserving ¼ cup of the liquid; chop the mushrooms.

**SOAK** the bulgur in the remaining ½ cup water for 30 minutes or until the liquid is absorbed.

**PREHEAT** the oven to 375°F. Coat a 9" × 5" loaf pan with cooking spray.

**COMBINE** the mushrooms, reserved mushroom liquid, and bulgur in a large bowl. Add the beef, egg whites, onions, bread crumbs, wine, garlic, thyme, oregano, salt, pepper, and tomato sauce (reserving 1 tablespoon for the gravy). Gently mix to combine. Place in the pan. Bake for 1 hour 15 minutes.

To Make the Gravy:

**HEAT** the oil in a medium skillet over medium heat. Cook the onion, stirring, for 3 minutes. Add the mushrooms and cook, stirring, for 5 minutes. Stir in the garlic and reserved 1 tablespoon tomato sauce. Cook for 1 minute. Add the broth, wine, thyme, and salt. Bring to a boil. Reduce the heat to low, cover, and simmer for 10 minutes.

**WHISK** together the cornstarch and water in a small bowl. Add to the gravy. Stir until thickened.

Total time: 2 hours  ✳  Makes 8 servings

Per serving: 218 calories, 23 g protein, 19 g carbohydrate, 6 g fat, 2 g saturated fat, 669 mg sodium, 6 g fiber

✳

Flavor boosters such as mushrooms, garlic, herbs, and wine enhance the flavor of lean beef. For easier slicing, let the meat loaf cool 10 minutes before serving.

# Kidney Bean and Beef Chili

6 ounces lean top round beef, cut into 1" pieces

1 tablespoon olive oil

1 onion, chopped

1 cup canned crushed tomatoes

1 cup reduced-sodium chicken broth

1 green bell pepper, chopped

1 clove garlic, minced

1½ teaspoons chili powder

1 teaspoon ground cumin

½ teaspoon salt

½ teaspoon black pepper

1 can (15 ounces) kidney beans, rinsed and drained

4 teaspoons sour cream

4 teaspoons shredded extra-sharp Cheddar cheese

**PLACE** the beef in the food processor and pulse for 1 minute or until coarsely ground.

**HEAT** the oil in a large skillet over medium-high heat. Cook the beef and onion for 5 minutes or until browned.

**PLACE** in a 4- to 6-quart slow cooker. Stir in the tomatoes, broth, bell pepper, garlic, chili powder, cumin, salt, and pepper.

**COVER** and cook on low for 4 to 6 hours. Add the beans and cook on high, stirring occasionally, for 1 hour. Spoon into 4 bowls. Top each with 1 teaspoon each of the sour cream and cheese.

---

Total time: 7 hours  ✳  Makes 4 servings

Per serving: 260 calories, 19 g protein, 26 g carbohydrate, 9 g fat, 3 g saturated fat, 370 mg sodium, 9 g fiber

✳

Friends are coming to supper on a weeknight. Impress them with this lively, classic chili. Prepare in the morning for a hearty meal when you arrive home. Serve with low-fat cornbread and crudités for a meal that's sure to please.

## NUTRITION NEWS TO USE

Here's an easy swap to drastically cut calories: Trade the beef in your recipes for mushrooms. Research from Johns Hopkins University showed that when adults ate a mushroom-based version of four beef dishes such as lasagna and chili, not only were they just as full, but they also ate around 420 fewer calories and 30 fewer grams of fat. Subbing 1 cup of mushrooms for 3 ounces of 85% lean ground meat twice a week could add up to a 6-pound weight loss over 1 year.

# Quick and Easy Polenta Supper

1 tablespoon olive oil

1 pound precooked polenta roll, cut into 12 slices

¾ cup shredded Italian cheese blend, divided

½ pound extra-lean ground beef (95% lean)

2 cups chunky pasta sauce

**HEAT** the oil in a large nonstick grill pan or skillet over medium-high heat. Add the polenta and cook for 15 minutes or until lightly browned, turning once. Remove the pan from the heat and sprinkle with ½ cup of the cheese. Cover with a lid or foil to melt the cheese.

**MEANWHILE**, stir the beef in a medium saucepan over medium heat for 5 minutes or until browned. Add the pasta sauce and cook for 3 minutes or until heated through. Divide the sauce among 4 plates. Top with the polenta and sprinkle with the remaining ¼ cup cheese.

Total time: 20 minutes ✹ Makes 4 servings

Per serving: 283 calories, 20 g protein, 24 g carbohydrate, 12 g fat, 6 g saturated fat, 715 mg sodium, 0 g fiber

Craving comfort food? Reach for precooked polenta, cornmeal that's been simmered until it's thick and creamy, then cooled to firm it up. Use it as a lower-cal, lower-carb alternative to pasta. Add steamed broccoli or a salad—and dinner's done.

[
**SUPERFOOD
SPOTLIGHT:
HUMMUS**
]

Hummus is an inexpensive, high-fiber, protein-packed food—yet only 5% of U.S. households dabble with this dip. And while it makes a perfect partner for fresh veggies, the Middle Eastern mixture of chickpeas and tahini has endless possibilities. Here, three we love:

✹ As a topping: Slather it on broiled chicken or salmon and sprinkle with diced tomatoes and sliced black olives.

✹ As a filling: Dot the center of an egg white omelet with ¼ cup hummus. Top with sautéed asparagus and diced onion and bell pepper.

✹ As a sauce: Mix 2 parts pesto with 1 part hummus, then add chopped tomatoes and toasted pine nuts. Toss with whole wheat pasta.

# Fast Lamb Curry

- 1 **pound lean ground lamb**
- 5 **teaspoons curry powder**
- ½ **teaspoon salt**
- 1 **container (15 ounces) fresh marinara sauce**
- ½ **cup water**
- 1 **package (6 ounces) baby spinach**

**STIR** the lamb, curry powder, and salt in a large skillet over medium-high heat for 8 minutes or until well browned. Drain any fat.

**STIR** in the marinara sauce, water, and spinach. Bring to a simmer. Reduce the heat to low and simmer, uncovered, for 5 minutes.

Total time: 20 minutes ✱ Makes 4 servings

Per serving: 308 calories, 22 g protein, 15 g carbohydrate, 18 g fat, 7 g saturated fat, 571 mg sodium, 5 g fiber

✱

The key ingredient in this Indian-inspired dish is—surprise—Italian marinara sauce! The warm flavors of curry powder add dimension, and ground lamb cooks quickly, saving you time at the stove. Serve with whole wheat couscous, which cooks in the same time as the curry.

# Stir-Fried Pork with Ginger

2 tablespoons olive oil, divided

¾ pound stir-fry pork strips

2 bags (12 ounces each) fresh Asian vegetable mix

4 teaspoons bottled minced ginger

1 tablespoon water

⅓ cup stir-fry sauce

**HEAT** 1 tablespoon of the oil in a large skillet over medium-high heat. Add the pork and cook, stirring, for 4 minutes or until no longer pink. Remove to a serving plate.

**HEAT** the remaining 1 tablespoon oil in the same skillet and cook the vegetables, stirring, for 2 minutes. Add the garlic and water. Cover and steam until crisp-tender. Add the stir-fry sauce and pork and cook, stirring, for 1 minute.

Total time: 10 minutes ✳ Makes 6 servings

Per serving: 259 calories, 21 g protein, 11 g carbohydrate, 14 g fat, 3 g saturated fat, 904 mg sodium, 2 g fiber

✳

Nothing's quicker than a stir-fry—but only if there's nothing more to it than stirring and frying. Buy precut meat and vegetables, break out your wok or skillet, and get this one-dish meal on the table in a flash. Serve over instant brown rice.

# Grilled Pork Tenderloin Tacos with Corn and Black Bean Salsa

1   pound pork tenderloin

½   teaspoon salt

½   teaspoon black pepper

2   tomatoes, chopped

1   cup frozen whole kernel corn, thawed

1   can (15 ounces) black beans, rinsed and drained

½   small red onion, chopped

½   cup chopped cilantro

1   jalapeño pepper, finely chopped (wear plastic gloves when handling)

1   lime, juiced

¼   teaspoon ground cumin

8   corn tortillas, warmed

**COAT** a grill rack or broiler pan with cooking spray. Preheat the grill or broiler. Rub the pork with the salt and pepper.

**STIR** together the tomatoes, corn, beans, onion, cilantro, jalapeño, lime juice, and cumin in a medium bowl.

**GRILL** or broil the pork for 15 to 20 minutes, turning occasionally, until an instant-read thermometer inserted in the center reaches 155°F and the juices run clear. Let stand for 10 minutes before slicing.

**PLACE** the sliced pork on warm tortillas and top with salsa.

Total time: 1 hour  ✱  Makes 4 servings

Per serving: 357 calories, 32 g protein, 48 g carbohydrate, 6 g fat, 2 g saturated fat, 579 mg sodium, 10 g fiber

✱

Corn tortillas can be difficult to warm without having them fall apart. For perfect tortillas every time, wrap them in white paper towels and microwave on high for 30 seconds.

# Shepherd's Pie

2 pounds russet potatoes, peeled and cubed

⅓ cup 1% buttermilk

¼ cup grated Parmesan cheese

1 pound lean ground lamb

2 carrots, chopped

2 cloves garlic, minced

1 cup chopped cauliflower

1 can (8 ounces) reduced-sodium chopped tomatoes

1 cup frozen white pearl onions

1 cup frozen peas

2 teaspoons Worcestershire sauce

1 teaspoon Italian seasoning

1 teaspoon cornstarch

¼ cup apple juice

**PREHEAT** the oven to 350°F. Coat a 9" round baking dish with cooking spray.

**PLACE** the potatoes in a large saucepan. Add enough cold water to cover. Bring to a boil over high heat. Reduce the heat to medium and cook for 15 minutes or until very tender. Drain and place in a medium bowl. Mash well with a potato masher or electric mixer, adding the buttermilk and cheese to the potatoes.

**COAT** a large nonstick skillet with cooking spray and heat over medium-high heat until hot. Cook the lamb, carrots, and garlic for 5 minutes, stirring, until the lamb is browned. Add the cauliflower, tomatoes (with juice), onions, peas, Worcestershire sauce, and Italian seasoning. Bring to a boil.

**WHISK** together the cornstarch and apple juice in a small bowl. Add to the skillet and cook, stirring, for 3 minutes or until the sauce thickens.

**SPOON** the mixture into the prepared baking dish. Top with the mashed potatoes. Bake for 40 minutes or until the top is golden brown. Let stand 10 minutes before serving.

Total time: 1 hour 20 minutes ✱ Makes 6 servings

Per serving: 433 calories, 26 g protein, 46 g carbohydrate, 16 g fat, 7 g saturated fat, 305 mg sodium, 4 g fiber

Adding buttermilk and Parmesan cheese to the mashed potatoes gives them the richness of butter and cream without the added fat and calories.

# Spicy Sausage Sandwiches

1 tablespoon olive oil

½ pound hot Italian turkey sausages, sliced

2 cups fat-free tomato-basil pasta sauce

1 cup rinsed and drained canned chickpeas

4 whole grain rolls, halved

**HEAT** the oil in a large skillet over high heat. Cook the sausage, stirring, for 5 minutes or until browned. Stir in the sauce and chickpeas and cook for 5 minutes or until heated through and the flavors blend.

**PLACE** the rolls on plates and spoon the sausage mixture onto them.

Total time: 15 minutes  ✳  Makes 4 servings

Per serving: 496 calories, 23 g protein, 74 g carbohydrate, 16 g fat, 2 g saturated fat, 1,363 mg sodium, 10 g fiber

✳

Hot Italian turkey sausage gives these saucy skillet sandwiches a peppery kick, while fiber-rich chickpeas provide bursts of nutty flavor. Rinse beans to remove as much as one-third of the sodium.

# Very Veggie Skillet Casserole

¾ pound ground turkey breast (99% lean)

2 tablespoons olive oil

1 onion, chopped

2 cloves garlic, minced

1 medium yellow squash, halved and sliced

1 tomato, chopped

1 green bell pepper, chopped

1 carrot, chopped

1 cup instant brown rice

1½ cups reduced-sodium chicken broth

4 cups baby spinach

**COOK** the turkey in a large nonstick skillet over medium-high heat, stirring to breaking up the meat, for 8 minutes or until no longer pink. Remove the turkey to a medium bowl.

**HEAT** the oil in same skillet over medium heat. Cook the onion and garlic, stirring, for 5 minutes or until tender. Add the squash, tomato, pepper, and carrot. Cook, stirring, for 5 minutes or until vegetables are crisp-tender.

**RETURN** the turkey and any juices to the pan. Stir in the rice and broth. Bring to a boil. Reduce the heat to low, cover, and simmer for 15 minutes or until the rice is tender. Stir in the spinach. Cook, stirring, for 1 minute or until the spinach is wilted.

---

Total time: 40 minutes  ✽  Makes 4 servings

Per serving: 261 calories, 26 g protein, 22 g carbohydrate, 9 g fat, 1 g saturated fat, 315 mg sodium, 4 g fiber

Here's a great way to use garden-fresh vegetables at their peak.

# Turkey Burgers with Chili Beans

### Beans

- 1 teaspoon olive oil
- 1 onion, chopped
- 2 teaspoons chili powder
- ½ teaspoon whole cumin seeds
- ⅛ –¼ teaspoon ground red pepper
- 1 can (15 ounces) navy beans, rinsed and drained
- 1 can (15 ounces) red kidney beans, rinsed and drained
- 1 can (8 ounces) no-salt-added tomato sauce
- ½ cup jarred roasted red peppers, chopped and drained
- ¼ cup water

### Burgers

- 1¼ pounds ground turkey breast (99% lean)
- ¼ cup jarred roasted red peppers, chopped and blotted dry
- 2 scallions, chopped
- 2 tablespoons dried bread crumbs
- 2 tablespoons chopped parsley
- 1 tablespoon Dijon mustard
- ½ teaspoon black pepper

**To Make the Beans:**

**HEAT** the oil in a large nonstick skillet over medium-high heat. Cook the onion for 5 minutes, stirring, until browned. Stir in the chili powder, cumin seeds, and ground red pepper. Cook, stirring, for 30 seconds.

**STIR** in the beans, tomato sauce, peppers, and water. Bring to a boil. Reduce the heat to low, cover, and simmer for 10 minutes. Remove from the heat and keep warm.

**To Make the Burgers:**

**COAT** a grill rack or broiler pan with cooking spray. Preheat the grill or broiler.

**COMBINE** the turkey, chopped peppers, scallions, bread crumbs, parsley, mustard, and pepper in a large bowl. Mix gently but thoroughly until blended. Shape into four 1"-thick burgers.

**GRILL** the burgers for 10 minutes, turning once, until an instant-read thermometer inserted in the center registers 165°F and the meat is no longer pink. Serve with the beans.

----

Total time: 30 minutes  ✱  Makes 4 servings

Per serving: 369 calories, 47 g protein, 39 g carbohydrate, 4 g fat, 1 g saturated fat, 667 mg sodium, 12 g fiber

✱

Ground turkey makes a mean, lean burger—if you're choosy about the meat. Make sure the label reads "ground turkey breast" (or specifies 99% fat free); using plain old "ground turkey" (about 13% fat) tacks on an additional 80-plus calories and 11 grams of fat per serving!

# Turkey Spinach Burgers

1 **pound ground turkey breast (99% lean)**

1 **package (10 ounces) frozen chopped spinach, thawed and squeezed dry**

2 **tablespoons barbecue sauce**

½ **teaspoon salt**

¼ **teaspoon black pepper**

4 **whole wheat hamburger buns, toasted**

4 **tomato slices**

4 **lettuce leaves**

**COAT** a grill rack or broiler pan with cooking spray. Preheat the grill or broiler.

**COMBINE** the turkey, spinach, barbecue sauce, salt, and pepper in a large bowl. Shape mixture into four 1"-thick burgers.

**GRILL** the burgers for 10 minutes, turning once, until an instant-read thermometer inserted in the center registers 165°F and the meat is no longer pink. Serve on the buns with tomato and lettuce.

Total time: 20 minutes   ✱   Makes 4 servings

Per serving: 305 calories, 29 g protein, 30 g carbohydrate, 10 g fat, 3 g saturated fat, 723 mg sodium, 6g fiber

✱

A healthy dose of spinach makes these patties juicy and flavorful. Toast the buns right on the grill during the last few minutes of cooking.

What's more indulgent than a big, juicy burger? Lucky for us, with a little imagination you can turn the all-American favorite into a disease-fighting dinner. Here are five better-for-you burgers, paired with delicious health-boosting toppings. Choose the one that best matches your eating style:

### IF YOU'RE A: MEAT LOVER

**Try:** Lean beef (look for 90% lean or higher)

**For its:** Immune-boosting zinc

**Top with:** Fresh tomato slices and basil for extra antioxidants

**Look for:** Laura's Lean Beef 92% lean ground beef patties; laurasleanbeef.com

### IF YOU'RE A: DIETER

**Try:** Veggie

**For its:** Filling fiber

**Top with:** Avocado slices, rich in belly fat–busting MUFAs

**Look for:** Dr. Praeger's California Veggie Burger; drpraegers.com

### IF YOU'RE A: SEAFOOD FAN

**Try:** Salmon

**For its:** Heart disease–fighting omega-3 fats

**Top with:** Peppery, vitamin K–packed watercress and a teaspoon of wasabi mayonnaise

**Look for:** Vital Choice wild Alaskan sockeye salmon burgers; vitalchoice.com

### IF YOU'RE A: GOURMET

**Try:** Buffalo

**For its:** Energizing iron

**Top with:** Organic ketchup for cancer-fighting lycopene and grilled onion slices for disease-fighting flavonoids

**Look for:** NorthStar Bison ground grass-fed patties; northstarbison.com

### IF YOU'RE A: VEGETARIAN

**Try:** Soy

**For its:** Heart-healthy plant protein

**Top with:** Sautéed red bell pepper. Its vitamin C boosts iron absorption, crucial if you don't eat meat

**Look for:** Boca meatless burger original; bocaburger.com

[
**BURGERS WITH BENEFITS**
]

—Catherine A. Swiech, Buffalo, New York

# Apple Sausage Penne

2 cups low-carb penne pasta

1 pound Italian low-fat turkey sausage, diagonally cut into ¼" slices

4 red Delicious apples, cubed

½ cup half-and-half

¼ cup crumbled low-fat Gorgonzola or other blue cheese

¼ cup chopped fresh basil

**PREPARE** the pasta according to the package directions; drain.

**MEANWHILE.** stir the sausage in a large saucepan over medium-high heat until well browned. Add the apples and stir for 5 minutes or until the apples are golden. Add the pasta, half-and-half, and cheese and cook for 2 minutes, stirring, until heated through. Sprinkle with the basil before serving.

Total time: 15 minutes ✳ Makes 4 servings

Per serving: 448 calories, 44 g protein, 46 g carbohydrate, 12 g fat, 6 g saturated fat, 1,037 mg sodium, 12 g fiber

✳

Here's a great way to introduce moderation into your meals. The low-carb pasta and the apple provide plenty of fiber, while the half-and-half adds a touch of decadence. Choosing low-fat turkey sausage keeps the fat and calories lower than if using regular sausage or kielbasa.

# Quick and Light Pad Thai

8 ounces rice-flour noodles

¼ cup reduced-sodium fish sauce

3 tablespoons packed brown sugar

2½ tablespoons reduced-sodium soy sauce

1 lime, juiced

1 tablespoon rice wine vinegar

½ teaspoon ground red pepper

3 teaspoons toasted sesame oil, divided

4 ounces firm tofu, cubed

3 cloves garlic, minced

1 large egg + 2 large egg whites, lightly beaten

½ pound lean ground chicken breast

4 cups bean sprouts

4 scallions, including green tops, thinly sliced

2 tablespoons roughly chopped roasted, unsalted peanuts

1 cup chopped cilantro

**SOAK** the noodles (see tip below). Set aside.

**WHISK** together the fish sauce, brown sugar, soy sauce, lime juice, vinegar, pepper, and 1 teaspoon of the oil in a small bowl. Set aside.

**HEAT** the remaining 2 teaspoons oil in a wok or large nonstick skillet over medium heat. When the oil is hot but not smoking, add the tofu and cook, turning once, for 3 minutes or until lightly browned. Add the garlic and cook for 2 minutes. Add the eggs. When they are just set, stir and gently push to the side of the pan.

**ADD** the chicken to the pan and cook, stirring, for 5 minutes or until no longer pink. Add the sprouts and stir gently until just combined. Stir in the drained noodles, scallions, and fish sauce mixture and simmer for 5 to 10 minutes or until sauce thickens slightly.

**SPRINKLE** with the peanuts and cilantro.

---

Total time: 30 minutes   ✳   Makes 4 servings

Per serving: 496 calories, 26 g protein, 71 g carbohydrate, 14 g fat, 3 g saturated fat, 973 mg sodium, 6 g fiber

The complex blend of salty, sweet, tart, and hot comes mainly from pantry items, requiring only measuring, no prep, in this favorite dish.

## QUICK TIP: 3 WAYS TO SOAK RICE-FLOUR NOODLES

**Easiest:** Soak in enough cold water to cover for 40 to 50 minutes.

**Quicker:** Cover with boiling water. Let stand 20 minutes.

**Quickest:** Barely cover with water in a shallow dish. Microwave 3 to 4 minutes on high.

# California Comfort Chicken

1 cup reduced-sodium chicken broth

1 cup fat-free plain Greek yogurt

½ cup apple cider

1 tablespoon ground cinnamon

1 teaspoon vanilla extract

4 bone-in skinless chicken breast halves

1 red apple, chopped

1 cup chopped apricots

¼ cup dried currants

¼ cup chopped walnuts

**COMBINE** the broth, yogurt, cider, cinnamon, and vanilla in a large skillet over medium heat. Bring to a simmer. Add the chicken. Reduce the heat to low, cover, and simmer for 20 minutes.

**ADD** the apple, apricots, currants, and walnuts. Simmer, uncovered, for 15 minutes or until an instant-read thermometer inserted in the thickest portion of a breast registers 170°F and the juices run clear.

Total time: 45 minutes  ✳  Makes 4 servings

Per serving: 352 calories, 26 g protein, 49 g carbohydrate, 6 g fat, 1 g saturated fat, 112 mg sodium, 8 g fiber

✳

Serve these chicken breasts with brown rice and steamed broccoli. Start the rice just before cooking the chicken and they'll both be ready at the same time. Prepare the broccoli after adding the fruit and nuts to the chicken. If fresh apricots are not available, use ¼ cup dried.

## QUICK TIP: MICROWAVE DOS AND DONT'S

More than 90% of U.S. homes have a microwave. Although immeasurably convenient, they're not foolproof when it comes to food safety. Here's how to use your without harm:

✳ Do cook leftovers until they're steaming hot. They can still harbor dangerous bacteria if not warmed to 165°F throughout. If there are cold spots, stir, rotate, and reheat.

✳ Don't ignore instructions calling for standing or resting time. Microwaves cook from the outside in, usually to a depth of only 1 to 1½ inches. When a food rests, it's using conduction to heat more thoroughly.

✳ Do use microwave-safe cookware. Avoid dishes or containers that are metallic, including decorative paint and trim, which can cause sparks to form when heated. And skip plastic take-out bowls and food containers, as well as plastic wraps and foam trays, such as those used for ground beef and turkey: They may leach harmful chemicals into foods when heated.

# Neapolitan Chicken Cacciatore

1 whole chicken (3–3½ pounds), skinned and cut up

½ teaspoon salt

½ teaspoon black pepper

1 tablespoon olive oil

1 onion, chopped

1 rib celery, chopped

1 green bell pepper, chopped

3 cloves garlic, chopped

6 ounces mushrooms, sliced

1 can (28 ounces) crushed tomatoes with added puree

½ cup dry red wine

1 cup reduced-sodium chicken broth

1 tablespoon tomato paste

¼ teaspoon crushed red-pepper flakes

¼ cup grated Romano cheese

**SEASON** the chicken with the salt and pepper. Heat the oil in a large nonstick skillet over medium-high heat. Add chicken in batches and cook for 5 minutes, turning, until browned.

**MEANWHILE,** layer the onion, celery, bell pepper, garlic, and mushrooms in a 6-quart slow cooker. As the chicken browns, place it on top of the vegetables in an even layer.

**STIR** together the tomatoes, wine, broth, tomato paste, and pepper flakes. Pour over the chicken. Cover and cook on high for 3 to 4 hours or on low for 8 hours. Remove the chicken to a platter.

**POUR** the vegetables from the slow cooker into a saucepan and simmer for 10 to 15 minutes to thicken the sauce. Spoon the sauce over the chicken. Serve with the cheese.

Total time: 8 hours 40 minutes  ✳  Makes 6 servings

Per serving: 265 calories, 28 g protein, 17 g carbohydrate, 10 g fat, 3 g saturated fat, 888 mg sodium, 4 g fiber

My husband has high blood pressure and cholesterol, so healthy cooking has become a lifestyle. With a little imagination, you can cook delicious meals.
**—Gilda**

# Pesto Chicken Bake

2½ pounds chicken thighs or drumsticks, skinned

1½ pounds baby potatoes

1 pint cherry or grape tomatoes

½ cup prepared pesto

2 teaspoons olive oil

½ teaspoon black pepper

¼ teaspoon salt

**PREHEAT** the oven to 425°F.

**COMBINE** the chicken, potatoes, and tomatoes in a large roasting pan. Drizzle with the pesto, oil, pepper, and salt. Toss to coat well and spread the chicken in an even layer.

**BAKE** for 45 minutes or until an instant-read thermometer inserted in the thickest portion of the chicken registers 170°F and the juices run clear.

Total time: 50 minutes  ✱  Makes 6 servings

Per serving: 666 calories, 66 g protein, 35 g carbohydrate, 28 g fat, 7 g saturated fat, 641 mg sodium, 4 g fiber

This weeknight dinner comes together in no time—and leaves only one pan to clean. Just sit back while the chicken and veggies bake, filling your kitchen with the aroma of a healthy, home-cooked meal.

—Mylane Wilson, Atlanta, Georgia

# Picante Chicken

1 pound boneless, skinless chicken breasts, cut into strips

8 ounces sliced mushrooms

1 can (2.25 ounces) sliced black olives, drained

1 jar (8 ounces) picante sauce

2 cups low-sodium chicken broth

2 tablespoons yellow mustard

2 cups hot cooked long-grain brown rice

**PLACE** the chicken, mushrooms, olives, sauce, broth, and mustard in a 3- to 6-quart slow cooker and stir to combine. Cook on high for 3 to 4 hours or on low for 6 to 8 hours. Serve over the rice.

Total time: 3 hours 10 minutes ✱ Makes 4 servings

Per serving: 301 calories, 33 g protein, 34 g carbohydrate, 5 g fat, 1 g saturated fat, 1,101 mg sodium, 3 g fiber

Throw together this zesty dish before heading out for the day and you'll come home to a warm, delicious meal. Serve with baked corn chips as an alternative to the rice.

# Chicken and Dumplings

1 **pound Idaho or russet potatoes, peeled and cubed**

1 **large egg, lightly beaten**

¾ **teaspoon salt, divided**

½ **teaspoon baking powder**

½ **cup all-purpose flour**

1 **tablespoon olive oil**

1 **onion, chopped**

3 **ribs celery, sliced**

2 **carrots, sliced**

5 **cups reduced-sodium chicken broth**

2 **tablespoons chopped fresh thyme or 2 teaspoons dried**

½ **teaspoon black pepper**

1½ **pounds boneless, skinless chicken breasts, cut into 1" pieces**

½ **cup reduced-fat sour cream**

2 **tablespoons dry sherry (optional)**

1 **tablespoon cornstarch or arrowroot**

1½ **cups frozen peas, thawed**

3 **tablespoons chopped fresh chives, tarragon, or parsley (optional)**

1 **tablespoon lemon juice**

**BOIL** the potatoes in a large pot of water for 15 minutes or until tender. Drain and press through a potato ricer or coarse sieve into a medium bowl. Let cool for 10 minutes. Stir in the egg, ½ teaspoon of the salt, and the baking powder. Add enough flour to form a soft dough.

**PLACE** on a floured surface. Roll into 1" balls.

**HEAT** the oil in a Dutch oven or large pot over medium-high heat. Cook the onion, celery, and carrots for 2 minutes or until lightly browned. Add the broth, thyme, pepper, and the remaining ¼ teaspoon salt. Simmer for 10 minutes.

**ADD** the chicken to the simmering broth. Return to a simmer, cover, and cook for 10 minutes or until the chicken is no longer pink. Add the dumplings and simmer 1 minute longer.

**WHISK** together the sour cream, sherry, and cornstarch in a small bowl. Add to the broth along with the peas. Cook over medium-low heat for 3 minutes or until thickened. Stir in the chives and lemon juice.

Total time: 40 minutes ✳ Makes 6 servings

Per serving: 361 calories, 35 g protein, 36 g carbohydrate, 9 g fat, 3 g saturated fat, 936 mg sodium, 4 g fiber

✳

Making the sauce with reduced-fat sour cream instead of heavy cream slashes the saturated fat in this all-in-one main dish. Add the gnocchi-like dumplings to the simmering broth at the last minute to preserve their light, tender texture. For variety, replace the thyme with sage, rosemary, or a combination of the herbs.

# Buttermilk "Fried" Chicken

⅓ cup all-purpose flour

2 teaspoons chopped fresh
  thyme leaves or 1 teaspoon
  dried

¾ teaspoon salt

¼ teaspoon black pepper

½ cup 1% buttermilk

1 large egg white

¾ cup seasoned bread crumbs

1 whole chicken (3–3½ pounds),
  skinned and cut up

1 lemon, cut into wedges
  (optional)

**PREHEAT** the oven to 400°F. Coat a baking sheet with cooking spray.

**COMBINE** the flour, thyme, salt, and pepper in a shallow dish and mix with a fork. Pour the buttermilk into another shallow dish and whisk in the egg white. Put the bread crumbs in a third shallow dish.

**DREDGE** a piece of chicken in the flour mixture and shake off the excess. Using tongs, dip into buttermilk to coat and transfer to the dish with bread crumbs. Coat evenly with crumbs and put on the prepared baking sheet. Repeat with remaining chicken pieces.

**BAKE** for 40 minutes or until an instant-read thermometer inserted in the thickest portion registers 170°F and the juices run clear. Serve with lemon wedges.

Total time: 1 hour ✱ Makes 4 servings

Per serving: 364 calories, 47 g protein, 25 g carbohydrate, 8 g fat, 2 g saturated fat, 951 mg sodium, 1 g fiber

A cut-up whole bird gives you a delicious—and money-saving—mix of light and dark meat. Oil the baking sheet well so the crispy coating sticks to the chicken, not the pan.

—Josie A.G. Shapiro, Chicago, Illinois

# Chicken Tikka Kabobs with Coconut "Cream"

- 1 tablespoon olive oil
- 1 tablespoon garam masala
- 1 teaspoon ground turmeric
- ½ teaspoon ground red pepper
- 5 tablespoons lime juice, divided
- 1½ pounds boneless, skinless chicken breasts, cut into 24 (1") cubes
- 1 cup fat-free plain Greek yogurt
- ¼ cup shredded coconut
- ½ small cucumber, peeled and shredded
- 2 tablespoons chopped fresh mint
- ¼ teaspoon salt
- ¼ teaspoon honey
- 1 pound broccoli florets, separated into 24 large florets
- 2 medium red onions, each cut into 8 wedges

**COAT** a grill rack or broiler pan with cooking spray. Preheat the grill or broiler.

**COMBINE** the oil, garam masala, turmeric, pepper, and 4 tablespoons of the lime juice in a large bowl. Add the chicken, tossing to coat. Let stand for 30 minutes.

**MEANWHILE.** combine the yogurt, coconut, cucumber, mint, salt, honey, and remaining lime juice in a small bowl. Cover and refrigerate.

**STEAM** the broccoli for 2 minutes or until bright green. Thread the marinated chicken cubes on eight 12" metal or presoaked bamboo skewers, alternating with onion wedges and broccoli florets.

**GRILL** or broil 6" from the heat for 8 to 12 minutes, turning occasionally, until browned and the chicken is no longer pink.

**SERVE** with the yogurt mixture.

---

Total time: 35 minutes + marinating time  ✱  Makes 4 servings

Per serving: 332 calories, 46 g protein, 20 g carbohydrate, 8 g fat, 3 g saturated fat, 328 mg sodium, 6 g fiber

159

Main Dishes

✱

Yogurt forms the base of this flavorful sauce studded with coconut. To save calories, look for unsweetened coconut flakes in the natural section of your supermarket or at health food stores.

# Chinese Chicken and Noodles

- 4 ounces whole wheat fettuccine
- ½ cup reduced-sodium chicken broth
- ¼ cup reduced-sodium soy sauce
- 2 tablespoons packed brown sugar
- 2 tablespoons frozen orange juice concentrate, thawed
- 3 cloves garlic, minced
- 1 tablespoon grated fresh ginger
- 1 red bell pepper, finely chopped
- 1 onion, finely chopped
- ½ pound boneless, skinless chicken breasts, cut into strips
- ½ cup snow peas, cut into thirds diagonally
- 2 scallions, thinly sliced

**PREPARE** the pasta according to the package directions. Drain well.

**WHISK** together the broth, soy sauce, brown sugar, and juice concentrate in a medium bowl.

**COAT** a large nonstick skillet with cooking spray and heat over medium-high heat. Cook the garlic and ginger, stirring, for 2 minutes or until fragrant. Add the pepper and onion. Cook, stirring, for 5 minutes or until the onion is soft but not browned.

**ADD** the chicken. Cook, stirring, for 5 minutes or until the chicken is no longer pink. Add the snow peas, pasta, and broth mixture. Cook, stirring occasionally, for 1 minute or until the sauce thickens. Sprinkle with scallions.

Total time: 20 minutes ✱ Makes 4 servings

Per serving: 252 calories, 20 g protein, 39 g carbohydrate, 2 g fat, 1 g saturated fat, 622 mg sodium, 3 g fiber

✱

No need for takeout. This delicious meal is ready faster than delivery. Serve with iced herb tea and orange wedges for a lovely meal in minutes.

# Spice-Rubbed Chicken with Millet Pilaf

- 1 teaspoon ground paprika
- 1 teaspoon ground cumin
- ¾ teaspoon salt
- 4 bone-in, skinless chicken thighs (about 1½ pounds)
- 2 tablespoons canola oil, divided
- 1 onion, chopped
- 2 cloves garlic, minced
- 1 cup millet
- 1 can (14.5 ounces) diced tomatoes, drained
- 1 cup reduced-sodium chicken broth
- 1 bay leaf
- ¼ teaspoon black pepper
- 1 cup frozen peas, thawed

**COMBINE** the paprika, cumin, and salt in a small bowl. Rub on all surfaces of the chicken.

**HEAT** 1 tablespoon of the oil in a Dutch oven or large saucepan over medium-high heat. Add the chicken and cook for 6 minutes, turning once, until browned. Remove to a plate.

**ADD** the remaining 1 tablespoon oil to the same pan over medium heat. Cook the onion and garlic, stirring, for 3 minutes. Stir in the millet, tomatoes, broth, and bay leaf. Nestle the chicken into the mixture and sprinkle with the pepper. Bring to a boil over medium-high heat.

**REDUCE** the heat to low, cover, and simmer for 20 minutes or until the millet is tender and an instant-read thermometer inserted in the thickest portion of the chicken registers 170°F.

**REMOVE** from the heat and stir in the peas. Cover and let stand for 10 minutes. Discard the bay leaf.

Total time: 55 minutes ✳ Makes 4 servings

Per serving: 436 calories, 29 g protein, 49 g carbohydrate, 13 g fat, 2 g saturated fat, 944 mg sodium, 7 g fiber

If your family is skeptical about trying new foods, we recommend this fiber-packed dish. Mellow millet paired with familiar ingredients, such as tomatoes and peas, is sure to please. Plus, there's only one pot to clean!

## NUTRITION NEWS TO USE

**Myth** 38% of consumers say organically grown produce is no healthier than conventionally grown.

**Fact** 75 published studies have found that organic food is more nutritious than nonorganic.

**The winner:** Organic

# Dijon Chicken Patties
# with Cider Mashed Sweet Potatoes

### Sweet Potatoes

- **4 medium sweet potatoes**
- **¼ cup packed light brown sugar**
- **½ cup apple cider**

### Patties

- **1 pound ground chicken breast**
- **2 tablespoons country-style Dijon mustard**
- **½ teaspoon dried herbes de Provence**
- **⅛ teaspoon black pepper**
- **¼ teaspoon salt**
- **2 tablespoons extra virgin olive oil**

To Make the Sweet Potatoes:

**PREHEAT** the oven to 425°F. Pierce the potatoes with a fork. Bake for 1 hour or until very tender. Cut the potatoes in half and scoop the flesh into a medium bowl. Add the brown sugar and cider and mash until smooth.

To Make the Patties:

**STIR** together the chicken, mustard, herbes de Provence, pepper, and salt in a medium bowl. Shape into 4 patties.

**HEAT** the oil in a large nonstick skillet over medium-high heat; cook the patties for 10 minutes or until an instant-read thermometer inserted in the center registers 165°F and the meat is no longer pink.

**SERVE** with the mashed sweet potatoes.

----

Total time: 1 hour 10 minutes  ✱  Makes 4 servings

Per serving: 404 calories, 35 g protein, 44 g carbohydrate, 9 g fat, 1 g saturated fat, 507 mg sodium, 4 g fiber

✱

Be sure to opt for ground chicken breast and not just ground chicken. You'll know you've selected the correct package if the fat content is around 1 gram per serving versus more than 10 grams in the full-fat ground chicken.

# Chicken Vegetable Pot Pie

1 teaspoon olive oil

2 carrots, thinly sliced

2 ribs celery, thinly sliced

1 pound cooked chicken, chopped

½ cup frozen peas, thawed

1 can (15 ounces) fat-free chicken gravy

½ teaspoon salt

¼ teaspoon black pepper

2 tablespoons parsley (optional)

1 deep-dish refrigerated double pie crust

**PREHEAT** the oven to 350°F. Coat a 9" × 9" baking dish with cooking spray.

**HEAT** the oil in a large skillet over medium-high heat. Cook the carrots and celery, stirring, for 7 minutes or until tender. Stir in the chicken, peas, gravy, salt, pepper, and parsley.

**PLACE** 1 pie crust in the baking dish. Add the chicken mixture. Top with the second crust. Trim the edges and crimp.

**BAKE** for 50 minutes or until brown and bubbling.

---

Total time: 1 hour ✳ Makes 8 servings

Per serving: 281 calories, 13 g protein, 25 g carbohydrate, 15 g fat, 3 g saturated fat, 585 mg sodium, 3 g fiber

Nothing says homemade like the aroma of bubbling hot chicken pot pie. A great way to use leftover chicken, this dish comes together in minutes. Relax while it cooks and enjoy the familiar fragrance.

# Curried Chicken-Broccoli Casserole

1 pound broccoli florets

¼ cup water

1 can (10.75 ounces) reduced-sodium cream of mushroom soup

¼ cup mayonnaise

1 tablespoon lemon juice

1½ teaspoons curry powder

½ teaspoon salt

½ teaspoon black pepper

1½ pounds boneless, skinless chicken breasts, cut into bite-size pieces

¼ cup shredded reduced-fat Colby or Swiss cheese

**PREHEAT** the oven to 350°F. Coat a 13" × 9" baking dish with cooking spray.

**PLACE** the broccoli and water in a large resealable plastic bag. Microwave on high, rotating occasionally, for 3 to 5 minutes or until bright green. Drain and set aside.

**STIR** together the soup, mayonnaise, lemon juice, curry powder, salt, and pepper in a medium bowl.

**LINE** the baking dish with the broccoli. Top with the chicken. Cover evenly with the soup mixture. Sprinkle with the cheese. Cover and bake for 25 minutes. Uncover and bake for 15 to 20 minutes more, until golden and bubbling.

-----

Total time: 1 hour ✱ Makes 6 servings

Per serving: 255 calories, 30 g protein, 9 g carbohydrate, 11 g fat, 2 g saturated fat, 571 mg sodium, 3 g fiber

✱

Like chicken divan, this layered casserole gets a bit of zing from curry powder and lemon juice.

# White Chicken Chili

1 tablespoon olive oil

3 pounds boneless, skinless chicken breasts, cut into 1" pieces

2 onions, chopped

2 cloves garlic, minced

2 cans (14.5 ounces each) reduced-sodium chicken broth

4 cans (15 ounces each) cannellini beans, rinsed and drained

1 can (4.5 ounces) chopped green chile peppers

1 teaspoon ground cumin

1 teaspoon salt

¾ teaspoon dried oregano

½ teaspoon chili powder

⅛ teaspoon ground cloves

⅛ teaspoon ground red pepper

**HEAT** the oil in a large pot over medium-high heat. Cook the chicken, onions, and garlic for 5 minutes or until the chicken is lightly browned.

**PLACE** in a 4- to 6-quart slow cooker. Stir in the broth, beans, chile peppers (with juice), cumin, salt, oregano, chili powder, cloves, and pepper.

**COVER** and cook on low for 4 to 6 hours. Uncover and cook for 1 hour, stirring occasionally, until the flavors are blended.

--------------------------------------

Total time: 7 hours 30 minutes ✱ Makes 10 servings

Per serving: 232 calories, 35 g protein, 12 g carbohydrate, 4 g fat, 1 g saturated fat, 537 mg sodium, 3 g fiber

Perfect for a cold-weather gathering, chicken and beans are blended with Tex-Mex flavors for a satisfying dish. Freeze any leftovers in an airtight container for up to 3 months.

# Mustard- and Brown Sugar–Rubbed Salmon

2 tablespoons packed dark brown sugar

1½ teaspoons salt

1 teaspoon black pepper

½ teaspoon ground cumin

¼ teaspoon mustard powder

4 salmon fillets (6 ounces each), skin removed

1 teaspoon olive oil

**STIR** together the sugar, salt, pepper, cumin, and mustard in a small bowl. Press the sugar mixture evenly onto the top surface of the fish.

**HEAT** the oil in a large nonstick skillet over medium heat. Cook the fish, rub side down, for 4 minutes or until the rub dissolves and darkens slightly (being careful not to burn). Flip the fish and cook for 3 minutes or until the fish is opaque.

Total time: 20 minutes   ✱   Makes 6 servings

Per serving: 351 calories, 34 g protein, 7 g carbohydrate, 20 g fat, 4 g saturated fat, 823 mg sodium, 0 g fiber

✱

One bite of this salmon and it's sure to become a family favorite. The sugar caramelizes, glazing the fish with outstanding flavor.

## NUTRITION NEWS TO USE

A daily serving of red wine may boost the effects of heart-healthy omega-3 fatty acids, reports new research. Women ages 26 to 65 who drank one glass daily had higher blood levels of omega-3s—regardless of their fish consumption (the nutrient's top source). Scientists say the polyphenols in wine may alter the metabolism of omega-3s. One caution: Women with a family history of breast cancer should get omega-3s from fish, as studies show that even one daily drink may increase risk of the disease.

# Salmon with Red Salsa

2 tablespoons olive oil, divided

1 large salmon fillet (about 1½ pounds)

3 limes, divided

½ teaspoon black pepper

1 cup dry red wine

1 cup salsa

¼ cup pitted green olives

1 teaspoon agave syrup or honey

½ teaspoon chili powder

2 cups hot cooked brown basmati rice

1 avocado, pitted, peeled, and sliced

1 tomato, sliced

Cilantro sprigs

**PREHEAT** the oven to 425°F.

**DRIZZLE** 1 tablespoon oil in a 13" × 9" glass baking dish. Place the salmon in the dish, skin side down. Squeeze the juice of 2 limes over the salmon. Sprinkle with the pepper. Top with the red wine and salsa. Place the olives around the salmon. Drizzle the agave evenly over the salmon and dust lightly with the chili powder.

**BAKE** for 15 to 20 minutes, depending on the thickness of the fillet, until the fish is opaque.

**TO** serve, mound the rice on a large serving platter. Using 2 spatulas, place the salmon in the center of the rice. Spoon the pan juices over the salmon and rice. Slice the remaining lime and serve the salmon with slices of avocado, lime, and tomato. Garnish with the cilantro.

---

Total time: 55 minutes ✱ Makes 4 servings

Per serving: 599 calories, 38 g protein, 47 g carbohydrate, 28 g fat, 4 g saturated fat, 915 mg sodium, 7 g fiber

167

Main Dishes

Agave is the syrup of the agave cactus. It is a natural sweetener that is very low on the glycemic index and thus can be tolerated by many who must watch their intake of sugars. The Native Americans here in New Mexico believe it to be a natural antihistamine and helpful for arthritis. —**Marla**

—Michelle Anderson, Eagle, Idaho

# Salmon and Mango Wraps

1 cup flaked cooked salmon

1 cup rinsed and drained canned black beans

1 cup frozen shelled edamame (soybeans), thawed

1 cup cold cooked brown rice

1 large mango, cut into bite-size pieces

1 small red bell pepper, julienned

2 scallions, thinly sliced

½ cup loosely packed cilantro, chopped

⅓ cup prepared low-fat Asian salad dressing

6 whole grain tortillas (8" diameter)

2 cups baby greens

**STIR** together the salmon, beans, edamame, rice, mango, pepper, scallions, cilantro, and salad dressing in a large bowl until well blended.

**EVENLY** divide the mixture among the tortillas, top with the greens, and fold to enclose the filling.

Total time: 10 minutes   ✱   Makes 6 servings

Per serving: 361 calories, 20 g protein, 47 g carbohydrate, 10 g fat, 1 g saturated fat, 533 mg sodium, 7 g fiber

This quick and easy recipe is not only flavorful but also packed with nutrient-dense ingredients.

## NUTRITION NEWS TO USE
A recent study comparing the habits of nearly 300 Parisians and Chicagoans explains one possible reason why more than 20% of Americans fell into the overweight category, compared with just 5% in the French group, who weighed 21 pounds less on average. When it comes to putting their forks down, our croissant-loving counterparts are more likely to rely on internal cues, including feeling full, wanting to save room for dessert, or not liking the taste of a food. Americans, on the other hand, tend to be triggered by external cues, such as stopping when food is gone or a TV show is over.

# Fish en Papillote

¼ cup dry white wine

¼ cup seafood stock or clam broth

1 bay leaf

8 whole peppercorns

¾ teaspoon salt, divided

6 fish fillets (4–6 ounces each)

⅓ cup nonfat dry milk powder

2 tablespoons butter

1 cup thinly sliced mushrooms

¼ cup chopped scallions

2 tablespoons chopped parsley

2 tablespoons all-purpose flour

⅛ teaspoon black pepper

6 ounces cooked, peeled, and deveined small shrimp

**PREHEAT** the oven to 400°F.

**COMBINE** the wine, stock, bay leaf, peppercorns, and ½ teaspoon salt in a large skillet. Bring to a simmer over medium heat.

**ADD** the fish. Reduce the heat to low, cover, and simmer for 3 to 5 minutes or until the fish flakes easily. Place the fish on a plate; keep warm. Discard the bay leaf and peppercorns. Place the broth in a large measuring cup. If necessary, add water to equal ⅔ cup. Stir in the milk powder.

**WIPE** the skillet clean. Melt the butter in the skillet. Add the mushrooms, scallions, and parsley and cook, stirring, for 4 minutes. Whisk in the flour, pepper, and remaining ¼ teaspoon salt; cook for 1 minute. Gradually whisk in the reserved broth. Cook, stirring constantly, until the mixture comes to a boil and thickens.

**CUT** six 12" × 16" pieces of parchment paper. Place 1 fillet on one-half of each piece. Divide the shrimp and sauce over the fillets. Fold the paper over the fillets so the edges meet. Starting at the top end, fold the edges over twice to crimp and work around to the end. Place on a baking sheet and bake for 10 to 12 minutes or until the paper begins to turn golden. Serve immediately.

Total time: 55 minutes ✱ Makes 6 servings

Per serving: 215 calories, 31 g protein, 7 g carbohydrate, 6 g fat, 3 g saturated fat, 490 mg sodium, 0 g fiber

✱

To prepare a day ahead of time: Poach the fish, cover, and refrigerate. Prepare the sauce, cover, and refrigerate. Bring the fish to room temperature and heat the sauce. Assemble and bake per directions. May be assembled and refrigerated up to 2 hours before baking, but bring to room temperature before baking.

I have been making this for years. I had seen recipes for fish in parchment, but they were almost always made with a heavy, fatty cream sauce. By using the poaching stock and dry milk powder, I was able to make a healthy, tasty sauce. Fillets like snapper, tilapia, sole, and flounder work well.—**Virginia**

# Pan-Seared Tilapia

1 tablespoon butter or trans-free margarine

2 tilapia fillets (6 to 8 ounces each)

1 tablespoon chopped parsley

1 clove garlic, minced

1 teaspoon Cajun seasoning

1 lemon, juiced

**COAT** a large skillet with cooking spray. Add the butter and melt over medium heat. Add the tilapia and sprinkle with the parsley, garlic, and Cajun seasoning. Drizzle with the lemon juice. Cook for 5 minutes, turning the fillets once, until the fish flakes easily.

Total time: 15 minutes ✳ Makes 2 servings

Per serving: 228 calories, 35 g protein, 4 g carbohydrate, 9 g fat, 5 g saturated fat, 363 mg sodium, 1 g fiber

Serve this simple yet flavorful fish dish with whole grain couscous and steamed green beans for a delicious meal in minutes. If using frozen tilapia, thaw before preparing.

With its reputation for toughness, you probably pass up this superstar for more tender-sounding baby spinach. Don't. Kale is rich in vitamins A, C, and K and is a great source of calcium. What's more, eating cruciferous veggies like kale may lower your cancer risk.

**Try:** Chopping and drizzling it with olive oil, salt, and pepper, and baking it at 350°F for about 15 minutes to create kale "chips"—a crispy side you can eat with your fingers.

**Buy:** Deep green, smaller leaves (they are more tender and have a milder flavor than the larger ones). Because kale gets sweeter as the weather gets colder, fall is the perfect time to pick some up.

[ **SUPERFOOD SPOTLIGHT: KALE** ]

# Baked Parmesan Tilapia

8 tilapia fillets (4 to 6 ounces each)

⅓ cup dried minced onion

2 tablespoons dried parsley flakes

2 teaspoons ground paprika

1½ teaspoons garlic powder

¼ teaspoon cracked black pepper

⅛ teaspoon ground red pepper (optional)

4 tablespoons grated Parmesan cheese

4 teaspoons trans-free margarine

**PREHEAT** the oven to 350°F. Coat a rimmed baking sheet with cooking spray.

**PLACE** the fillets on the baking sheet and sprinkle with the onion, parsley, paprika, garlic powder, black pepper, and red pepper. Top each fillet with ½ tablespoon cheese. Place ½ teaspoon margarine on each fillet.

**BAKE** for 8 to 10 minutes or until the fish flakes easily.

-------------------------------------------

Total time: 10 minutes ✳ Makes 4 servings

Per serving: 297 calories, 48 g protein, 6 g carbohydrate, 9 g fat, 5 g saturated fat, 199 mg sodium, 1 g fiber

✱

Most often sold frozen, tilapia is a great staple to have on hand for last-minute dinners. You could substitute another white fish in this dish, such as sole, flounder, or red snapper.

## NUTRITION NEWS TO USE

Omega-3s and monounsaturated fats are good for our hearts, but might they also strengthen our spines? Researchers from Athens, Greece, studied the diets of 220 Greek women and found that those who followed key components of the Mediterranean diet—they ate plenty of fish and olive oil and minimal red meat—had the greatest bone density. To eat like the Greeks, try replacing your regular fats and oils with 8 to 10 teaspoons of olive oil per day, incorporate 2 or 3 servings of fish (2 to 3 ounces each) per week, and limit weekly red meat consumption to 1 to 3 ounces (or 1 serving).

—Kristina Vanni, North Hollywood, California

# Rye-Crusted Whitefish Fillets with Tomato Mushrooms

### Fish

- ⅔ **cup rye flour**
- ½ **teaspoon salt**
- ¼ **teaspoon ground white pepper**
- 1 **large egg**
- 1 **large egg white**
- 1¼ **pounds skinned whitefish fillet, cut into 4 equal pieces**
- 2 **tablespoons butter**

### Topping

- 1 **tablespoon butter**
- 4 **ounces small cremini mushrooms, thinly sliced**
- 1 **cup small cherry tomatoes, halved**
- 1 **tablespoon minced flat-leaf parsley**
- ¼ **teaspoon salt**
- ¼ **teaspoon lemon pepper**
- 1 **tablespoon snipped chives**

To Make the Fish:

**COMBINE** the rye flour, salt, and pepper on a shallow plate. Beat together the egg and egg white in a shallow bowl. Dip the fillets into the eggs. Dredge in the flour mixture.

**MELT** the butter in a large skillet over medium-high heat. Cook the fillets for 6 minutes, turning once, until the fish flakes easily. Place on a plate; keep warm.

To Make the Topping:

**MELT** the butter in the same skillet over medium-high heat. Add the mushrooms and cook, stirring, for 2 minutes. Stir in the cherry tomatoes, parsley, salt, and lemon pepper. Cook, stirring, for 1 minute or until the tomatoes are just heated.

**SPOON** the tomato mixture over the fish and sprinkle with the chives.

---

Total time: 20 minutes  ✱  Makes 4 servings

Per serving: 364 calories, 32 g protein, 17 g carbohydrate, 18 g fat, 7 g saturated fat, 545 mg sodium, 3 g fiber

✱

Easy enough for any night, impressive enough for company. Tomatoes and mushrooms are sautéed with chives and lemon pepper, creating a zesty, flavorful topping for delicately sautéed whitefish fillets.

# Low-Fat Seafood Newburg

3 tablespoons trans-free margarine

4 shallots, finely chopped

2 tablespoons all-purpose flour

1 cup reduced-sodium chicken broth

¼ cup white wine

2 cups fat-free half-and-half

1 pound frozen cooked medium shrimp

8 ounces imitation crabmeat

**MELT** the margarine in a medium saucepan over medium-high heat. Add the shallots and cook for 5 minutes or until translucent.

**SPRINKLE** with the flour and whisk to make a paste. Whisk in ¼ cup of the broth until well blended. Whisk in the remaining broth, wine, and half-and-half. Bring to a simmer and cook, stirring often, for 10 minutes or until thickened.

**STIR** in the shrimp and crabmeat; cook for 3 minutes or until heated through.

Total time: 20 minutes ✱ Makes 4 servings

Per serving: 375 calories, 41 g protein, 19 g carbohydrate, 11 g fat, 4 g saturated fat, 569 mg sodium, 0 g fiber

✱

Wow! A great way to get the rich, creamy flavors of the classic without the fat. Serve over brown rice and asparagus for an elegant meal.

# Tuna Noodle Casserole

6 ounces whole wheat egg noodles

1 can (10.7 ounces) lower-fat, reduced-sodium cream of celery soup

1 can (10.7 ounces) lower-fat, reduced-sodium cream of mushroom soup

1 cup fat-free milk

2 tablespoons dried parsley

½ teaspoon red-pepper flakes

1 package (16 ounces) California blend frozen vegetables

2 cans (6 ounces each) solid white tuna packed in water, drained and flaked

½ cup sliced almonds

**COAT** a 4- to 6-quart slow cooker with cooking spray.

**PREPARE** the noodles according to the package directions, using the minimum cooking time listed. Drain and refrigerate until needed.

**MIX** the soups, milk, parsley, and pepper flakes in the slow cooker. Stir in the vegetables and tuna.

**COVER** and cook on high for 3 to 4 hours or on low for 7 to 8 hours, adding the cooked noodles during the last 30 minutes. Serve sprinkled with the almonds.

---

Total time: 3 hours 10 minutes ✱ Makes 8 servings

Per serving: 243 calories, 17 g protein, 27 g carbohydrate, 7 g fat, 1 g saturated fat, 476 mg sodium, 3 g fiber

Here's a healthy version of a calorie-dense classic. Switching to lighter soups and nonfat milk along with adding plenty of veggies makes this dish a dieter's delight.

## NUTRITION NEWS TO USE

Drastically cutting carbohydrates to lose weight may diminish your memory. In a study at Tufts University, researchers asked women ages 22 to 55 to follow either a low-carb Atkins-style diet or a low-calorie diet rich in fruits, vegetables, and whole grains. After 1 week of eating very few carbs, the women on the Atkins-style diet performed, on average, 50% worse on memory tasks than those on the low-calorie diet. Once the women started eating carbs again, their scores improved.

# Vegetarian Chili

4 ribs celery, chopped

4 cloves garlic, minced

2 large onions, chopped

2 large green bell peppers, chopped

2 cans (14.5 ounces each) diced tomatoes, drained

1 can (15 ounces) pinto beans, rinsed and drained

1 can (15 ounces) black beans, rinsed and drained

1 can (15 ounces) kidney beans, rinsed and drained

1 can (15 ounces) chickpeas, rinsed and drained

2 cups frozen whole kernel corn

1 can (4 ounces) chopped green chiles

1 cup salsa

1 cup low-sodium tomato or vegetable juice

1½ cups reduced-sodium beef broth

1 tablespoon ground cumin

1 tablespoon chili powder

1 teaspoon ground smoked paprika

**COMBINE** the celery, garlic, onions, bell peppers, tomatoes, beans, chickpeas, corn, chiles, salsa, juice, broth, cumin, chili powder, and paprika in a large stockpot.

**BRING** to a boil over medium-high heat. Reduce the heat to low, cover, and simmer for 1½ to 2 hours.

---

Total time: 2 hours 30 minutes  ✻  Makes 8 servings

Per serving: 220 calories, 11 g protein, 43 g carbohydrate, 2 g fat, 0 g saturated fat, 585 mg sodium, 9 g fiber

✻

Bursting with protein and fiber, this chili makes a hearty dinner. Serve with brown rice and a green salad.

# Easy Black Bean Enchiladas

4 cloves garlic, minced

1 onion, chopped

1 green bell pepper, chopped

1 teaspoon ground red pepper

1 teaspoon chili powder

1 teaspoon ground cumin

1 teaspoon dried oregano

1 teaspoon black pepper

2 cans (15 ounces each) black beans, rinsed and drained

1½ cups salsa, divided

12 corn tortillas (6" each), warmed according to package directions

1 can (14.5 ounces) diced tomatoes, well drained

1 cup shredded reduced-fat Cheddar cheese

3 cups finely shredded lettuce

6 tablespoons fat-free sour cream

**PREHEAT** the oven to 350°F. Coat a 13" × 9" baking dish with cooking spray.

**COAT** a large nonstick skillet with cooking spray and heat over medium-high heat. Cook the garlic, onion, bell pepper, red pepper, chili powder, cumin, oregano, and black pepper for 5 to 7 minutes or until the vegetables are tender.

**MASH** the beans and add to the skillet with ¾ cup of the salsa. Cook for 5 minutes or until heated through.

**SPOON** about ¼ cup of bean mixture onto each tortilla. Roll loosely and place seam side down in the baking dish.

**COMBINE** the tomatoes and the remaining salsa and pour over the enchiladas. Sprinkle with the cheese. Bake for 15 to 20 minutes or until hot.

**DIVIDE** the lettuce among 6 plates. Top each with 2 enchiladas and 1 tablespoon sour cream.

Total time: 55 minutes * Makes 6 servings

Per serving: 345 calories, 14 g protein, 59 g carbohydrate, 7 g fat, 3 g saturated fat, 836 mg sodium, 10 g fiber

I am a firm believer in the power of food to mitigate and prevent disease, so finding healthy, fiber-rich foods that even kids love is a challenge I relish daily. This dish is delicious, simple to prepare, and kid approved, not to mention nutritious! Make it as spicy or mild as you wish by using your favorite variety of salsa.

**—Christina**

# Curried Chickpeas and Rice

1 cup instant brown rice

1 cup frozen peas

3 tablespoons olive oil

1 large onion, chopped

4 large cloves garlic, minced

½ teaspoon red-pepper flakes

2 teaspoons hot curry powder

1 tablespoon grated fresh ginger

¾ teaspoon seasoned salt

1 can (15 ounces) chickpeas, drained and rinsed

¼ cup golden raisins

¼ cup dark raisins

¾ cup light coconut milk

¼ cup lightly salted cashew halves

**COOK** the rice according to the package directions. Add the peas and remove from the heat. Cover and let stand for 10 minutes.

**HEAT** the oil in a large skillet over medium heat. Add the onion, garlic, and pepper flakes; cook, stirring constantly, for 3 minutes or until lightly browned. Add the curry powder, ginger, and seasoned salt; cook for 1 minute, stirring constantly.

**ADD** the chickpeas, raisins, and coconut milk; bring to a boil, reduce the heat to low, cover, and simmer for 15 minutes, stirring occasionally, until thickened.

**PLACE** the rice in a serving bowl and top with the curry mixture. Sprinkle with the cashews.

---

Total time: 40 minutes  ✱  Makes 4 servings

Per serving: 475 calories, 12 g protein, 64 g carbohydrate, 19 g fat, 4 g saturated fat, 608 mg sodium, 8 g fiber

180

Main Dishes

I was in the mood for curry one night, so I just tinkered around with some ingredients I had on hand. And voilà! This is a quick, easy and nutritious dish—light enough for a late supper, hearty enough for a cold winter's meal.
—**Mary**

# Fettuccine Alfredo with Broccoli

| 1 | tablespoon all-purpose flour |
| ¼ | teaspoon salt |
| ⅛ | teaspoon black pepper |
| 1½ | cups 1% milk, divided |
| ¾ | cup grated Romano cheese |
| 1 | teaspoon butter or trans-free margarine |
| 6 | ounces whole wheat fettuccine |
| 4 | cups bite-size broccoli florets |
| ½ | cup frozen peas |
| 12 | grape tomatoes, halved |
| ⅓ | cup chopped parsley |

**WHISK** together the flour, salt, pepper, and ½ cup of the milk in a medium saucepan. Whisk in the remaining 1 cup milk. Cook over medium heat, stirring, for 4 minutes or until just simmering. Stir in the cheese and butter; cook, stirring, for 3 to 4 minutes or until slightly thickened. Remove from the heat and cover to keep the sauce warm.

**PREPARE** the pasta according to the package directions. Add the broccoli to the pasta water during the last 5 to 7 minutes of cooking. Place the peas in a colander. Drain the pasta and broccoli over the peas.

**PLACE** the pasta and vegetables in a serving bowl. Top with the cheese sauce, tomatoes, and parsley. Toss gently to coat.

Total time: 25 minutes ✱ Makes 4 servings

Per serving: 304 calories, 19 g protein, 41 g carbohydrate, 7 g fat, 4 g saturated fat, 449 mg sodium, 8 g fiber

Cheesy, creamy pasta is the ultimate indulgence, but it's usually loaded with refined carbohydrates and artery-damaging saturated fat. To the rescue: this good-for-you version of fettuccine Alfredo made healthy with whole grain pasta and delicious vegetables.

# Dreamy Creamy Macaroni and Cheese

1¼ cups whole grain or low-carb elbow pasta

2 teaspoons butter or trans-free margarine

2 tablespoons all-purpose flour

2 cups 2% milk

½ teaspoon salt

⅛ teaspoon black pepper

Dash of hot sauce (optional)

1½ cups shredded reduced-fat Cheddar cheese, divided

¼ cup whole wheat bread crumbs

**PREHEAT** the oven to 350°F. Coat a 3-quart baking dish with cooking spray.

**PREPARE** the pasta according to the package directions (reduce the cooking time by 2 to 3 minutes). Drain.

**MELT** the butter in a medium saucepan over medium heat. Stir in the flour and cook, stirring constantly, for 2 minutes or until browned. Whisk in the milk, salt, pepper, and hot sauce. Cook, stirring frequently, over medium heat for 5 minutes or until just boiling.

**ADD** 1¼ cups of the cheese and cook, stirring constantly, for 2 minutes or until melted.

**MIX** the pasta and cheese sauce and pour into the prepared baking dish. Combine the remaining ¼ cup cheese and bread crumbs in a small bowl. Sprinkle over the casserole. Bake for 30 minutes or until bubbling and golden brown.

----

Total time: 50 minutes  ✱  Makes 4 servings

Per serving: 368 calories, 34 g protein, 23 g carbohydrate, 16 g fat, 9 g saturated fat, 842 mg sodium, 6 g fiber

✱

Classic rich and creamy mac 'n' cheese is made healthier by using low-fat milk and reduced-fat cheese. The result: You'll never miss the fat and will love each bite of this favorite casserole. For a change of pace, try whole grain penne or rotini pasta.

## NUTRITION NEWS TO USE

New research suggests that low-fat dairy doesn't just reduce high blood pressure—it may also prevent it. In a study of nearly 29,000 middle-aged women, Harvard researchers found that those who had the highest intake of low-fat dairy—between 2 and 9.6 servings per day—were 11% less likely to develop hypertension than those who consumed hardly any. For a bundle of BP benefits, pair low-fat dairy with hypertension-quashing foods rich in potassium and magnesium (such as fruits and nuts). Some of our fav duos: chevre or feta with figs; reduced-fat cottage cheese and fruit salad.

# Spicy Mac 'n' Cheese

3 cups whole grain rotini pasta

3 tablespoons all-purpose flour

2¼ cups 1% milk, divided

3 scallions, chopped

2 cups shredded reduced-fat Mexican blend cheese

½ cup reduced-fat sour cream

2 tablespoons Dijon mustard

1 teaspoon chopped chipotle chile pepper in adobo sauce

½ teaspoon salt

½ teaspoon black pepper

3 tablespoons whole wheat bread crumbs

2 tablespoons grated Parmesan cheese

2 teaspoons olive oil

**PREHEAT** the oven to 400°F. Coat a 3-quart baking dish with cooking spray.

**PREPARE** the pasta according to the package directions (reduce the cooking time by 2 to 3 minutes). Drain.

**WHISK** the flour and ½ cup of the milk in a small bowl.

**COOK** the scallions and the remaining 1¾ cups milk in a large saucepan over medium heat for 4 minutes or until just simmering. Whisk in the flour mixture. Cook, stirring, for 3 minutes or until thickened. Remove from the heat and gradually stir in the cheese until smooth. Stir in the sour cream, mustard, chipotle, salt, pepper, and the pasta. Place in the prepared baking dish.

**COMBINE** the bread crumbs, Parmesan, and oil in a small bowl. Sprinkle over the casserole. Bake for 25 minutes or until bubbling and golden brown.

Total time: 45 minutes ✽ Makes 6 servings

Per serving: 357 calories, 19 g protein, 43 g carbohydrate, 13 g fat, 7 g saturated fat, 728 mg sodium, 2 g fiber

✽

Chipotle chile pepper and a blend of cheeses lend an unexpected but enticing kick to this classic comfort food—made healthier by using reduced-fat dairy products.

# Baked Penne with Zucchini

- 2 cups whole wheat penne pasta
- 2 teaspoons olive oil
- 2 medium zucchini, cut into ½" cubes
- 12 ounces green beans, cut diagonally in half
- 1 can (14.5 ounces) no-salt-added diced tomatoes
- 1 cup tomato-basil pasta sauce
- ½ cup water
- ½ teaspoon salt-free Italian seasoning
- ¼ teaspoon salt
- ⅛ teaspoon black pepper
- ½ cup shredded reduced-fat mozzarella cheese
- 2 tablespoons grated Parmesan cheese

**PREHEAT** the oven to 375°F. Coat a 2-quart baking dish with cooking spray.

**PREPARE** the pasta according to the package directions (reduce the cooking time by 2 to 3 minutes). Drain.

**HEAT** the oil in a large nonstick skillet over medium-high heat. Add the zucchini and beans. Cover and cook, stirring occasionally, for 8 minutes or until the vegetables are lightly browned. Stir in the tomatoes (with juice), pasta sauce, water, Italian seasoning, salt, and pepper. Cover and simmer for 4 minutes.

**SPREAD** half of the pasta in the prepared baking dish and cover with half of the vegetable mixture. Repeat. Sprinkle with the cheese. Cover and bake for 30 minutes or until bubbling and golden brown. Uncover and bake for 10 minutes.

---

Total time: 1 hour 10 minutes ✳ Makes 6 servings

Per serving: 208 calories, 10 g protein, 34 g carbohydrate, 5 g fat, 2 g saturated fat, 336 mg sodium, 6 g fiber

✳

When cooking pasta for a baked dish, you can reduce the cooking time by 2 to 3 minutes, because the pasta will continue to cook as it bakes. This will save a little time but, more important, prevent the pasta from becoming overcooked.

# Spinach Lasagna

12 whole wheat lasagna noodles

8 ounces button mushrooms, chopped

1 onion, chopped

2 cloves garlic, minced

2 tablespoons olive oil

2 cans (14.5 ounces each) diced tomatoes

2 cans (15 ounces each) tomato sauce

1 bag (16 ounces) frozen spinach, thawed and squeezed dry

1 tablespoon Italian seasoning

1 container (16 ounces) 1% cottage cheese

5 cups shredded reduced-fat mozzarella cheese

**PREHEAT** the oven to 375°F. Coat a 13"× 9" baking dish with cooking spray.

**PREPARE** the noodles according to the package directions. Drain.

**COOK** the mushrooms, onion, and garlic in the oil in a medium saucepan over medium-high heat for 7 to 10 minutes or until soft. Add the tomatoes, tomato sauce, spinach, and Italian seasoning. Bring to a boil. Reduce the heat to low; simmer for 15 minutes.

**PLACE** half of the noodles in the prepared baking dish. Spread with half of the cottage cheese. Sprinkle with 2 cups of the mozzarella. Cover with half of the tomato mixture. Repeat.

**COVER** and bake for 30 minutes. Uncover and sprinkle with the remaining 1 cup cheese. Bake for 12 to 15 minutes or until hot in the center.

Total time: 1 hour 30 minutes  ✱  Makes 12 servings

Per serving: 310 calories, 25 g protein, 31 g carbohydrate, 10 g fat, 5 g saturated fat, 1,058 mg sodium, 6 g fiber

✱

A simple way to determine if lasagna and other casseroles are hot all the way through is to insert a knife in the center. As soon as you remove it, carefully feel the knife with your fingers. If it's hot, the lasagna is ready.

# Stuffed Shells with Artichokes

24 jumbo pasta shells

1 teaspoon extra virgin olive oil

8 ounces sliced mushrooms

1 can (14.5 ounces) no-salt-added diced tomatoes

1 can (14 ounces) artichoke hearts packed in water, drained and coarsely chopped

1 package (10 ounces) frozen spinach, thawed and squeezed dry

1½ cups 1% cottage cheese

2 carrots, shredded

½ teaspoon dried thyme

⅛ teaspoon salt

⅛ teaspoon black pepper

½ cup shredded reduced-fat mozzarella cheese

**PREHEAT** the oven to 400°F. Coat a 13" × 9" baking dish with cooking spray.

**PREPARE** the pasta according to the package directions (reduce the cooking time by 2 to 3 minutes). Drain.

**HEAT** the oil in a large nonstick skillet over medium-high heat. Cook the mushrooms, stirring occasionally, for 5 minutes. Add the tomatoes (with juice) and artichokes. Cover and simmer for 4 minutes.

**COMBINE** the spinach, cottage cheese, carrots, thyme, salt, and pepper in a large bowl. Fill the shells with the cheese mixture and place in the baking dish. Top with the sauce. Cover loosely with foil and bake for 20 minutes. Sprinkle with the cheese and bake uncovered for 10 minutes or until bubbling.

Total time: 55 minutes  ✱  Makes 8 servings

Per serving: 176 calories, 14 g protein, 25 g carbohydrate, 3 g fat, 1 g saturated fat, 385 mg sodium, 3 g fiber

A great way to make healthier versions of creamy Italian dishes is to switch part-skim ricotta to 1% cottage cheese. This will save 90 calories and 8.5 grams of fat per ½ cup—while maintaining creaminess.

**[ SUPERFOOD SPOTLIGHT: TAHINI ]**

This traditional Middle Eastern puree of ground sesame seeds is a great source of protein, calcium, and "good" monounsaturated fats (MUFAs). If you like hummus, chances are you'll love tahini, one of the dip's main ingredients.

**Try:** Using it as an alternative to mayo: Tahini tastes great spread on bread in a turkey sandwich or mixed into tuna. It's also delicious as a topping for crackers or as an ingredient in salad dressing.

**Buy:** Arrowhead Mills Organic Sesame Tahini ($6 for a 16-ounce jar; arrowheadmills.com).

# French Roasted-Vegetable Sandwich

2 tablespoons olive oil

2 cloves garlic, minced

½ teaspoon crushed dried rosemary

1 small eggplant, peeled and cut into thick slices

1 red bell pepper, quartered

1 tomato, halved

1 small onion, cut into thick slices

1 round loaf whole wheat Italian bread (8" diameter)

2 tablespoons fat-free plain Greek yogurt

3 tablespoons balsamic vinegar

2 teaspoons grated Parmesan cheese

½ cup tightly packed spinach leaves

**PREHEAT** the oven to 400°F. Coat a large baking sheet with cooking spray. Combine the oil, garlic, and rosemary in a small bowl.

**ARRANGE** the eggplant, pepper, tomato, and onion on the baking sheet. Brush with the oil mixture. Bake for 45 minutes or until the vegetables are golden brown and tender.

**SPLIT** the bread horizontally and scoop out the interior, leaving a 1" shell. (Reserve the crumbs for another use.) Spread the yogurt over the bottom of the shell and sprinkle with the vinegar. Arrange the vegetables over the vinegar. Sprinkle with the Parmesan. Top with the spinach.

**PLACE** the top of the bread over the filling. Press on the bread to make good contact with the vegetables. Wrap tightly in plastic wrap and chill for 30 minutes or until chilled. Cut into wedges.

Total time: 1 hour + chilling time ✱ Makes 6 servings

Per serving: 219 calories, 7 g protein, 36 g carbohydrate, 6 g fat, 1 g saturated fat, 346 mg sodium, 4 g fiber

Similar to muffuletta, this sandwich has roasted vegetables layered in place of the heavy deli meats. Perfect for picnics or large parties (cut into smaller wedges if part of a buffet), this sandwich can be made early in the morning and refrigerated until serving time.

# Pescado Con Salsa Roja

2 tablespoons olive oil, divided

1 large salmon filet, about 1½ pounds

3 limes, divided

½ teaspoon salt

½ teaspoon pepper

1 cup dry good quality red wine

1 cup salsa

¼ cup good quality pitted green olives

1 teaspoon agave syrup or honey

½ teaspoon chili powder

2 cups steamed basmati brown rice

1 avocado, sliced (garnish)

1 tomato, sliced (garnish)

Cilantro sprigs for garnish

**PREHEAT** the oven to 425°F. Drizzle 1 tablespoon oil in a 13" × 9" glass baking dish. Place the salmon in the dish, skin side down. Squeeze the juice of 2 limes over the salmon. Sprinkle with the salt and pepper. Top with the red wine and salsa. Place the olives around the salmon. Drizzle the agave evenly over salmon and dust lightly with the chili powder.

**BAKE** for 15 to 20 minutes (depending on thickness of the fillet) , or until the fish is opaque.

**TO** serve, mound the rice on a large serving platter. Using 2 spatulas, place the salmon in the center of the rice. Spoon the pan juices over the salmon and rice. Slice the remaining lime and serve salmon with slices of avocado, lime and tomato. Garnish with the cilantro.

Total time: 25 minutes ✱ Makes 4 servings

Per serving: 599 calories, 38 g protein, 47 g carbohydrate, 28 g fat, 4 g saturated fat, 915 mg sodium, 7 g fiber

191

Main Dishes

# Apple, Gouda, and Crispy Prosciutto Panini

2 ounces prosciutto slices

4 teaspoons honey Dijon mustard

8 slices (½" thick) whole grain baguette

2 McIntosh apples, halved, cored, and thinly sliced lengthwise

2 ounces light Gouda cheese, thinly sliced

**HEAT** a grill pan or large nonstick skillet over medium heat and cook the prosciutto for 8 minutes, turning occasionally, until crispy. Remove to a paper towel.

**SPREAD** the mustard on 4 slices of the bread. Layer the apples, prosciutto, and cheese on the bread and top with the remaining bread slices. Press lightly to compact the filling.

**SPRAY** the top of the sandwiches with cooking spray and place, sprayed side down, in the same grill pan or skillet. Spray the tops. Place a heavy pan over the top of the sandwiches. Cook for 4 minutes, turning once, or until golden brown on both sides and the cheese is melted.

Total time: 20 minutes  ✽  Makes 4 servings

Per serving: 224 calories, 13 g protein, 33 g carbohydrate, 5 g fat, 2 g saturated fat, 826 mg sodium, 3 g fiber

✽

A panini or sandwich press works well for making these sandwiches; however, an indoor grill (such as George Foreman's) also does the trick: Cook the prosciutto slices on the grill, remove them, and carefully wipe the grill surface clean. Place the sandwiches, coated with cooking spray, on the grill. Instead of using a heavy pan to weight the sandwiches, simply close the lid and press slightly. There's no need to turn the sandwiches.

—Kathryn Rezza, Glen Cove, New York

# Spaghetti Squash and Meatballs

- 1 **spaghetti squash (about 5 pounds), halved lengthwise and seeds removed**
- 1 **pound 99% fat-free ground turkey breast**
- 1 **egg, lightly beaten**
- ¼ **cup chopped onion**
- 1 **teaspoon chopped garlic**
- 1 **tablespoon dried parsley**
- 1 **teaspoon salt, divided**
- 1 **teaspoon black pepper, divided**
- 3 **cans (8 ounces) no-salt-added tomato sauce**
- ½ **cup water**
- 2 **teaspoons Italian seasoning**
- ½ **teaspoon dried basil**

  **Grated Parmesan cheese**

**PREHEAT** the oven to 400°F. Coat a baking sheet with nonstick spray.

**PLACE** the squash, cut side down, on the baking sheet. Bake for 30 to 40 minutes or until tender when pierced with a fork. Let cool slightly. With a fork, scrape the squash strands into a large platter.

**MEANWHILE.** combine the turkey, egg, onion, garlic, parsley, ½ teaspoon salt, and ½ teaspoon pepper in a large bowl. Shape into twelve 2" meatballs.

**COAT** a large saucepan with cooking spray. Cook the meatballs over medium-high heat for 5 minutes, turning often, until browned. Add the tomato sauce, water, Italian seasoning, basil, and the remaining ½ teaspoon salt and ½ teaspoon pepper. Bring to a simmer. Cover and simmer for 15 to 20 minutes or until an instant-read thermometer inserted in the center of a meatball registers 165°F and the meat is no longer pink.

**PLACE** the meatballs and sauce over the spaghetti squash. Serve sprinkled with Parmesan.

Total time: 1 hour 5 minutes ❋ Makes 4 servings

Per serving: 324 calories, 35 g protein, 43 g carbohydrate, 5 g fat, 1 g saturated fat, 816 mg sodium, 3 g fiber

193

Main Dishes

This version of spaghetti and meatballs is low in calories, high in fiber, and a good source of nutrition. I think everyone will agree it's quite tasty. If you like a spicy sauce, add red-pepper flakes to the sauce.

—**Kathryn**

[ it worked for me ]

# 152 lbs lost!

## ✳ STACY ZANDEE

**When nurse Stacy Zandee took herself on as a patient, her daughter followed suit—and together they lost 212 pounds**

### My Story

When I became a nurse in 1981, I was already on the road to obesity. I gained 80 pounds during my first pregnancy, and they stuck. With my next four children came more weight, and by 2006 I'd hit 277 pounds. I felt embarrassed on the job because I advised patients on nutrition and diet, and they always looked at me sideways as if to say, "Yeah sure, I can see how well you follow your own advice."

They were right to scoff. With my long hours, my meals frequently came from vending machines—MandM's, doughnuts, and soda. I knew my diet was unhealthy, but I was ashamed, and I relied on food to conceal my emotional pain.

### An Unkind Legacy

By the time I was 35 years old, I had high blood pressure and diabetes. I was going to have to start injecting insulin. My doctor said my only hope of getting

Pounds Lost: 152

Age: 46

Height: 5'8"

Weight Then: 277 pounds

Weight Now: 125 pounds

Health Bonus: "We lost
big as a team!"

healthy was with bariatric surgery. That was the wake-up call I needed. As a nurse, I refused to believe it was my only option. Plus, my second-youngest child, Payton, who was 13 at the time and 60 pounds overweight, was picking up my bad habits and insecurities. So, in December 2006, we decided to change our lives together.

## Weight Loss, Family Style

Payton and I became avid readers of nutrition books, magazines, and Web sites. We collected new recipes and combed the supermarket aisles seeking smart substitutions: We traded whole milk for fat-free, white rice for brown, and soda for water. To ward off hunger, we ate small meals every 3 hours.

After 4 months, Payton and I began exercising. At first, we'd walk several blocks and return home huffing and puffing. But by the end of the summer, we were walking 5 miles at a stretch.

In just 2 years, I went from a size 24 to a size 4. I no longer need medication for high blood pressure or diabetes, and I have loads of energy. Best of all, 60 pounds lighter, Payton is healthier and more

confident. Watching her blossom has been the biggest reward of all.

## My Top Tips

* Sneak in good deeds and exercise.

* My family "pays it forward" by helping neighbors with odd jobs—mowing lawns, raking leaves, and shoveling snow—that also keep us active.

* Keep experimenting. Payton and I try new recipes often, and they've led us to new favorites: Spaghetti squash is the perfect pasta impostor.

* Pack in the produce. I up my intake of fruits and veggies by eating at least one portion at every meal. Since I eat every 3 hours, the servings really add up.

* Make food count . . . is my motto. Saying it out loud reminds me to eat in moderation and savor every bite.

* Be like a mail carrier. Rain or shine, I exercise. When my husband wants to go out to dinner, I lace up my sneakers and meet him there. Walking has not only lowered my blood sugar but also boosted my energy and my mood.

195

Main Dishes

# side dishes

# Garlic Mashed Potatoes

2 pounds Yukon gold potatoes, peeled and cut into 2" pieces

3 cloves garlic, sliced

¾ cup 1% buttermilk

1 tablespoon butter

½ teaspoon salt

½ teaspoon black pepper

**COMBINE** the potatoes and garlic in a medium saucepan with salted water to cover. Bring to a boil. Reduce the heat to a simmer and cook for 20 minutes or until tender.

**WARM** the buttermilk in a small saucepan over medium-low heat.

**DRAIN** the potatoes and garlic. Push through a potato ricer or food mill into a medium bowl or mash with a potato masher.

**MASH** in the buttermilk, butter, salt, and pepper.

Total time: 35 minutes  ✱  Makes 8 servings

Per serving: 121 calories, 3 g protein, 24 g carbohydrate, 2 g fat, 1 g saturated fat, 453 mg sodium, 2 g fiber

✱

Buttermilk might sound as rich as cream, but it actually has 98% less fat. Crush the garlic before you slice it and let it stand while you peel the potatoes to maximize its heart-protective compounds.

# Roasted Herbed New Potatoes

2 pounds new potatoes, halved or quartered

1 tablespoon olive or canola oil

1 tablespoon chopped fresh thyme or 1 teaspoon dried

2 teaspoons chopped fresh oregano or ½ teaspoon dried

1 teaspoon salt

¼ teaspoon black pepper

**PREHEAT** the oven to 400°F.

**TOSS** together the potatoes, oil, thyme, oregano, salt, and pepper in a medium bowl.

**ARRANGE** in a single layer on a nonstick or foil-lined baking sheet. Roast for 30 minutes, turning occasionally with a metal spatula, until browned and tender.

Total time: 50 minutes  ✱  Makes 6 servings

Per serving: 125 calories, 3 g protein, 24 g carbohydrate, 3 g fat, 1 g saturated fat, 397 mg sodium, 4 g fiber

✱

Potatoes are called "new" when they're harvested young and small before they reach maturity. The skins are extra thin and are generally left on. You can substitute red bliss or fingerling potatoes.

## NUTRITION NEWS TO USE

Consuming just ½ teaspoon of heart-healthy flaxseed oil every day may soothe irritated skin. In a 12-week study of 45 women, those taking flaxseed oil supplements daily saw a 45% reduction in redness and 25% less water loss, resulting in smoother, softer skin. Flaxseed oil is rich in omega-3s, fats that combat inflammatory damage and keep skin supple. Try it with yogurt and grain dishes; its mild flavor makes it an easy add-in.

# Slow-Cooked Sweet Potatoes

4 sweet potatoes (8–10 ounces each)

1 tablespoon canola oil

1 tablespoon trans-free margarine, melted

1 tablespoon honey

1 teaspoon ground cinnamon

¼ teaspoon ground nutmeg

3 tablespoons water

**SCRUB** the sweet potatoes and pierce with a fork on all sides. Combine the oil, margarine, honey, cinnamon, nutmeg, and water in a 4- to 6-quart slow cooker. Add the potatoes, tossing to coat well.

**COVER.** Cook on low for 4 to 6 hours, or until tender when pierced with a fork.

---

Total time: 6 hours  ✽  Makes 4 servings

Per serving: 313 calories, 4 g protein, 61 g carbohydrate, 6 g fat, 1 g saturated fat, 102 mg sodium, 7 g fiber

✽

Reap the benefits of one of nature's truly perfect foods. Sweet potatoes are low in calories, high in fiber, great for those who are carb-sensitive, and packed with vitamins and minerals.

## SWEET OR SAVORY
### 5 WAYS TO ENJOY SLOW-COOKED SWEET POTATOES

**1.** Puree 2 or 3 peeled potatoes with 2 cups milk or broth in a blender until smooth. Microwave for a quick, easy soup.

**2.** Use 1 cup of cubed potatoes and stir cubes into soups and stews.

**3.** Peel 4 potatoes and mash them with ½ cup milk and ¼ cup trans-free margarine.

**4.** Sprinkle sliced potatoes with brown sugar or honey and cinnamon. Dot with trans-free margarine and bake at 350°F for 15 to 20 minutes.

**5.** Try twice-"baked" sweet potatoes: Halve 4 potatoes, then scoop flesh into a bowl, reserving skins. Add ¼ to ½ cup milk and ¼ cup trans-free margarine to bowl and mix well. Spoon mixture into reserved skins and bake at 350°F for 20 minutes.

# Wheat Berry–Sweet Potato Bake

3 cups water

1 cup wheat berries

½ teaspoon salt, divided

2 pounds sweet potatoes, peeled and cut into ⅛"-thick slices

2 cloves garlic, minced

2 tablespoons finely chopped fresh thyme or 2 teaspoons dried

1 tablespoon finely chopped fresh rosemary or 1 teaspoon dried

2 cups shredded Gruyere cheese, divided

½ cup reduced-sodium chicken broth

**BRING** the water and wheat berries to a boil in a medium saucepan. Reduce the heat, cover, and simmer, stirring occasionally, for 1 hour or until the wheat berries are tender and the liquid has been absorbed. Stir in ¼ teaspoon salt.

**PREHEAT** the oven to 350°F. Coat a 13" × 9" baking dish with cooking spray.

**PLACE** half of the sweet potatoes in the prepared baking dish. Sprinkle with half of the garlic, 1 tablespoon thyme, ½ tablespoon rosemary, and ⅛ teaspoon salt. Top with half of the wheat berries and ⅔ cup of the cheese. Repeat (reserving ⅔ cup of the cheese). Pour the broth over all.

**COVER** with foil and bake for 45 minutes or until the potatoes are tender. Uncover, top with the remaining ⅔ cup cheese, and bake 5 minutes longer.

Total time: 2 hours 5 minutes  ✱  Makes 8 servings

Per serving: 262 calories, 13 g protein, 33 g carbohydrate, 9 g fat, 5 g saturated fat, 298 mg sodium, 5 g fiber

✱

Chewy wheat berries make a more interesting contrast to tender sweet potatoes than marshmallows do! You can prepare this dish in stages: Cook the wheat a day or two ahead, then assemble the casserole a few hours before baking.

> ## QUICK TIP
> Add wheat berries to your meals to include another whole grain bursting with fiber. Here are two simple ways to use them.
> ✱ Add cooked wheat berries 10 minutes before any meat or poultry stir-fry is done.
> ✱ The berries' sweetness makes them a great substitute for rice in rice pudding or bread in bread pudding.

201

Side Dishes

# Chile-Corn Casserole

1 package (8 ounces) corn muffin mix

2 cans (15.25 ounces each) cream-style corn

1 cup fat-free plain yogurt

1 can (4.5 ounces) chopped mild green chiles, drained

¼ cup chopped red bell pepper

3 scallions, thinly sliced

1 large egg

2 tablespoons chopped fresh dill

**PREHEAT** the oven to 350°F. Coat a 9" or 10" cast-iron skillet or 11" × 8" baking dish with cooking spray.

**COMBINE** the muffin mix, corn, yogurt, chiles, bell pepper, scallions, egg, and dill in a large bowl. Stir well with a wooden spoon until blended. Pour the batter into the prepared skillet.

**BAKE** for 35 to 40 minutes or until the casserole is lightly browned and a toothpick inserted in the center comes out clean. Let cool slightly before serving.

Total time: 40 minutes  ✱  Makes 8 servings

Per serving: 113 calories, 4 g protein, 23 g carbohydrate, 1 g fat, 0 g saturated fat, 456 mg sodium, 2 g fiber

✱

Cornbread lovers, this one's for you! Now your favorite treat can become a main dish. Creamed corn, mild green chiles, and spices blend together for the ultimate comfort food casserole.

# Penne with Feta

8 ounces whole grain penne pasta

1 teaspoon olive oil

½ cup frozen broccoli florets, thawed and chopped

½ cup frozen chopped red bell peppers

½ cup chopped tomatoes

2 cloves garlic, minced

¼ teaspoon dried thyme

¾ cup crumbled feta cheese

3 tablespoons chopped parsley

¼ teaspoon black pepper

**PREPARE** the pasta according to the package directions. Drain and return to the pot.

**COAT** a large nonstick skillet with cooking spray and place over medium-high heat. Add the oil, broccoli, bell peppers, tomatoes, garlic, and thyme. Cook, stirring, for 5 to 8 minutes or until the vegetables are tender.

**ADD** the cheese. Cook, stirring, for 2 minutes or until the cheese begins to melt. Add the pasta, parsley, and pepper. Mix well.

Total time: 30 minutes ✱ Makes 6 servings

Per serving: 204 calories, 8 g protein, 31 g carbohydrate, 6 g fat, 3 g saturated fat, 221 mg sodium, 2 g fiber

Be sure to always use whole grain or whole wheat pasta. Just one serving can provide 5 to 6 grams of fiber, about 25 percent of your daily requirement. A recent study found that women who got their fiber from whole grains had a 50 percent lower chance of gaining weight during their lifetime.

# Zucchini Rotini

¼ cup whole wheat rotini pasta

¾ cup 1% cottage cheese

1 tablespoon salt-free Italian seasoning

½ cup shredded zucchini

1 cup canned no-salt-added diced tomatoes, drained

¼ cup shredded reduced-fat mozzarella cheese

20 kalamata olives, sliced

**PREPARE** the pasta according to the package directions. Drain.

**COMBINE** the cottage cheese and Italian seasoning in a microwave-safe dish. Stir in the pasta and zucchini. Top with the tomatoes and sprinkle with the cheese. Microwave on high for 3 minutes or until warmed through. Divide the pasta evenly between 2 plates and sprinkle olives on top.

Total time: 15 minutes  ✱  Makes 2 servings

Per serving: 223 calories, 18 g protein, 20 g carbohydrate, 8 g fat, 3 g saturated fat, 864 mg sodium, 4 g fiber

✱

What's for dinner? Keep the ingredients on hand for this recipe that comes together in just minutes. If you don't have the zucchini, try shredded carrots or spinach instead.

**NUTRITION NEWS TO USE**
People who eat rapidly until they are full are three times more likely to be overweight than slow eaters.

# Farfalle with Kasha, Mushrooms, and Onion

1 tablespoon olive oil

8 ounces sliced mushrooms

1 onion, sliced

¼ teaspoon salt

⅛ teaspoon black pepper

1 cup reduced-sodium chicken broth

½ cup kasha

2 tablespoons egg white

3 ounces farfalle (bowtie) pasta

**HEAT** the oil in a nonstick Dutch oven over medium-high heat. Add the mushrooms, onion, salt, and pepper and cook, stirring, for 8 minutes or until browned and tender. Remove to a bowl.

**BRING** the broth to a simmer in a small saucepan. Stir the kasha and egg white in a small bowl.

**HEAT** the same Dutch oven over medium-high heat. Toast the kasha mixture in the hot pan for 1 to 2 minutes, stirring, until the grains are separate. Reduce the heat to low, stir in the hot broth and the mushroom mixture, cover, and simmer for 10 minutes or until the liquid is absorbed and the kasha is tender.

**PREPARE** the pasta according to the package directions while the kasha cooks. Stir into the kasha mixture.

Total time: 35 minutes  ✱  Makes 4 servings

Per serving: 214 calories, 9 g protein, 37 g carbohydrate, 5 g fat, 1 g saturated fat, 304 mg sodium, 4 g fiber

✱

Full-flavored kasha mixes beautifully with pasta and mushrooms in our healthy version of this classic Jewish side dish.

# Spring Risotto

3 cups reduced-sodium chicken or vegetable broth, heated, divided

1 tablespoon butter

1 tablespoon olive oil

1 onion, chopped

½ teaspoon salt

1½ cups Arborio or Carnaroli rice

12 ounces fresh peas in the pod, shelled, or 1 cup frozen peas

1 tablespoon lemon juice

¼ cup grated Parmesan cheese

**BRING** the broth to a boil in a small saucepan over high heat. Reduce the heat to low. Cover.

**MELT** the butter and oil in a medium saucepan over medium-low heat. Add the onion and salt. Cover and cook, stirring occasionally, for 3 minutes or until the onion is translucent.

**ADD** the rice and stir. Add about 1½ cups of the broth and adjust the heat to maintain a good simmer. Stir occasionally until most of the liquid has been absorbed. Add 1 cup of the remaining broth and continue simmering and stirring until absorbed. Add the remaining ½ cup broth and peas and continue to simmer and stir for 4 minutes or until the rice is just tender. If you run out of broth before the rice is cooked through, use water.

**STIR** in the lemon juice and cheese. Serve immediately.

Total time: 35 minutes  ✱  Makes 4 servings

Per serving: 384 calories, 13 g protein, 66 g carbohydrate, 9 g fat, 3 g saturated fat, 857 mg sodium, 5 g fiber

✱

Chefs swoon over delicate, flavorful green peas in season. If you have a garden or a nearby farmers' market, use your just-picked young peas in this recipe. If not, choose frozen with confidence. They're often tastier than the overgrown, starchy peas generally available in supermarkets.

—Greg Fontenot, The Woodlands, Texas

# Brown Rice with Black Beans

1 tablespoon olive oil

1 onion, chopped

1 can (4 ounces) diced green chile peppers, drained

1 clove garlic, minced

3 tablespoons chili powder

1 tablespoon ground cumin

1 teaspoon dried oregano

2 teaspoons ground coriander (optional)

2 cups brown rice

3 cups reduced-sodium vegetable or chicken broth

2 cups water

1 can (15 ounces) black beans, rinsed and drained

2 tablespoons chopped cilantro

**HEAT** the oil in a medium saucepan over medium heat. Add the onion, peppers, and garlic. Cook for 5 minutes or until tender. Add the chili powder, cumin, oregano, and coriander. Cook for 1 minute. Stir in the rice, broth, and water. Bring to a boil.

**REDUCE** the heat to low, cover, and simmer for 40 to 45 minutes or until the liquid is absorbed and the rice is tender. Stir in the beans and cook 1 minute. Sprinkle with the cilantro.

Total time: 45 minutes  ✳  Makes 8 servings

Per serving: 262 calories, 8 g protein, 50 g carbohydrate, 3 g fat, 1 g saturated fat, 104 mg sodium, 7 g fiber

207

Side Dishes

✳

This Southwest side dish is full of bold flavor and heart-healthy fiber. Serve it with any Mexican entrée to help fill out the meal.

# Mediterranean Couscous

1¼ cups water

¾ cup whole wheat couscous

½ teaspoon salt, divided

2 tablespoons lemon juice

1 tablespoon olive oil

¼ teaspoon black pepper

½ cup rinsed and drained canned red kidney beans

½ medium cucumber, peeled, seeded, and chopped

½ green bell pepper, chopped

¼ red onion, chopped

½ cup crumbled reduced-fat feta cheese

2 tablespoons chopped fresh dill

1 tablespoon capers, rinsed and drained

**BRING** the water to a boil in a medium saucepan over medium-high heat. Stir in the couscous and ¼ teaspoon of the salt. Return to a boil, reduce the heat to low, cover, and simmer for 2 minutes. Remove from the heat and let stand for 5 minutes. Fluff with a fork and cool for 5 minutes longer.

**WHISK** together the lemon juice, oil, pepper, and the remaining ¼ teaspoon salt in a large bowl. Add the kidney beans, cucumber, bell pepper, onion, feta, dill, capers, and couscous; toss to coat well.

---

Total time: 30 minutes ✻ Makes 4 servings

Per serving: 186 calories, 8 g protein, 27 g carbohydrate, 6 g fat, 1 g saturated fat, 520 mg sodium, 6 g fiber

✻

Couscous, a North African type of pasta, is commonly available in supermarkets. Look for it near the rice. Be sure to get the whole wheat variety, which is much higher in fiber than white. This recipe can be made up to 1 day ahead. Store it in an airtight plastic container in your refrigerator.

Break out of that brown rice rut! You can find a host of more exotic grains, with interesting flavors and intriguing textures, right in the supermarket. Check out mild and fluffy quinoa, nutty bulgur, earthy kasha, chewy wheat berries, hearty farro, and delicate millet. They're all as simple to prepare as rice, and most are just as quick, too! Since these lesser-known grains are whole, not refined, they still have the bran, germ, and endosperm, with their wholesome vitamins, minerals, and fiber. You can wake up meals, enjoy terrific taste, and reap health benefits besides.

## HOW TO COOK WHOLE GRAINS

✱ Quinoa, mild and tender with a subtle pop, is a complete protein, just like meat or eggs.

**Grain:** 1 cup     **Water:** 2 cups     **Yield:** 3½ cups
**Method:** Rinse quinoa. Bring liquid to a boil, add quinoa, cover, and simmer 15 minutes.

✱ Bulgur is boiled, dried, and cracked wheat kernels. For a chewy texture, simply reconstitute it by soaking in liquid. For a fluffy grain, cook it further.

**Grain:** 1 cup     **Water:** 1½ cups     **Yield:** 3 cups
**Method:** To reconstitute: Bring liquid to a boil, add bulgur, remove from heat, cover, and let stand 10 minutes.
**To cook:** Bring liquid to a boil, add bulgur, cover, and simmer 15 minutes.

✱ Kasha, aka roasted buckwheat, tastes nutty and earthy. It's quick-cooking and especially good when you want a bold grain flavor.

**Grain:** 1 cup     **Water:** 2 cups     **Yield:** 4 cups
**Method:** Stir 1 beaten egg or egg white into each cup kasha before toasting in nonstick pan over medium-high heat 1 to 2 minutes. Bring liquid to a boil, add kasha, cover, and simmer 10 minutes.

✱ Wheat berries boast sturdy texture and complex flavor. When cooked, they plump up to a sweet treat.

**Grain:** 1 cup     **Water:** 3 cups     **Yield:** 2½ cups
**Method:** Bring liquid and wheat berries to a boil. Reduce heat, cover, and simmer 1 hour.

✱ Farro (hulled) has a light yet toothsome texture similar to that of barley. It's quick and easy to cook.

**Grain:** 1 cup     **Water:** 2 cups     **Yield:** 2½ cups
**Method:** Bring liquid to a boil, add farro, cover, and simmer 20 minutes.

✱ Millet, a tiny grain, explodes into fluffy, crumblike morsels. Mild-mannered millet soaks up flavor from anything it's cooked with.

**Grain:** 1 cup     **Water:** 2½ cups     **Yield:** 4 cups
**Method:** Bring liquid to a boil, add millet, cover, and simmer 20 minutes.

[ **GREAT GRAINS** ]

## THE BEST PLACE TO STORE GRAINS

Whole grains still have their germ, with its tiny amount of nutrient-packed oil. Just like any oil that you don't use up in a couple of weeks, raw grains should be kept in the refrigerator. When chilled, they'll stay fresh for months.

# Couscous with Chickpeas, Pine Nuts, and Peppadew

1 box (6 ounces) couscous mix with toasted pine nuts

2 tablespoons olive oil

1 clove garlic, minced

1 cup canned chickpeas, rinsed and drained

1½ cups reduced-sodium vegetable broth

¼ cup drained jarred Peppadew or pimientos, chopped

**REMOVE** the seasoning packet from the couscous. Set aside.

**HEAT** the oil and garlic in a large saucepan over high heat for 30 seconds or until sizzling. Add the chickpeas and the contents of the reserved seasoning packet.

**COOK,** stirring, for 2 minutes or until the chickpeas are thoroughly coated with the seasonings. Add the broth and couscous. Bring to a boil. Stir. Reduce the heat to medium-low. Cover and simmer for 4 minutes or until all the broth is absorbed. Stir in the Peppadew.

---

Total time: 10 minutes  ✱  Makes 6 servings

Per serving: 221 calories, 7 g protein, 32 g carbohydrate, 7 g fat, 1 g saturated fat, 902 mg sodium, 4 g fiber

Peppadew, a sweet-hot bright red chile from South Africa, adds interest to this good grain side dish. Serve with everything from roast chicken to grilled shrimp.

# Spinach Casserole

1 package (10 ounces) frozen chopped spinach, thawed and drained

1 container (15 ounces) part-skim ricotta cheese

6 ounces feta cheese, crumbled

4 large egg whites

1 teaspoon dried basil

½ teaspoon lemon pepper seasoning

**PREHEAT** the oven to 350°F. Coat a 9" round baking dish with cooking spray.

**COMBINE** the spinach, ricotta, feta, egg whites, basil, and lemon pepper seasoning in a large bowl. Pour the mixture into the prepared baking dish. Bake for 1 hour or until the casserole is set and lightly browned around the edges.

Total time: 1 hour 5 minutes  ✽  Makes 6 servings

Per serving: 197 calories, 16 g protein, 7 g carbohydrate, 12 g fat, 8 g saturated fat, 478 mg sodium, 2 g fiber

Spinach is an excellent source of vitamin A and a good source of vitamin C and folic acid. Keep boxes of frozen spinach in the freezer to pump up the nutrition of your recipes. Add to soups, sauces, and casseroles for a touch of color and flavor.

# Grilled Mexican Corn

½ cup reduced-fat sour cream

½ teaspoon ground cumin

½ teaspoon salt

¼ teaspoon garlic powder

⅛ teaspoon black pepper

4 ears corn, husked

¼ cup chopped cilantro

1 teaspoon chili powder

**COAT** a grill rack or broiler pan with cooking spray. Preheat the grill or broiler.

**STIR** together the sour cream, cumin, salt, garlic powder, and pepper in a large shallow dish.

**GRILL** the corn for 8 to 10 minutes or until browned in spots, turning occasionally. Coat with the sour cream mixture. Sprinkle with the cilantro and chili powder.

Total time: 15 minutes   ✱   Makes 4 servings

Per serving: 127 calories, 4 g protein, 19 g carbohydrate, 5 g fat, 3 g saturated fat, 324 mg sodium, 3 g fiber

✱

Don't wait for the county fair for this yummy corn. It's quick and easy to make yourself. You'll never miss the butter!

## QUICK TIP: THE BEST GRILLED VEGGIES

Many kinds, in addition to corn, get sweeter and juicier on the grill. Just coat lightly with olive oil and cook. Finish off with a touch of balsamic vinegar and chopped mixed herbs, if you like. Try:

✱ Whole small mushrooms or large ones cut into ½"-thick slices

✱ Whole asparagus stalks

✱ Zucchini or yellow summer squash, cut lengthwise into ½"-thick strips

✱ Multicolored bell peppers, quartered

✱ Eggplant, peeled and cut lengthwise into ½"-thick strips

✱ Onions, sliced into ½"-thick rounds

# New Green Bean Casserole

½ cup 1% buttermilk

½ cup bread crumbs

1 onion, cut crosswise into ¼"-thick slices and separated into rings

8 ounces mushrooms, sliced

1 small onion, chopped

½ teaspoon dried thyme

¼ teaspoon salt

¼ cup all-purpose flour

3 cups 1% milk

1 bag (16 ounces) frozen French-cut green beans, thawed and drained

**PREHEAT** the oven to 500°F. Coat a medium baking dish and a baking sheet with cooking spray.

**PLACE** the buttermilk in a shallow bowl and the bread crumbs in another bowl. Dip the onion rings into the buttermilk, then dredge in the bread crumbs. Place on the baking sheet. Coat with cooking spray. Bake for 20 minutes or until tender and golden brown.

**COAT** a medium saucepan with cooking spray and heat over medium heat. Add the mushrooms, onion, thyme, and salt. Cook, stirring occasionally, for 4 to 5 minutes or until the mushrooms give off their liquid. Sprinkle with the flour. Cook, stirring, for 1 minute. Add the milk. Cook, stirring constantly, for 3 to 4 minutes, or until thickened. Stir in the beans.

**REDUCE** the oven temperature to 400°F. Pour the bean mixture into the prepared baking dish. Scatter the onion rings over the top. Bake for 25 to 30 minutes or until hot and bubbly.

Total time: 55 minutes  ✹  Makes 8 servings

Per serving: 121 calories, 7 g protein, 21 g carbohydrate, 2 g fat, 1 g saturated fat, 184 mg sodium, 3 g fiber

✳

Here's a healthy version of an American favorite. Homemade onion rings baked to a crisp top a casserole of mushrooms and green beans bathed in a creamy sauce.

# Seared Green Beans

2 tablespoons canola or peanut oil

1 pound whole green beans, trimmed

Salt

2 cloves garlic, minced

⅛ teaspoon red-pepper flakes (more if desired)

**HEAT** a large skillet over medium-high heat until very hot. Add the oil and swirl to coat the pan.

**INCREASE** the heat to high and wait 30 seconds. Add the beans and season with salt. Cook for 3 minutes, shaking the pan or using tongs to turn and move the beans so they cook quickly and evenly. Carefully taste the beans (they may be crunchy) and cook to the desired doneness.

**SEASON** with the garlic and pepper flakes. Cook 1 minute longer. Serve hot, warm, or at room temperature.

Total time: 15 minutes ✱ Makes 4 servings

Per serving: 98 calories, 2 g protein, 8 g carbohydrate, 7 g fat, 1 g saturated fat, 7 mg sodium, 4 g fiber

Searing is a quick-cooking technique that coaxes the most flavor out of veggies in the shortest amount of time. You can use the same cooking method with virtually any vegetable that's cut into thin strips, so they heat through quickly. Try it with a mixture of fennel and bell peppers, carrots and celery, or zucchini and yellow squash.

# Southeast Asia–Style Eggplant

2 large eggplants (about 3 pounds)

2 tablespoons canola or peanut oil

1 medium red onion, sliced

¼ teaspoon salt

3 cloves garlic, minced

3 serrano chile peppers, thinly sliced (wear plastic gloves when handling)

⅓ cup dry sherry or ¼ cup rice wine vinegar

2 tablespoons packed brown sugar

2 tablespoons reduced-sodium soy sauce

2 tablespoons lime juice

¼ cup water

1 cup packed fresh mint leaves, coarsely chopped

**PEEL** the eggplant and slice lengthwise ½" thick; cut the pieces crosswise into ½"-thick sticks.

**HEAT** the oil in a large skillet over medium heat. Add the eggplant, onion, and salt. Cook, stirring, for 5 minutes. Add the garlic, peppers, and sherry and cook, stirring, for 5 minutes.

**COMBINE** the brown sugar, soy sauce, lime juice, and water in a small bowl. Stir until the sugar dissolves. Stir into the eggplant mixture. Cover, reduce the heat to low, and cook, stirring frequently, for 10 minutes or until the eggplant is tender and no longer bitter. Stir in the mint.

Total time: 30 minutes ✳ Makes 4 servings

Per serving: 212 calories, 5 g protein, 33 g carbohydrate, 8 g fat, 1 g saturated fat, 428 mg sodium, 13 g fiber

✳

Eggplant notoriously absorbs a lot of oil, so don't be tempted to add more. If you need more liquid for cooking, simply splash in a bit of water.

# Baked Eggplant with Tomato Chutney

1 medium eggplant

2 tablespoons olive oil, divided

¼ teaspoon salt

¼ teaspoon black pepper

1 onion, chopped

1 clove garlic, chopped

¼ cup balsamic vinegar

1 tablespoon chopped fresh basil or 1 teaspoon dried

1 can (14.5 ounces) diced tomatoes

¼ cup pine nuts

**PREHEAT** the oven to 425°F. Coat a 13" × 9" baking dish with cooking spray. Cut the eggplant into ½" slices and brush with 1 teaspoon of the oil. Sprinkle each side with salt and pepper; lay the slices in the baking dish. Bake for 30 minutes or until the eggplant is tender.

**HEAT** the remaining oil in a nonstick saucepan over medium-high heat. Cook the onion and garlic for 3 minutes, stirring, until softened. Add the vinegar and basil and cook, stirring, for 1 minute. Add the tomatoes and simmer for 5 minutes. Remove from the heat and stir in the pine nuts. Spoon over the eggplant and bake for 10 minutes.

Total time: 1 hour ✱ Makes 4 servings

Per serving: 169 calories, 3 g protein, 14 g carbohydrate, 13 g fat, 1 g saturated fat, 155 mg sodium, 5 g fiber

Full of flavor, this is low in fat and sugar. It is a very filling main dish or can be used as a side dish or even served over pasta.

—**Greg**

# Portobello Parmesan

1 tablespoon extra virgin olive oil

4 firm portobello mushrooms (4" diameter), stems and gills removed (leave edges of caps intact)

¾ cup fat-free ricotta cheese

½ cup shredded reduced-fat mozzarella cheese

1 clove garlic, minced

   black pepper

1 medium firm-ripe tomato, thinly sliced

1 tablespoon fresh thyme leaves

3 tablespoons grated Parmesan cheese

**HEAT** the oil in a large ovenproof skillet over medium heat. Lay the mushrooms cap side down in the skillet and cook, undisturbed, for 10 minutes. Turn and cook for 10 minutes. Turn over again.

**COMBINE** the ricotta, mozzarella, and garlic in a small bowl. Season with pepper.

**SPOON** about 3 tablespoons of the ricotta mixture into each mushroom cap (leave in pan), spreading gently into place.

**PREHEAT** the broiler.

**ARRANGE** a few tomato slices on each mushroom and sprinkle evenly with thyme and Parmesan. Broil for 3 to 5 minutes or until the tops are golden brown.

---

Total time: 30 minutes  ✱  Makes 4 servings

Per serving: 156 calories, 12 g protein, 11 g carbohydrate, 7 g fat, 3 g saturated fat, 214 mg sodium, 2 g fiber

Portobello mushrooms are one of the best sources of selenium, which may help protect against cancer. Adequate selenium is also required for DNA repair.

—Isabella Djordjevski, Brighton, Michigan

# Beans with Herbed Tomatoes and Goat Cheese

3 medium tomatoes, seeded and chopped

¼ cup chopped fresh basil or 1 tablespoon dried

¼ cup chopped fresh oregano or 1 tablespoon dried

2 scallions, sliced

2 cloves garlic, minced

¼ teaspoon salt

¼ teaspoon black pepper

1 can (15 ounces) kidney beans, rinsed and drained

1 can (15 ounces) navy beans, rinsed and drained

1 cup crumbled semisoft goat cheese or feta cheese

**COMBINE** the tomatoes, basil, oregano, scallions, garlic, salt, and pepper in a medium bowl. Let stand at room temperature for 30 minutes to 2 hours.

**PLACE** the beans in a medium microwave-safe bowl. Microwave on medium for 1 to 2 minutes, stirring once. Stir the beans into the tomato mixture and sprinkle with the cheese.

Total time: 15 minutes + marinating time ✷ Makes 4 servings

Per serving: 275 calories, 15 g protein, 33 g carbohydrate, 10 g fat, 6 g saturated fat, 624 mg sodium, 8 g fiber

Serve this hearty fresh tomato dish with steamed fish or chicken and whole grain rolls.

—Jackie Ortega, San Lorenzo, California

# Cauliflower Supreme

6–8 **cups cauliflower florets, steamed until crisp-tender**

1 **can (10 ounces) reduced-fat, reduced-sodium cream of mushroom soup**

1 **cup shredded reduced-fat Cheddar cheese**

2 **slices bacon, cooked and crumbled**

**PREHEAT** the oven to 350°F. Coat a 2-quart baking dish with cooking spray.

**MIX** the cauliflower and soup in the prepared baking dish. Bake for 15 minutes. Top with the cheese and bake for 5 minutes or until the cheese melts. Sprinkle with the bacon and serve.

Total time: 30 minutes　✶　Makes 6 servings

Per serving: 124 calories, 8 g protein, 9 g carbohydrate, 7 g fat, 4 g saturated fat, 377 mg sodium, 3 g fiber

Reminiscent of a rich stuffed baked potato, here high-fiber, low-carb cauliflower takes the place of the potato. It's coated with flavorful Cheddar cheese and a touch of bacon for a delicious side dish.

**SUPERFOOD SPOTLIGHT: WINTER WHITES**

When nutrition experts tell you to avoid "white food," they mean refined foods such as white flour, rice, and pasta. White vegetables, beans, and nuts may also lack the vibrant color connected with many disease-fighting antioxidants, but they can lower risks of high blood pressure and heart attack, and more.

✶ Turnips: One-half cup has only 18 calories but is rich in cancer-fighting compounds called glucosinolates. Blend turnips into your favorite mashed potato recipe for lower-calorie comfort food.

✶ Cauliflower: One cup of this cruciferous veggie (cooked) contains nearly 20% of your daily need for bone-building vitamin K. Toss florets with oil and red-pepper flakes and roast.

✶ Jicama: A cup provides nearly one-quarter of the daily fiber requirement and one-third of your need for the antioxidant vitamin C. Slice thinly into strips and dip into salsa.

✶ Radishes: A peppery addition to salads, ½ cup has 9 calories and is a good source of vitamin C.

✶ Cannellini beans: Just 1 cup provides nearly half of your daily fiber need and 14 g of filling protein. Sauté with olive oil and rosemary for a quick side.

✶ Parsnips: This carrot cousin is packed with vitamin C and fiber. Slice, drizzle with oil and maple syrup, and roast in the oven.

✶ Pine nuts: They're rich in manganese, a mineral crucial for metabolism and bone health. Toast and toss onto soups and salads.

# Stewed Tomatoes

2 slices high-fiber whole wheat bread

1 tablespoon trans-free margarine

1 can (14.5 ounces) Italian stewed tomatoes

2 tablespoons dried onions

1 tablespoon sugar or granular sugar substitute

Pinch of garlic salt

**PREHEAT** the oven to 350°F. Coat a small baking dish with cooking spray.

**SPREAD** the bread with the margarine, cut into cubes, and place in the prepared baking dish. Stir in the tomatoes, onions, sugar, and garlic salt. Let stand for 5 minutes or until the bread is soaked through.

**BAKE** for 10 to 15 minutes or until heated through.

---

Total time: 25 minutes ✳ Makes 2 servings

Per serving: 205 calories, 5 g protein, 34 g carbohydrate, 7 g fat, 2 g saturated fat, 688 mg sodium, 2 g fiber

This was my mother's idea of a vegetable. Of course she used real butter and white bread, but I find it tastes just as good with my modifications.
**—Elizabeth**

—Dorthy Steffan, Sequim, Washington

# Veggie Boats

4 medium zucchini or large
   yellow summer squash

1 tablespoon olive oil

1 medium sweet onion, chopped

1 can (8 ounces) tomato sauce

2 tablespoons orange juice

½ teaspoon dried basil

½ cup seasoned bread crumbs

½ cup grated Parmesan cheese

1 tablespoon butter, melted

**PREHEAT** the oven to 350°F. Coat a 13" × 9" baking dish with cooking spray.

**CUT** the zucchini in half lengthwise. Scoop out the center of each zucchini, leaving a ¼" shell. Place the shells, skin side down, in the prepared baking dish. Chop the removed squash.

**HEAT** the oil in a large nonstick skillet over medium-high heat. Add the onion and chopped zucchini. Cook, stirring, for 5 to 7 minutes or until tender.

**ADD** the tomato sauce, orange juice, and basil. Bring to a simmer over medium-high heat and cook for 5 minutes or until the mixture thickens. Fill each shell with the mixture. Cover and bake for 25 minutes.

**STIR** together the bread crumbs, Parmesan, and butter. Sprinkle over the zucchini. Bake uncovered for 10 minutes or until the cheese is melted and slightly golden brown.

Total time: 1 hour ✱ Makes 4 servings

Per serving: 224 calories, 10 g protein, 26 g carbohydrate, 10 g fat, 4 g saturated fat, 735 mg sodium, 5 g fiber

✱

A perfect recipe to prepare with an abundance of squash from your garden, this different variation of the vegetable is sure to become a summertime favorite.

Side Dishes

# Curried Spring Vegetables

2 tablespoons extra virgin olive oil

1 onion, chopped

4 teaspoons grated fresh ginger

2 cloves garlic, minced

1½ teaspoons mild curry powder

½ medium zucchini, chopped

2 carrots, chopped

2 ribs celery, thinly sliced

4 ounces mushrooms, sliced

¾ cup fresh or frozen whole corn kernels

1 green bell pepper, chopped

½ cup fresh or frozen peas

½ teaspoon salt

4 scallions, chopped

**HEAT** the oil in a large nonstick skillet over medium heat. Add the onion and cook, stirring, for 6 minutes or until softened. Add the ginger, garlic, and curry powder. Cook, stirring frequently, for 5 minutes, or until the onion is golden.

**ADD** the zucchini, carrots, celery, mushrooms, corn, pepper, peas, and salt. Cover and cook over medium-low heat, stirring occasionally, for 15 minutes or until the vegetables are tender. Sprinkle with the scallions.

Total time: 1 hour ✳ Makes 4 servings

Per serving: 104 calories, 3 g protein, 13 g carbohydrate, 5 g fat, 1 g saturated fat, 238 mg sodium, 3 g fiber

These spicy vegetables perk up broiled chicken, pork, or seafood. For a flavorful soup, heat them in some chicken broth.

## NUTRITION NEWS TO USE

Americans are shelling out more for "natural" foods than ever before—but does the label guarantee healthier picks? Not always. Here's what you need to know:

✳ Trust it when it's on meat and poultry packaging. The USDA requires these products to be free of artificial ingredients, colorings, preservatives, and unnecessary processing.

✳ Use caution when it's on anything else. Products can be packed with sweeteners or flavorings and still carry a "natural" sticker.

✳ Our advice: Check the nutrition label. All of the ingredients—good for you and not so good—are listed there. Our rule of thumb: Avoid anything you can't pronounce.

# Vegetable Ragout

2 cups frozen cut green beans

1 can (14.5 ounces) stewed tomatoes

1 can (8.75 ounces) whole kernel corn, drained

2 tablespoons olive oil

**PLACE** the beans, tomatoes, corn, and oil in a medium saucepan over medium-high heat. Bring to a boil and turn the heat to medium. Cook for 10 to 15 minutes or until the tomatoes break down a little and the flavors blend.

Total time: 20 minutes　✱　Makes 4 servings

Per serving: 159 calories, 4 g protein, 23 g carbohydrate, 8 g fat, 1 g saturated fat, 437 mg sodium, 3 g fiber

This works well with just about any meat. But I love it with chicken and fish. It's easy and can be ready in a jiff. By the time you cook the meat, it's ready.　　　　**—Geneva**

[ it worked for me ]

# 110 lbs lost!

## ✳ MELISSA BENAVIDES

**Tired of being tired, Melissa Benavides took a long, hard look at her diet and lost 110 pounds**

### My Story

Growing up in San Antonio, I savored the Mexican dishes my family ate—enchiladas smothered in cheese, tacos stuffed with meat—not to mention lots of cookies and cake. But it wasn't until I got married and had two children that my weight spiraled out of control. I gained 60 pounds with each pregnancy, and although I tried several diets, I always gained it all back.

Between work and kids, I didn't have time to cook, so I picked up burgers, pizza, and, of course, Mexican for lunch and dinner. Whenever I felt sluggish, I opened a soda. At one point, I was drinking a six-pack a day! By age 37, I weighed 250 pounds. I had asthma, my knees ached, and I suffered constant headaches. Even worse, I couldn't play with my children. When I offered to walk my older son to school, he'd decline. It broke my heart that he was ashamed to be seen with me.

## VITAL STATS

Pounds Lost: 110

Age: 40

Height: 5'5"

Weight Then: 250 pounds

Weight Now: 140 pounds

Health Bonus: "I went from size 24 to size 6"

## Small Steps, Big Impact

When my father was diagnosed with colon cancer, it finally hit me: If I continued on this path, I might not see my kids grow up. It terrified me. That's when I happened to read a magazine article about a woman who slimmed down at a local LA Weight Loss Center. The program sounded simple: Meet with a counselor weekly and learn about portion control and smart substitutions. Best of all, the plan didn't have its own brand of required food—I loved that.

I worried that I'd hate my new lifestyle, but I discovered I didn't mind trading soda for water or cutting back on sweets. I began eating more salads, fish, and baked chicken—and I even learned to cook leaner and lighter versions of my beloved Mexican fare that were surprisingly satisfying.

## Total Transformation

Today I'm 110 pounds lighter—and my weight loss has brought my family closer. When my kids want to play soccer in the park, I race them there. And now my son asks me to walk him to school. My doctor says I've added 10 years to my life. Knowing that my hard work has given me extra time with my family is what thrills me the most.

## My Top Tips

✻ Modify your favorites . . . I didn't want to give up Mexican food, so I lightened it with low-fat cheese, whole wheat tortillas, and sautéed vegetables.

✻ Practice self-reflection . . . Keep a food journal and analyze it every night. If you've gotten off course, you can make an adjustment the next day.

✻ Carry backup snacks . . . I used to grab fast food when the hunger pangs hit. Now I have healthy, portion-controlled snacks in plastic bags on hand at all times so I don't blow my diet.

✻ Don't arrive hungry . . . To avoid over-indulging at events, I fill up on fruits and veggies before I head out. Then I have just a taste of dessert later on.

✻ Appreciate feeling energized . . . When I lost the weight, all of my health problems—the headaches, sore knees, and asthma—disappeared, too. In their place: immense self-confidence!

# snacks & little

# bites

—Eric Stevens, Portsmouth, Virginia

# Anytime Veggie Snack

½ seedless cucumber, peeled and chopped

2 plum tomatoes, chopped

1 tablespoon light mayonnaise

12 jarred sliced jalapeño peppers or black olives, chopped

½ cup chopped red onion

Dash of hot sauce (optional)

12 whole grain crackers

**COMBINE** the cucumber, tomatoes, mayonnaise, jalapeños, onion, and hot sauce in a medium bowl. Spread on the crackers.

Total time: 10 minutes  **✻**  Makes 4 servings

Per serving: 76 calories, 2 g protein, 13 g carbohydrate, 2 g fat, 0 g saturated fat, 560 mg sodium, 2 g fiber

Here's a great way to add some fiber to your day. Be sure to read the labels of the crackers and opt for ones that have the most fiber per serving.

# White Bean Dip with Pistachios and Cilantro

1 can (15.5 ounces) cannellini beans, rinsed and drained

4 teaspoons lemon juice

1 teaspoon coriander seed, crushed or ground

1 clove garlic, halved

3 tablespoons finely chopped cilantro

3 tablespoons olive oil

3 tablespoons finely chopped pistachios

1 tablespoon finely chopped scallion (white part only)

Salt and black pepper

**PUREE** the beans, lemon juice, coriander, and garlic in a food processor until smooth.

**STIR** in the cilantro, oil, pistachios, and scallion. Season with salt and pepper.

Total time: 20 minutes ✻ Makes 6 servings

Per serving: 145 calories, 4 g protein, 12 g carbohydrate, 9 g fat, 1 g saturated fat, 169 mg sodium, 3 g fiber

Similar to hummus, this dip gets a boost of flavor from cilantro and scallions. Enjoy it on pita wedges, carrot or celery sticks, or bell pepper strips.

**QUICK TIP: THE RIGHT TIME TO PICK HERBS**

Snip herbs in the morning rather than in the afternoon or evening. The flavorful oils of the plants are most concentrated just after the dew evaporates.

—Alyson Widen, Shaker Heights, Ohio

# Do-It-Your-Way Red Salsa and Chips

3 small plum tomatoes, chopped

1 red bell pepper, chopped

1 small red onion, finely chopped

2 tablespoons lime juice

2 tablespoons chopped cilantro

6 ounces baked tortilla chips

**COMBINE** the tomatoes, pepper, onion, and lime juice in a medium bowl. Let stand 5 minutes to allow the flavors to blend. Just before serving, add the cilantro. Serve with the tortilla chips.

Total time: 15 minutes   ✳   Makes 6 servings

Per serving: 157 calories, 3 g protein, 22 g carbohydrate, 7 g fat, 2 g saturated fat, 172 mg sodium, 2 g fiber

Snacks &
Little Bites

I love this California salsa recipe because it is so easy to fix. Vary the recipe to your liking by adding minced seeded jalapeño pepper for spice or sliced scallions for zest.

—**Alyson**

# Pitas with Tzatziki

2 cups low-fat plain Greek yogurt

1 cup peeled, grated cucumber, spun dry in salad spinner

4 cloves garlic, grated

1 teaspoon lemon juice

¾ teaspoon salt

⅛ teaspoon ground red pepper

6 whole wheat pitas (6"–7" diameter)

1 tablespoon extra virgin olive oil

**STIR** together the yogurt, cucumber, garlic, lemon juice, salt, and pepper in a medium bowl. Chill, covered, for 1 hour.

**BRUSH** both sides of the pitas lightly with the oil. Heat in batches in a large skillet over medium heat for 5 minutes, turning once, until golden and puffed. Serve with the chilled tzatziki.

Total time: 15 minutes + chilling time  ✻  Makes 6 servings

Per serving: 241 calories, 12 g protein, 39 g carbohydrate, 6 g fat, 2 g saturated fat, 603 mg sodium, 5 g fiber

✻

Tzatziki—a yogurt and cucumber condiment that graces nearly every table in Greece—has an incredibly pungent flavor laced with lots of garlic.

[ **NUTRITION NEWS TO USE**
Three handfuls of candy corn between trick-or-treater visits can equal as much as 770 calories—the caloric equivalent of a Big Mac and small fries! ]

# Simple Radish Canapés

18 slices (¼" each) from small, rustic, whole grain baguette

5 ounces Boursin Garlic and Fine Herbs

8 radishes, trimmed and sliced into very thin rounds (use up to 12 as desired)

Black pepper

**SPREAD** each slice of bread with 1½ teaspoons Boursin. Layer radishes on top, overlapping slightly. Season with pepper.

Total time: 15 minutes ✽ Makes 6 servings

Per serving: 125 calories, 3 g protein, 7 g carbohydrate, 10 g fat, 7 g saturated fat, 214 mg sodium, 1 g fiber

✽

Boursin is a mild creamy cheese spread that complements the peppery radishes. Extra-thin slices of baguette and radish make these bites taste better—and easier to eat. Or try crisp flatbread.

# Roasted Mixed Nuts

1 cup mixed raw pecans, walnuts, and macadamia nuts

1½ tablespoons apple cider or juice

½ teaspoon celery salt or curry powder

**PREHEAT** the oven to 350°F.

**STIR** together the nuts, cider, and celery salt in a small bowl. Toss to coat and spread in a single layer on a baking sheet. Roast for 4 to 6 minutes or until light golden. Let cool before serving.

-------------------------------------------------------------

Total time: 15 minutes ✱ Makes 4 servings

Per serving: 200 calories, 3 g protein, 5 g carbohydrate, 20 g fat, 2 g saturated fat, 126 mg sodium, 2 g fiber

✱

Change up the flavors of these nuts by using different juices and seasonings. Try peach nectar with cardamom, grape juice and nutmeg, or pear juice and cinnamon.

## NUTRITION NEWS TO USE

Macadamia nuts may have a bad rap because of their high calorie count, but a moderate serving can help keep your arteries clear. A new study found that adding 1½ ounces (the size of a shot glass, about 305 calories' worth) of macs daily to a typical diet lowered total cholesterol and "bad" LDL by about 9% each after 5 weeks. And the results weren't due to weight loss; the subjects weighed the same over the course of the study. Crush the nuts and "dust" salads, vegetables, and yogurt.

# Cereal-Nut Mix

- **4 cups whole grain cereal**
- **½ cup raw almonds**
- **½ cup unsalted roasted peanuts**
- **¼ cup unsalted roasted sunflower seeds**

**MIX** the cereal, almonds, peanuts, and sunflower seeds in a large bowl. Divide evenly among 6 resealable plastic bags.

Total time: 5 minutes ✻ Makes 6 servings

Per serving: 237 calories, 8 g protein, 21 g carbohydrate, 15 g fat, 2 g saturated fat, 198 mg sodium, 5 g fiber

✻

Here's a great snack to have on hand for midafternoon cravings. Grab a bag for the office or when running errands. This packable snack mix provides more than 90 percent of your daily vitamin E requirement and is a source of vitamins $B_2$ (riboflavin) and $B_3$ (niacin).



## NUTRITION NEWS TO USE

Forget butter-flavored popcorn and king-size candy (hello, 800+ calories!). We asked you to share your favorite healthier movie snacks. Here are our top four:

- ✻ Shelled, salted edamame
- ✻ A mix of pretzels, almonds, raisins, and mini marshmallows
- ✻ Jicama matchsticks, tossed with lime juice and chili powder
- ✻ Frozen red or green grapes

—Mylane Wilson, Atlanta, Georgia

# Fruit Roll-Up Snacks

2 tablespoons fat-free cream cheese, softened

1 whole wheat 96% fat-free tortilla (8" diameter)

½ teaspoon Splenda or other granular sugar substitute

¼ cup blueberries, raspberries, or chopped strawberries

**SPREAD** the cream cheese on the tortilla. Sprinkle with the Splenda. Place the fruit on one end of the tortilla. Fold in the bottom and sides of the tortilla and roll around the fruit. Cut diagonally in half.

---

Total time: 5 minutes   ✱   Makes 1 serving

Per serving: 50 calories, 4 g protein, 7 g carbohydrate, 1 g fat, 0 g saturated fat, 158 mg sodium, 1 g fiber

Experiment with a variety of tortillas until you find your favorite. Try low-carb, low-fat, or whole grain—being sure that whichever ones you pick are made from whole wheat and not white flour.

# Apricots with Yogurt and Honey

1 cup low-fat plain Greek yogurt

2 tablespoons honey

½ teaspoon vanilla extract

9 apricots, halved

**WHISK** together the yogurt, honey, and vanilla in a small bowl. Place the apricots on a serving plate and top with the yogurt mixture.

---

Total time: 5 minutes  ✻  Makes 6 servings

Per serving: 74 calories, 3 g protein, 13 g carbohydrate, 1 g fat, 1 g saturated fat, 11 mg sodium, 1 g fiber

Fruit is a common dessert for those on the Mediterranean diet. Any fresh fruit will work in this recipe; try plums, peaches, figs, or nectarines. To add some flavor to the yogurt, stir in a pinch of cinnamon, nutmeg, or cardamom.

## NUTRITION NEWS TO USE

Americans are consuming 46 more calories a day from sugar-sweetened beverages than they were 2 decades ago, according to a study in the *American Journal of Clinical Nutrition*—enough to gain 5 pounds in a year if calories are not cut elsewhere. Get flavor without the sugar by adding citrus wedges, chopped mint, or crushed fresh or frozen berries to seltzer water or unsweetened iced tea; once your tastebuds adjust, the sweet stuff will taste overly sweet.

# Cinnamon Applesauce

7 crisp apples, such as Granny Smith or Golden Delicious, peeled, cored, and chopped

2 teaspoons ground cinnamon

¾ cup water

½ cup packed brown sugar

**PLACE** the apples in a 4- to 6-quart slow cooker and sprinkle with the cinnamon. Stir in the water.

**COVER.** Cook on low for 2 to 4 hours, or until the apples become soft and mushy.

**STIR** in the brown sugar and mix well. Serve warm or cool.

Total time: 4 hours  ✱  Makes 6 servings

Per serving: 143 calories, 0 g protein, 38 g carbohydrate, 0 g fat, 0 g saturated fat, 8 mg sodium, 2 g fiber

To can this sauce, pour the hot sauce into hot, scalded preserving jars, leaving ½" headspace. Wipe the rims clean, attach the lids, and tightly screw on the caps. Invert the jars for 10 seconds. Store in the refrigerator.

**5 WAYS TO ENJOY CINNAMON APPLESAUCE**

**1.** Stir applesauce into yogurt or oatmeal or use it instead of sugary syrup to top pancakes and waffles.

**2.** Freeze it up to 4 months. Make single-serving portions and simply defrost for a healthy anytime snack.

**3.** Replace half of the oil in cake and muffin recipes with just-as-moist applesauce.

**4.** Serve applesauce beside savory meats or pair the sweet side with steamed or sautéed veggies.

**5.** Make stuffing: Mix 4 cups stale bread cubes with ¼ teaspoon dried thyme and ¼ cup each chopped celery, chopped onion, and golden raisins. Add 1 cup applesauce and bake in 1½-quart casserole dish coated with cooking spray at 350°F for 30 to 35 minutes.

[ **SUPER SAUCE** ]

# Lemon Bars

2¼ cups all-purpose flour, divided

⅔ cup + 2 tablespoons confectioners' sugar, divided

½ cup (1 stick) trans-free margarine or butter, cut into small pieces

3 lemons

1 cup fat-free egg substitute

1½ cups granulated sugar

**PREHEAT** the oven to 350°F. Coat a jelly-roll pan with cooking spray.

**STIR** together 2 cups of the flour and ⅔ cup of the confectioners' sugar in a medium bowl. Cut in the spread until the mixture resembles coarse meal. Press firmly and evenly onto the bottom of the prepared pan. Bake for 10 to 15 minutes or until lightly browned. Cool in the pan on a rack.

**GRATE** the zest from 2 lemons into a medium bowl. Cut all the lemons in half and squeeze their juice into the same bowl. Whisk in the egg substitute, granulated sugar, and the remaining ¼ cup flour until smooth. Pour over the crust.

**BAKE** for 18 to 20 minutes or until the filling is set when lightly touched in the center. Cool in the pan on a rack. When completely cooled, sift the remaining 2 tablespoons confectioners' sugar over the top. Cut into bars and serve.

-------------------------------------------

Total time: 40 minutes  ✱  Makes 6 servings

Per serving: 101 calories, 2 g protein, 17 g carbohydrate, 3 g fat, 2 g saturated fat, 13 mg sodium, 1 g fiber

✱

Here's a healthy version of a classic lemon bar. Serve with fresh berries—raspberries, blueberries, or strawberries—to increase the fiber and add a lovely flavor to the lemony bars.

—Diane Nemitz, Ludington, Michigan

# Coconut Pecan Oatmeal Bars

½ cup (1 stick) butter or trans-free margarine, softened

½ cup Splenda sugar blend

¼ cup packed brown sugar

½ teaspoon salt

1 large egg

¾ cup unsweetened applesauce

1 teaspoon vanilla extract

1 cup whole grain pastry flour

1 cup rolled oats

1¼ teaspoons baking powder

1 teaspoon ground nutmeg

1 cup chopped toasted pecans

¾ cup unsweetened shredded coconut

**PREHEAT** the oven to 350°F. Coat a 13" × 9" baking pan with cooking spray.

**BEAT** the butter, Splenda, brown sugar, and salt in a large bowl with an electric mixer on medium until creamed. Beat in the egg, applesauce, and vanilla. Beat in the flour, oats, baking powder, and nutmeg until well blended. Stir in the pecans and coconut.

**SPREAD** in the pan. Bake for 30 minutes or until golden and set. Cool in the pan on a rack. Cut into 24 bars.

---

Total time: 40 minutes ✳ Makes 24 bars

Per bar: 129 calories, 2 g protein, 10 g carbohydrate, 9 g fat, 4 g saturated fat, 83 mg sodium, 2 g fiber

This is my recipe for a low-sugar cookie that is absolutely scrumptious. I have tried to lower the sugar in all my recipes recently, as there is a history of diabetes in my family and I'm trying to stay healthy as long as I can.

—**Diane**

—Iris Davis, Houston, Texas

# Healthy Oatmeal Raisin-Nut Cookies

1 cup (2 sticks) trans-free margarine, softened

1 cup Splenda or other granular sugar substitute

⅓ cup fat-free milk

2 teaspoons vanilla extract

2 large eggs or 3 large egg whites

2 cups quick-cooking rolled oats

1½ cups buckwheat pancake mix

1 cup finely chopped walnuts

1½ cups raisins

**PREHEAT** the oven to 350°F. Line baking sheets with parchment paper.

**BEAT** the margarine and Splenda in a large bowl with an electric mixer on medium until well blended. Beat in the milk, vanilla, and eggs. Stir in the oats, pancake mix, walnuts, and raisins until well blended.

**DROP** by rounded spoonfuls onto the baking sheets and bake for 15 minutes or until set. Cool on a rack.

Total time: 35 minutes  ✱  Makes 36 cookies

Per cookie: 130 calories, 2 g protein, 13 g carbohydrate, 8 g fat, 2 g saturated fat, 120 mg sodium, 1 g fiber

✱

Packed with nuts and raisins, these cookies are also bursting with fiber from the buckwheat pancake mix. Look for it alongside other pancake mixes and syrups.

## NUTRITION NEWS TO USE

Attention, adults: Time to take a healthy eating lesson from the young ones in your life. Fresh fruit beat out cookies as the top snack food among children ages 2 to 12, according to a recent survey by market research firm NPD Group. Adults prefer gum and chocolate; in 2005, only 28.7% of grown women ate the recommended two or more servings of fruit per day. Toss a portable piece like a kiwifruit, banana, or pear into your purse so you have a healthy snack at the ready.

—Heather Dunning, Kirkland, Washington

# Whole Wheat Harvest Cookies

1½  cups whole wheat flour

1  teaspoon baking soda

¾  teaspoon ground nutmeg

1  teaspoon ground cinnamon

¼  teaspoon pumpkin pie spice

½  cup (1 stick) butter or trans-free margarine, softened

1  cup packed brown sugar

1  large egg

⅔  cup 1% buttermilk

1½  cups quick-cooking rolled oats

½  cup chopped walnuts

⅓  cup chopped dried apricots

⅓  cup dried cranberries

⅓  cup raisins

**PREHEAT** the oven to 350°F. Line baking sheets with parchment paper.

**COMBINE** the flour, baking soda, nutmeg, cinnamon, and pumpkin pie spice in a medium bowl.

**BEAT** the butter and brown sugar in a large bowl with an electric mixer on medium until creamed. Beat in the egg. Add the flour mixture alternately with the buttermilk, until well blended. Stir in the oats, walnuts, apricots, cranberries, and raisins.

**DROP** by rounded spoonfuls onto a baking sheet and bake for 12 to 15 minutes or until set. Cool on a rack.

---

Total time: 35 minutes  ✱  Makes 36 cookies

Per cookie: 103 calories, 2 g protein, 16 g carbohydrate, 4 g fat, 2 g saturated fat, 45 mg sodium, 1 g fiber

Cookies are a weakness of mine, but I feel better about eating cookies that use whole wheat flour and yet are so moist and chewy. I was inspired to make them because I love spices, and they remind me of a granola bar with all the oats, nuts, and dried fruit.

**—Heather**

—Angel Toledano, Campbell, California

# Almost-Sugar-Free Chocolate Chip Cookies

2¼ cups whole grain pastry flour

1 teaspoon baking soda

1 cup (2 sticks) trans-free margarine, softened

¾ cup Splenda or other granular sugar substitute

⅓ cup firmly packed Splenda brown sugar blend

1 teaspoon salt

2 large eggs

1 tablespoon vanilla extract

2 cups semisweet chocolate chips

**PREHEAT** the oven to 350°F. Line baking sheets with parchment paper.

**COMBINE** the flour and baking soda in a small bowl. Set aside.

**BEAT** the margarine, Splenda, brown sugar blend, and salt in a large bowl with an electric mixer on medium until creamed. Add the eggs, one at a time, beating well after each addition. Beat in the vanilla. Add the flour mixture and beat on low speed just until blended. Stir in the chips.

**DROP** by mounded teaspoonfuls about 2" apart on the prepared baking sheets. Bake each sheet for 9 to 11 minutes or until the cookies are golden. Cool on a rack.

---

Total time: 50 minutes  ✳  Makes 54 cookies

Per cookie: 79 calories, 1 g protein, 7 g carbohydrate, 5 g fat, 2 g saturated fat, 106 mg sodium, 1 g fiber

These cookies are great for those watching their sugar intake. While low in sugar, they taste so similar to the original recipe your entire family will love them.

# Orange Marmalade Cookies

½ cup (1 stick) trans-free margarine, softened

1 large egg

1 cup all-fruit orange marmalade spreadable fruit

2 cups whole grain flour

1 teaspoon baking soda

1 teaspoon salt

1 teaspoon vanilla extract

**PREHEAT** the oven to 350°F. Line baking sheets with parchment paper.

**BEAT** the margarine and egg together in a large bowl with an electric mixer on medium. Stir in the fruit spread. Add the flour, baking soda, salt, and vanilla and mix until well blended.

**DROP** by rounded teaspoons 2" apart on parchment-lined baking sheets. Bake each sheet for 15 to 20 minutes or until the cookies are lightly browned. Cool on the sheets for 5 minutes before transferring to a rack to cool completely.

Total time: 35 minutes  ✱  Makes 24 cookies

Per cookie: 98 calories, 1 g protein, 15 g carbohydrate, 4 g fat, 1 g saturated fat, 201 mg sodium, 1 g fiber

Marmalade cookies were developed during World War II when sugar was scarce and marmalade replaced the sugar in recipes. Using spreadable fruit that's sweetened with fruit juice only makes these treats healthier than the original recipe. For the flour, choose whole grain pastry flour or white whole wheat.

249

Snacks & Little Bites

## NUTRITION NEWS TO USE

More than a quarter of women over age 40 don't eat enough protein, even though it can help keep hunger pangs at bay. An easy solution: fat-free Greek-style yogurt. The creamy treat has twice the protein of regular yogurt (and is now hitting dairy aisles across the country). A straining process removes liquid, concentrating nutrients and making it thicker and richer than typical yogurt for fewer calories. Look for fat-free varieties like Oikos Organic Greek Yogurt (90 calories and 15 grams of protein per 5.3-ounce serving).

# Chocolate Waffle Cookies

½ cup (1 stick) butter or trans-free margarine, softened

⅔ cup sugar or granular sugar substitute

2 large eggs

1 teaspoon vanilla extract

1 cup whole grain pastry flour

6 tablespoons unsweetened cocoa powder

2 tablespoons canola oil

½ teaspoon espresso powder (optional)

Confectioners' sugar

**PREHEAT** a nonstick waffle iron.

**BEAT** the butter and sugar in a large bowl with an electric mixer on medium until creamed. Beat in the eggs and vanilla. Beat in the flour, cocoa powder, oil, and espresso powder until well blended.

**DROP** the batter by rounded teaspoonfuls about 1" apart onto the waffle iron. (To avoid burnt fingers, use two spoons, one to scoop and one to scrape dough onto the waffle iron.) Close and cook for 1 to 1½ minutes or until the cookies are puffed and cooked through.

**TRANSFER** to a wire rack to cool until just warm. Immediately dust the cookies with confectioners' sugar.

Total time: 45 minutes ✱ Makes 36 cookies

Per cookie: 186 calories, 3 g protein, 20 g carbohydrate, 11 g fat, 5 g saturated fat, 66 mg sodium, 2 g fiber

 I love to make these with my 10-year-old granddaughter! They are wonderful to make in the summer because you do not have to heat up the house. We even make them camping. They soon disappear!

—**Debi**

# Peanutty Treats

¼ cup low-fat vanilla soy milk

½ cup creamy peanut butter

¼ cup sugar

2–3 cups granola or granola-type cereal

¼ cup sesame seeds

**PLACE** 36 mini-muffin papers on a rimmed baking sheet.

**BRING** the soy milk, peanut butter, and sugar to a boil in a medium saucepan over medium heat, whisking until combined. Boil for 1 minute.

**REMOVE** from the heat. Stir in the granola. Spoon into the muffin papers. Sprinkle with the sesame seeds. Place in refrigerator to cool and set.

Total time: 10 minutes + chilling time　✱　Makes 36 cookies

Per cookie: 58 calories, 2 g protein, 7 g carbohydrate, 3 g fat, 0 g saturated fat, 23 mg sodium, 1 g fiber

I love this recipe because it easy enough for a child to make. I also like it because it gives my mother, who is diabetic, a treat that won't cause her blood sugar to spike.

**—Yolanda**

# Peanut Butter Cookies

1 cup all-purpose flour

¾ cup whole grain pastry flour

⅔ cup quick-cooking rolled oats

1 teaspoon baking powder

¼ teaspoon baking soda

¼ teaspoon salt

⅔ cup creamy peanut butter

½ cup (1 stick) trans-free margarine, softened

1 large egg

2 tablespoons fat-free milk

½ cup packed brown sugar

1 cup unsalted peanuts

**PREHEAT** the oven to 350°F. Line baking sheets with parchment paper.

**COMBINE** the flours, oats, baking powder, baking soda, and salt in a medium bowl.

**BEAT** the peanut butter, margarine, egg, milk, and brown sugar in a large bowl with an electric mixer on medium for 3 minutes or until well blended. Add the flour mixture and beat just until combined.

**ROLL** the dough into 1" balls. Place on the baking sheets about 3" apart. Flatten in crisscross pattern with the back of a fork. Press 3 or 4 peanuts into the top of each cookie. Bake for 10 minutes or until lightly browned. Cool on a rack.

Total time: 35 minutes   ✱   Makes 36 cookies

Per cookie: 115 calories, 3 g protein, 10 g carbohydrate, 7 g fat, 2 g saturated fat, 89 mg sodium, 1 g fiber

Reach for natural peanut butter to stay slim. Unlike typical peanut butter with added sugar and oil, the natural version is simply ground peanuts and salt.

—Susan Jerrott, Bedford, Nova Scotia

# Butter Pecan Cookies

3 cups reduced-fat biscuit mix

⅓ cup pecan pieces, finely ground

¾ cup pitted dates, chopped

2 large egg whites

⅓ cup water

½ cup (1 stick) butter or trans-free margarine, melted

2 teaspoons vanilla extract

3 tablespoons all-fruit apricot spreadable fruit

36 pecan halves

**SIFT** the biscuit mix into a medium bowl and stir in the ground pecans.

**PLACE** the dates, egg whites, and water in the blender and process until blended and creamy. Transfer to a large bowl and stir in the butter and vanilla.

**STIR** in the biscuit mixture just until blended. The dough will be very soft. Cover and chill for 30 minutes.

**PREHEAT** the oven to 350°F.

**DROP** the dough by teaspoons onto an ungreased baking sheet. Press a thumbprint into the middle of each cookie to form an indentation. Fill with ¼ teaspoon of the spreadable fruit and a pecan half.

**BAKE** for 8 to 10 minutes or until just light brown. Cool on a rack.

----

Total time: 30 minutes + chilling time ✻ Makes 36 cookies

Per cookie: 95 calories, 2 g protein, 10 g carbohydrate, 12 g fat, 4 g saturated fat, 295 mg sodium, 2 g fiber

Fill these tasty bites with your favorite flavor of all-fruit spread—apricot, raspberry, blueberry, or strawberry are all great options.

# Pecan Biscotti

1½ cups whole grain pastry flour

¼ cup sugar

1 teaspoon baking powder

¼ teaspoon salt

2 large eggs, lightly beaten

2 teaspoons almond extract

1¼ cups finely chopped pecans, divided

12 ounces 70% cocoa chocolate chips, melted

**PREHEAT** the oven to 350°F. Coat 2 rimmed baking sheets with cooking spray.

**COMBINE** the flour, sugar, baking powder, and salt in a large bowl.

**MIX** the eggs, almond extract, and ¾ cup of the pecans in a small bowl. Stir into the flour mixture until well blended. Divide the dough into 2 equal pieces.

**KNEAD** each piece of dough on a floured surface with floured hands for 2 minutes. Shape into a 10" log. Place each log in the center of a prepared baking sheet and pat to flatten slightly.

**BAKE** for 15 to 20 minutes, until very lightly browned and firm to the touch. Gently remove from the sheets to a cutting board.

**CUT** the logs diagonally into ½" slices. Lay the slices on a large wire rack and place the rack on a rimmed baking sheet.

**BAKE** for 20 to 30 minutes or until very firm and crispy.

**COOL** the biscotti completely on the rack. Dip half each biscotti into the melted chocolate and place on a rack; immediately sprinkle with chopped pecans.

Total time: 1 hour + cooling time  ✱  Makes 24 biscotti

Per biscotti: 145 calories, 2 g protein, 17 g carbohydrate, 9 g fat, 3 g saturated fat, 54 mg sodium, 2 g fiber

✱

Always opt for chocolate with the highest percentage of cocoa, preferably 60 to 72%. The higher the cocoa content, the greater the amount of flavonoids, the antioxidant also found in red wine and some berries. Studies have shown that people with high blood levels of flavonoids have a lower risk of heart disease, lung cancer, prostate cancer, asthma, and type 2 diabetes.

# Blueberry Yogurt Parfait

1 cup low-fat plain yogurt

2 teaspoons sugar or granular
   sugar substitute

1 teaspoon lemon juice

1 cup blueberries

½ cup Kashi Go Lean cereal

**STIR** together the yogurt, sugar, and lemon juice in a small bowl.

**LAYER** the yogurt, blueberries, and cereal into 2 parfait glasses.

--------------------------------------------------------

Total time: 10 minutes ✲ Makes 2 servings

Per serving: 171 calories, 10 g protein, 31 g carbohydrate, 2 g fat, 1 g saturated fat, 108 mg sodium, 4 g fiber

I love yogurt and blueberries. This easy homemade snack tastes better and is less expensive than most other snacks. And it's lower in sugar, salt, and fat.     **—Taliena**

# Banana-Mango Parfait

1 ripe mango, peeled, pitted, and cubed

2 tablespoons sugar

1 cup fat-free ricotta cheese

1 large banana, thinly sliced

1½ tablespoons chopped fresh mint leaves

**PUREE** the mango and sugar in a food processor or blender until smooth.

**SPOON** a scant 2 tablespoons of the ricotta into each of 3 parfait glasses. Top with a few banana slices, a few spoonfuls of mango sauce, and ½ teaspoon of the mint. Repeat twice to make 3 layers in each glass.

---

Total time: 10 minutes ✽ Makes 3 servings

Per serving: 184 calories, 8 g protein, 37 g carbohydrate, 0 g fat, 0 g saturated fat, 89 mg sodium, 2 g fiber

Here's a great late-night snack. The banana, mango, and fat-free ricotta cheese provide the tryptophan necessary for your brain to make serotonin, the neurotransmitter best known for creating feelings of calm and making you sleepy.

## NUTRITION NEWS TO USE

Stuck on a big decision? Have a healthy snack. In a new study, researchers found that people tend to react more aggressively and impulsively when levels of the brain chemical serotonin are low; eating regularly helps maintain serotonin, which keeps you on an even keel.

On two occasions, scientists gave adults either a drink that decreased serotonin levels or one that maintained them, and then asked the people to negotiate with a partner. Those with higher serotonin levels were less swayed by emotions and their decisions led to better outcomes. TIP: Before negotiating, think your options through over a snack that combines carbs and a tryptophan-rich food (dairy, soy, or poultry), such as whole grain crackers and cheese; both help keep serotonin high.

—Linda Cochran, Austell, Georgia

# Blender Ice Cream

1 cup low-fat soy milk

1 heaping tablespoon Splenda or other granular sugar substitute

2 cups ice cubes

4 tablespoons sugar-free maple syrup, divided

**COMBINE** the soy milk, Splenda, ice, and 2 tablespoons syrup in a blender. Puree for 2 to 3 minutes or until smooth. Pour into 4 glasses and drizzle each with ½ tablespoon of the syrup.

------------------------------------------------

Total time: 5 minutes  ✱  Makes 4 servings

Per serving: 37 calories, 1 g protein, 8 g carbohydrate, 1 g fat, 0 g saturated fat, 47 mg sodium, 0 g fiber

I hit on this idea one day when I was craving something sweet. I love this recipe because I am an ice-cream junkie. It provides about a pint or more of delicious frozen confection.          **—Linda**

—Peter Halferty, Corpus Christi, Texas

# Summertime Iced Cappuccino

1 cup fat-free vanilla or coffee frozen yogurt

1 cup strong brewed coffee

1 teaspoon unsweetened cocoa powder

1 teaspoon vanilla extract

1 tablespoon sugar or granular sugar substitute

**PLACE** the yogurt, coffee, cocoa powder, vanilla, and sugar in a blender. Process until smooth. Place the blender container in the freezer for 2 hours or until the top and sides of the mixture are partially frozen. Scrape down the sides of the container and process until smooth and frothy.

**POUR** into 2 chilled glasses and serve immediately.

Total time: 5 minutes + freezing time ✱ Makes 2 servings

Per serving: 129 calories, 5 g protein, 26 g carbohydrate, 0 g fat, 0 g saturated fat, 67 mg sodium, 0 g fiber

Cool off with this thick, rich drink bursting with coffee flavor and a hint of chocolate.

Snacks &
Little Bites

# Mango Orangeade

¼ cup sugar

2 cups water

2 cups mango nectar

1 tablespoon finely grated orange zest

1 cup orange juice

**BRING** the sugar and water to a boil in a medium saucepan. Stir until the sugar dissolves completely. Cool slightly.

**COMBINE** the mango nectar, orange zest, and orange juice in a large pitcher. Gradually stir in the sugar mixture. Let cool to room temperature. Serve in tall glasses over ice.

Total time: 5 minutes + cooling time  ✱  Makes 4 servings

Per serving: 149 calories, 1 g protein, 38 g carbohydrate, 0 g fat, 0 g saturated fat, 7 mg sodium, 1 g fiber

✱

Rich in beta-carotene, mangos are most flavorful when soft and ripe. Leave underripe mangos at cool room temperature for several days to soften.

**SUPERFOOD SPOTLIGHT: FRUIT JUICES**

Fruit juices account for 7 of the 10 most antioxidant-rich beverages—with pomegranate juice heading the list, reports a new study from UCLA. The juices, from highest to lowest antioxidant power, are pomegranate, Concord grape, blueberry, black cherry, açaí, cranberry, and orange. (Red wine and iced green and white tea also made the top 10.) Our recommendation: Whole fruit is always best, but one serving of pure or 100% juice a day is an easy way to get more produce into your diet.

# Mint and Tea Coolers with Lime

2 limes

8 cups water

4 green tea bags

4 mint tea bags

12 mint sprigs, divided

2 tablespoons agave nectar

**JUICE** 1 lime. Cut the remaining lime into 6 rounds. Set both aside.

**BRING** the water just to a boil. Place the tea bags in a large heatproof pitcher or measuring cup, pour the water over the tea bags, and let steep for 8 minutes. Remove the tea bags and cool the liquid to room temperature.

**ADD** the lime juice and half of the mint. Chill at least 1 hour or overnight. Sweeten with agave nectar (adding more to taste).

**FILL** 6 glasses with ice. Strain in the tea. Garnish with the lime rounds and the remaining mint.

----

Total time: 20 minutes + chilling time ✱ Makes 6 servings

Per serving: 21 calories, 0 g protein, 6 g carbohydrate, 0 g fat, 0 g saturated fat, 0 mg sodium, 0 g fiber

This tea is sweetened with agave nectar, a mild-flavored sweetener from the agave plant. It's excellent for iced tea because it dissolves rapidly even in cold liquid. (When you add sweetener to the liquid at drinking temperature, you can judge better how much you need.)

# Iced Pom-Mojito Spritzers

½ cup fresh mint leaves

2 tablespoons sugar

2 tablespoons lime juice

1 cup 100% pomegranate juice

2 cups chilled cranberry seltzer

**CRUSH** the mint leaves and sugar in bottom of a pitcher using a large wooden spoon. Add the lime juice and continue to crush.

**ADD** the pomegranate juice and seltzer and stir gently to combine. Serve in tall glasses over ice.

Total time: 5 minutes ✱ Makes 4 servings

Per serving: 76 calories, 1 g protein, 18 g carbohydrate, 0 g fat, 0 g saturated fat, 17 mg sodium, 1 g fiber

✱

So refreshing and delicious, no one will miss the alcohol from these drinks.

## NUTRITION NEWS TO USE

Fiber, fluid, and protein: three essential ingredients for a diet-friendly—and hunger-squashing—snack. To create the perfect combo, choose one item from each column below. Our favorites include a pear with a golf ball–size portion of almonds, or an apple and a dollop of peanut butter.

| FIBER AND FLUID | PROTEIN |
|---|---|
| Pear | Almonds |
| Baby carrots | Hummus |
| Celery | Almond butter |
| Kiwifruit | Walnuts |
| String beans | Low-fat cheese |
| Apple | Peanut butter |
| Red bell pepper slices | Greek yogurt |

# Juicy Fruit "Cocktail"

3 cups cranberry or
  pomegranate juice

2 cups sparkling cider

1 cup seltzer water

**POUR** the juice, cider, and water an ice-filled pitcher and stir gently with a long swizzle stick or iced-tea spoon.

----

Total time: 5 minutes   ✳   Makes 6 servings

Per serving: calories, g protein, g carbohydrate, g fat, g saturated fat, mg sodium, g fiber

As a lovely addition to any party, offer this colorful nonalcoholic option in a glass pitcher. Make it even prettier with a decorative mix of fruit—perhaps berries with lemon and lime wheels.

Noshing on crunchy veggie snacks to up your produce intake? Bad move. The following ingredients (from most to least plentiful) make these snacks high in fat, low on veggies. Here's the breakdown:

**Potato flour:** This gluten-free baking alternative is also used as a thickener. Made from dried potatoes, it lacks the robust nutritional profile of the unprocessed tuber.

**Canola oil:** It's a great source of heart-healthy monounsaturated fatty acids. But these snacks are still fried, supplying about the same amount of fat as regular chips.

**Tomato puree:** Straight from the can, it's a rich source of cancer-fighting lycopene. But here, the amount is minimal.

**Spinach and beet powders:** In whole-food form, these two veggies are packed with nutrients, but as a powder, there's not enough to make a difference.

**Salt:** One serving has nearly 300 milligrams of sodium—far more than most potato chips.

**Better Buy:** Just Tomatoes, Etc.! Organic Just Veggies. This crunchy mix uses peas, bell peppers, corn, tomatoes, and carrots. One serving has 100 calories, 1 g fat, 40 mg sodium, 60% of the Daily Value for vitamin A, and 45% for vitamin C. Go to justtomatoes.com for stores.

[ **WHAT'S IN YOUR . . . VEGGIE SNACK?** ]

[ it worked for me ]

# 63 lbs lost!

## ✳ CAROL CUCCARESE

**When a kids' game turned into a health scare, Carol Cuccarese made a big change**

### My Story

Like many women, I never had a weight problem until I had kids. I put on 25 pounds when my first daughter was born, and at 5-foot-2, it was noticeable! My cholesterol shot up, and my doctor prescribed medication to help control it. Meanwhile, I desperately wanted to look like my former 115-pound self, so I went for a quick fix with fen-phen. Although I lost all the weight in just 3 months, I wasn't happy. My blood pressure increased, and I had heart palpitations and anxiety attacks. I beat myself up for trying to take the easy way out. I stopped the drugs, and the weight came back. Of course, this made me feel worse, so I ate more. What a vicious cycle! By the time my second daughter was born, I had piled on another 30-plus pounds.

I'd always loved dancing around the living room with my girls, but by 2005, I weighed almost 190 pounds, and moving was becoming difficult. One day while my husband was away, we were having a dance party

## VITAL STATS

Pounds Lost: 63

Age: 39

Height: 5'2"

Weight Then: 189 pounds

Weight Now: 126 pounds

Health Bonus: "I lost 63 pounds!"

when my heart started pounding and I got dizzy. It was terrifying. What if I passed out while alone with my 8-year-old and 2½-year-old? I could not let that happen.

And just like that, I started walking 2 to 3 miles a day. After a few months, I lost 5 pounds but was sidelined with a foot injury. Before I could give up, a friend encouraged me to join her at a Weight Watchers meeting—which happened to be at a retirement community. I thought, How can I get motivated surrounded by older people in wheelchairs and with canes? Well, I did! I was impressed by their commitment despite their age and obstacles; they made me want to be healthier for my daughters and future grandchildren. My foot injury kept me from exercising until I lost more weight, but after 3 months of careful dieting, I was ready to move again.

While my husband watched the kids, I'd lift weights or do a fitness DVD. Eventually I started running. My cholesterol went from through-the-roof to a healthier 182—no more pills! My good health is rubbing off on my family. The kids now snack on veggies, and we go inline skating. I'm finally comfortable in my skin again and proud to be a healthy role model.

## My Top Tips

* Eat more fruits and vegetables, plus almonds and sesame seeds . . . "Also, I cut back on my portion sizes. Once I learned that I could have whatever I wanted—just not so much of it—things got a lot easier."

* Lose the sugary drinks . . . "I gave up my four-sodas-a-day habit and kept bottles of water in the fridge so they were cold and ready when I was thirsty."

* Find 30 minutes to exercise each day . . . "I exercised by going to the gym for cardio and weight training twice a week. Plus, I'd find some activity, such as swimming or inline skating, to do for at least 30 minutes every day. I get bored easily, so I like to mix it up."

# desserts

# Angelic Dessert

1 package (4-serving size) fat-free, sugar-free instant white chocolate pudding mix

1 cup fat-free milk

1 cup reduced-fat sour cream

12 ounces thawed light or fat-free frozen whipped topping

1 packaged angel food cake (10 ounces), cubed

3 cups quartered strawberries or whole raspberries or blueberries

1 cup almonds, toasted and chopped

**STIR** together the pudding mix and milk in a medium bowl for 1 minute or until well blended. Stir in the sour cream and whipped topping.

**PLACE** the cake in a 13" × 9" baking dish. Top with the pudding mixture. Sprinkle with the berries and almonds.

Total time: 20 minutes  ✱  Makes 8 servings

Per serving: 309 calories, 7 g protein, 46 g carbohydrate, 10 g fat, 3 g saturated fat, 361 mg sodium, 3 g fiber

✱

Assemble this rich dessert for your next potluck supper. It will become a favorite for years to come.

## NUTRITION NEWS TO USE

Covet candy and other sugary treats? It could be in your DNA. People with a certain variation of the gene called glucose transporter type 2 (GLUT2), which may help the brain regulate food intake, are more likely to crave sweet foods, new research recently revealed. In a study of 687 people, those with the gene variation ate more sugar than those who didn't have it; both groups consumed the same amount of protein, fat, and alcohol. To satisfy your sugar jones and stay fit, try a single serving of heart-healthy dark chocolate. We like CocoaVia's 100-calorie chocolate bars and chocolate-covered almonds, available in grocery and drug stores (cocoavia.com).

# Heavenly Tiramisu

1 cup fat-free ricotta cheese

8 ounces mascarpone

2 tablespoons 2% milk or water

1 teaspoon vanilla extract

¼ cup + 2 tablespoons sugar, divided

1½ cups hot brewed espresso or 4 teaspoons instant espresso powder dissolved in 1½ cups boiling water

24 store-bought crisp ladyfingers

2 teaspoons unsweetened cocoa powder, divided

**PLACE** the ricotta, mascarpone, milk, vanilla, and ¼ cup of the sugar in a food processor and process for 3 minutes or until smooth and creamy.

**COMBINE** the hot espresso and remaining 2 tablespoons sugar in a pie plate and stir until the sugar dissolves.

**DIP** each ladyfinger in the espresso mixture, working quickly, and arrange half of the ladyfingers in a single layer in an 8" × 8" baking dish. Spread half of the ricotta mixture evenly on top. Place 1 teaspoon of the cocoa in a small strainer and dust over the cream. Repeat with the remaining ladyfingers, ricotta mixture, and 1 teaspoon cocoa.

**COVER** with plastic wrap and refrigerate for 6 hours or overnight.

-------------------------------------------------

Total time: 15 minutes + chilling time ✽ Makes 9 servings

Per serving: 250 calories, 6 g protein, 28 g carbohydrate, 13 g fat, 7 g saturated fat, 83 mg sodium, 1 g fiber

✽

You won't miss the abundant fat found in traditional recipes! Just be sure to blend the ricotta mixture with a food processor—it creates a smooth, creamy texture you can't get mixing by hand.

# Banana Bread Cake

1 cup + 2 tablespoons finely chopped pecans, divided

2 cups mashed ripe bananas

1¼ cups Splenda sugar blend

⅔ cup unsweetened applesauce

2 large eggs

2 large egg whites

⅔ cup water

3⅓ cups all-purpose flour

2 teaspoons baking soda

1 teaspoon salt

½ teaspoon baking powder

**PREHEAT** the oven to 350°F. Coat a 12-cup bundt pan with cooking spray. Sprinkle 2 tablespoons of the pecans in the bottom of the pan.

**STIR** together the bananas, Splenda, and applesauce in a large bowl. Add the eggs, egg whites, and water; stir until well blended. Stir in the flour, baking soda, salt, baking powder, and the remaining 1 cup pecans just until blended. Pour into the bundt pan.

**BAKE** for 55 to 60 minutes or until a toothpick inserted in the center comes out clean. Cool in the pan on a rack for 30 minutes. Remove the cake from the pan and cool completely on the rack.

---

Total time: 1 hour 35 minutes + cooling time ✳ Makes 12 to 16 servings

Per serving: 268 calories, 7 g protein, 41 g carbohydrate, 9 g fat, 1 g saturated fat, 449 mg sodium, 3 g fiber

I love to bake banana bread cake. I work hard to make sure my two children have choices to snack on that are healthy and yummy!

**—Audrey**

—Leona Dachel, Chippewa Falls, Wisconsin

# Super Simple Cake

1  package (18.2 ounces) yellow cake mix

2  tablespoons canola oil

½  cup fat-free egg substitute

1  cup diet ginger ale

2  cups thawed fat-free frozen whipped topping

**PREHEAT** the oven to 325°F or as the package directs. Coat a 13" × 9" baking dish with cooking spray.

**PLACE** the cake mix in a large bowl and stir in the oil, egg substitute, and soda until well blended. Pour into the prepared baking dish.

**BAKE** according to the package directions. Cool in the pan on a rack for 10 minutes. Remove the cake from the pan and cool completely on the rack.

**PLACE** the cake on a serving plate and frost the top or top and sides with the whipped topping.

----

Total time: 40 minutes + cooling time   ✱   Makes 12 to 16 servings

Per serving: 244 calories, 2 g protein, 41 g carbohydrate, 8 g fat, 1 g saturated fat, 302 mg sodium, 0 g fiber

Try different mixes and soda flavors to find your favorites. "I made this cake for Easter using a white cake mix and a can of diet grape soda. It was a hit!"

# Easy Red Velvet Cake

1 package (18.2 ounces) red velvet cake mix

1 cup light mayonnaise

3 large egg whites

1 cup water

1 container (8 ounces) fat-free or light frozen whipped topping, thawed

**PREHEAT** the oven to 350°F. Coat two 8" cake pans with cooking spray. Sprinkle with 1 teaspoon of the cake mix; shake the pans to coat.

**WHISK** together the cake mix, mayonnaise, egg whites, and water until well blended. Divide the batter between the pans and bake for 30 minutes or until a toothpick inserted in the center comes out clean. Cool in the pans for 5 minutes; remove to a rack to cool completely.

**PLACE** one cake layer on a plate. Spread the top of the cake with half of the whipped topping. Repeat with the second layer and remaining topping.

Total time: 45 minutes + cooling time ✱ Makes 8 to 10 servings

Per serving: 434 calories, 5 g protein, 61 g carbohydrate, 20 g fat, 2 g saturated fat, 827 mg sodium, 2 g fiber

✱

Decorate this cake to suit the occasion. Chocolate curls and strawberry halves are perfect for Mother's Day. Top with jelly beans for Easter or candy corn for Halloween. Candy mint leaves and Red Hots make holly for a lovely Christmas cake.

# Chocolate Buttermilk Cake

### Cake

- 3 ounces unsweetened chocolate
- 1 cup water
- ¾ cup granulated sugar
- ⅓ cup canola oil
- ⅓ cup unsweetened applesauce
- 1 large egg
- 1 teaspoon vanilla extract
- ½ cup 1% buttermilk
- 1 teaspoon baking soda
- 1 cup all-purpose flour
- ¼ cup whole wheat flour
- ½ cup unsweetened cocoa powder
- Pinch of salt

### Frosting

- 1 teaspoon instant coffee or espresso powder
- 1 tablespoon hot water
- ½ cup (1 stick) 50–50 butter-blend spread, such as Smart Balance
- 1½ cups confectioners' sugar
- 2 teaspoons unsweetened cocoa powder
- 1 teaspoon vanilla extract

**PREHEAT** the oven to 350°F. Coat an 8" × 8" baking dish with cooking spray.

To Make the Cake:

**COMBINE** the chocolate and water in a medium saucepan and stir over medium-low heat until melted. Cool to lukewarm.

**ADD** the sugar, oil, applesauce, egg, and vanilla and whisk until smooth. Measure the buttermilk into a cup and stir in the baking soda. Set aside.

**WHISK** together the flours, cocoa, and salt in a large bowl until blended. Whisk in the chocolate mixture and buttermilk.

**POUR** the batter into the prepared baking dish and bake for 35 minutes or until a toothpick inserted in the center comes out clean. Cool in the pan on a rack to room temperature.

To Make the Frosting:

**DISSOLVE** the coffee powder in the water in a medium bowl. Add the spread, confectioners' sugar, cocoa, and vanilla. Beat with an electric mixer on medium speed until thoroughly blended. Spread on the cooled cake.

---

Total time: 1 hour + cooling time ✸ Makes 12 servings

Per serving: 354 calories, 4 g protein, 43 g carbohydrate, 21 g fat, 7 g saturated fat, 235 mg sodium, 3 g fiber

To reduce the fat and calories of a classic recipe, canola oil and applesauce—rather than the original stick of butter—keep this cake moist. The deep flavor of antioxidant-rich cocoa powder allowed us to cut back on the chocolate, and a butter-blend spread (like Smart Balance) slimmed down the frosting without sacrificing taste.

# Brownie Cake Squares

⅔ cup all-purpose flour

⅔ cup sugar

⅓ cup unsweetened cocoa powder

1 teaspoon baking powder

¼ teaspoon salt

⅔ cup fat-free evaporated milk

⅓ cup trans-free margarine, melted

1 large egg, lightly beaten

1½ teaspoons vanilla extract

1 cup semisweet mini chocolate chips

**COAT** a 4- to 6-quart slow cooker with cooking spray. Stir together the flour, sugar, cocoa powder, baking powder, and salt in a medium bowl.

**COMBINE** the milk, margarine, egg, and vanilla in a large bowl. Stir into the flour mixture until smooth, then stir in the chocolate chips. Spread the batter evenly in the slow cooker.

**COVER** and cook on low for 2 to 3 hours or until a toothpick inserted in the center comes out clean. Let cool, uncovered, for 15 minutes. Remove the insert from the cooker and invert the brownies onto a rack or let cool completely in the cooker before cutting into 12 squares.

---

Total time: 3 hours 30 minutes ✱ Makes 12 servings

Per serving: 200 calories, 3 g protein, 29 g carbohydrate, 9 g fat, 4 g saturated fat, 164 mg sodium, 2 g fiber

Surprise! These melt-in-your-mouth brownies come out of a slow cooker.

## NUTRITION NEWS TO USE

Trying to lose weight? Eat some dark chocolate. It may help you feel full, according to a new study from Denmark. Researchers gave 16 participants 100 grams of either dark or milk chocolate, and 2 hours later offered them pizza. Those who consumed the dark chocolate ate 15% fewer calories than those who had milk chocolate, and they were less interested in fatty, salty, and sugary foods. Try a chocolate with 70% or more cocoa. Two tablespoons of dark chocolate chips alongside fresh berries as a midafternoon snack should give you some of the benefits without breaking your calorie budget.

—Brigitta Larsson, Nashville, Tennessee

# Double Chocolate Cupcakes

## Cupcakes

- 1 large egg
- ¾ cup packed light brown sugar
- ½ cup Dutch process cocoa powder
- 3 tablespoons all-purpose flour
- 2 teaspoons instant espresso powder
- ⅛ teaspoon salt
  Pinch of black pepper
- ¾ cup fat-free milk
- 1 teaspoon vanilla extract
- 4 ounces 60–72% cacao bittersweet chocolate chips
- 3 large egg whites
- ⅛ teaspoon cream of tartar
- ⅓ cup granulated sugar

## Frosting

- 1 cup confectioners' sugar
- 3 tablespoons Dutch process cocoa powder
- 2–3 teaspoons trans-free margarine, softened
- 1 teaspoon vanilla extract
- 2–3 tablespoons fat-free milk

To Make the Cupcakes:

**PREHEAT** the oven to 350°F. Coat a 12-cup muffin pan with cooking spray. Beat the egg in a small bowl until blended; set aside.

**COMBINE** the brown sugar, cocoa, flour, espresso powder, salt, and pepper in a medium saucepan; gradually whisk in the milk and vanilla until smooth. Heat over medium heat, stirring frequently, until the mixture is hot and the sugar dissolves (do not boil).

**REMOVE** the saucepan from the heat; add the chocolate and stir until melted. Whisk about ½ cup of the chocolate mixture into the beaten egg; whisk the egg mixture back into the saucepan. Cool to room temperature.

**BEAT** the egg whites and cream of tartar in a large bowl with an electric mixer on high speed until soft peaks form. Continue beating, gradually adding the granulated sugar until stiff peaks form. Stir about one-quarter of the egg whites into the cooled chocolate mixture; fold the chocolate mixture into the remaining egg whites.

**DIVIDE** the batter among the muffin cups. Place the muffin pan in a large roasting pan; add 1 inch boiling water to the roasting pan.

**BAKE** for 25 to 30 minutes or until just firm when lightly touched (do not test with a toothpick as the cupcakes will still be soft in the center). Cool completely on a rack; chill, covered, for 8 hours or overnight.

To Make the Frosting:

**STIR** together the confectioners' sugar, cocoa, margarine, vanilla, and 1 tablespoon milk until creamy and spreadable, adding more milk as needed.

**LOOSEN** the sides of the cupcakes from the pan with a knife. Place on a serving plate. Frost the cupcakes.

Total time: 1 hour + chilling time  ✱  Makes 12 cupcakes

Per cupcake: 212 calories, 4 g protein, 44 g carbohydrate, 5 g fat, 3 g saturated fat, 42 mg sodium, 3 g fiber

—Terri A. Engelmann, Jacksonville, Illinois

# Chocolate Lava Cakes

¼ cup heavy cream

6 ounces 60–72% cacao bittersweet chocolate chips, divided

½ cup (1 stick) butter or trans-free margarine

2 large eggs

2 large egg yolks

⅓ cup Splenda or other granular sugar substitute

1 teaspoon vanilla extract

¼ cup cake flour

Light frozen whipped topping, thawed (optional)

1 cup raspberries

**COMBINE** the cream and 2 ounces of the chocolate chips in a small microwave-safe bowl. Microwave on medium for 1 to 2 minutes, stirring every 30 seconds, until well blended. Cover and chill for 2 hours or until firm. Roll into 6 balls; refrigerate until needed.

**PREHEAT** the oven to 400°F. Spray six 4-ounce ramekins or custard cups with cooking spray.

**COMBINE** the butter and the remaining 4 ounces chocolate chips in a medium microwave-safe bowl. Microwave on medium for 2 to 3 minutes, stirring every 30 seconds, until well blended.

**COMBINE** the eggs, yolks, Splenda, and vanilla in a large bowl and beat with an electric mixer on high speed for 5 minutes or until thick and light.

**FOLD** the melted chocolate and flour into the eggs just until combined. Spoon into the ramekins. Place the ramekins on a rimmed baking sheet. Place 1 chocolate ball in the center of each ramekin. Bake for 12 to 15 minutes or until firm to the touch.

**IF** desired, invert the ramekins onto individual dessert plates. Serve garnished with topping and raspberries.

---

Total time: 30 minutes + chilling time   ✱   Makes 6 servings

Per serving: 385 calories, 5 g protein, 27 g carbohydrate, 30 g fat, 14 g saturated fat, 197 mg sodium, 3 g fiber

✱

When melting chocolate in the microwave, it's essential to stir every 30 seconds. The chocolate will keep its shape even when melted. Stir well after each cook time until most pieces have melted. Then continue stirring so the residual heat can finish the melting process.

# Lemon Torte with Raspberry Sorbet

3 large eggs, separated

3 large egg whites

¼ teaspoon salt

6 tablespoons granulated sugar

¼ cup canola oil

2 teaspoons grated lemon zest

½ teaspoon lemon extract

2 teaspoons vanilla extract, divided

2 tablespoons cornstarch

6 tablespoons all-purpose flour

3 tablespoons raspberry 100% fruit spread, warmed

2 pints raspberry sorbet, softened

1 pint reduced-fat sour cream

⅓ cup confectioners' sugar

2 tablespoons sliced almonds

½ pint raspberries

**PREHEAT** the oven to 350°F. Coat a 9" × 5" loaf pan with cooking spray. Line with wax paper and spray again. Dust with flour.

**BEAT** the 6 egg whites and salt with an electric mixer on high speed until soft peaks form. Beat in the granulated sugar 1 tablespoon at a time. Continue beating for 3 minutes or until stiff peaks form.

**WHISK** together the egg yolks, oil, lemon zest, lemon extract, and 1 teaspoon of the vanilla in a medium bowl. Add a spoonful of the beaten whites and gently whisk to blend. Pour over the remaining whites. Do not stir. Sift the cornstarch and flour into the bowl. Gently fold until well combined. Spoon into the prepared loaf pan.

**BAKE** for 30 minutes or until golden and a toothpick inserted in the center comes out clean. Cool in the pan on a rack for 5 minutes. Remove the cake from the pan and cool on the rack for 15 minutes.

**TURN** the cake onto its side and cut lengthwise into thirds. Lay the slices flat and spread 1 tablespoon of the fruit spread on top of each.

**WASH** the loaf pan and line it with wax paper. Place one cake slice, spread side up, in the pan. Spread 1 pint sorbet over top. Top with the second cake. Repeat with remaining sorbet and cake (spread side down). Cover and freeze for 2 hours or overnight.

**STIR** together the sour cream, confectioners' sugar, and the remaining 1 teaspoon vanilla in a small bowl. Remove the cake from the pan and place on a serving platter. Quickly frost with the sour cream mixture and return to the freezer until serving time. Before serving, garnish with almonds and raspberries.

Total time: 1 hour 20 minutes + freezing time ✳ Makes 12 servings

Per serving: 277 calories, 4 g protein, 40 g carbohydrate, 12 g fat, 4 g saturated fat, 96 mg sodium, 2 g fiber

—Cheryl Lambert, Thorofare, New Jersey

# Cranberry-Peach Dessert Bars

1 cup fresh or frozen cranberries

¼ cup orange juice

1 cup finely ground almonds

1½ cups old-fashioned rolled oats, toasted

⅓ cup packed brown sugar

⅓ cup trans-free margarine, melted

2 packages (8 ounces each) fat-free cream cheese

1 package (4-serving size) fat-free instant vanilla pudding mix

½ cup reduced-fat sour cream

¼ cup confectioners' sugar

1 tablespoon vanilla extract

2 cups thawed frozen light whipped topping

1 package (4-serving size) sugar-free raspberry gelatin

2 cups boiling water

1 bag (16 ounces) frozen sliced peaches

1 cup shredded coconut, toasted

**PREHEAT** the oven to 350°F. Coat a 13" × 9" baking dish with cooking spray.

**COOK** the cranberries and orange juice in a small saucepan over medium heat for 5 minutes or until the cranberries pop. Drain the cranberries and set aside.

**STIR** together the almonds, oats, and brown sugar in a medium bowl. Drizzle with the margarine and stir to combine. Press into the bottom of the prepared baking dish to form a crust.

**BAKE** for 20 to 23 minutes or until lightly browned. Cool for 10 to 15 minutes on a rack.

**BEAT** the cream cheese, pudding mix, sour cream, confectioners' sugar, and vanilla in a large bowl with an electric mixer on medium speed until smooth. Fold in the whipped topping. Spread over the cooled crust. Sprinkle with the reserved cranberries. Refrigerate until needed.

**MIX** the gelatin and boiling water in a medium heatproof bowl until dissolved. Add the frozen peaches and stir. Chill for 20 minutes or until the mixture starts to thicken. Pour the mixture over the cranberries and spread evenly. Sprinkle with the coconut. Chill for 1 hour or until completely set.

Total time: 1 hour 10 minutes + chilling time ✱ Makes 12 to 16 servings

Per serving: 317 calories, 10 g protein, 33 g carbohydrate, 17 g fat, 8 g saturated fat, 87 mg sodium, 4 g fiber

✱

Toasting adds crunch and a deeper nutty flavor to coconut. To toast, spread out the coconut on a rimmed baking sheet and bake at 350°F for 3 to 7 minutes, stirring often. To prevent burning, be sure to check the coconut every minute.

—Marshall Sorgen, Brooklyn, New York

# Strawberry Cheesecake

6 plain low-fat graham wafers (2½" × 2½" each)

1½ tablespoons butter, melted

½ cup + 2 tablespoons cold water, divided

1 tablespoon gelatin powder

½ teaspoon grated lemon zest

½ cup lemon juice

⅓ cup boiling water

1 container (16 ounces) fat-free cream-style cottage cheese

½ cup sugar or ¼ cup Splenda or other granular sugar substitute

½ teaspoon lemon extract

12 strawberries, halved

**COAT** an 8" × 8" baking dish with cooking spray.

**PLACE** the graham crackers in a resealable plastic bag. Seal and roll with a rolling pin to crush. Place in a bowl and toss with the butter. Set aside.

**PLACE** ½ cup cold water in a medium bowl and sprinkle the gelatin over it. Let stand for 2 minutes to soften. Add the lemon zest, juice, and boiling water to the gelatin; stir until completely dissolved.

**CHILL** for 25 minutes or until almost set but still somewhat loose.

**COMBINE** the cottage cheese, sugar, lemon extract, and remaining 2 tablespoons water in a blender. Pulse for 15 seconds or until smooth. Add the gelatin mixture; blend on high for 15 seconds.

**POUR** into the prepared baking dish. Sprinkle with the crumbs. Garnish with strawberry halves. Chill for at least 3 hours or until set.

Total time: 15 minutes + chilling time ✱ Makes 8 servings

Per serving: 132 calories, 7 g protein, 22 g carbohydrate, 2 g fat, 1 g saturated fat, 225 mg sodium, 1 g fiber

✱

Cottage cheese blended until smooth takes the place of high-fat cream cheese in this yummy cheesecake. Be sure to blend completely until smooth and creamy.

# Caramel Applesauce Pie

¼ cup + 1 tablespoon jarred caramel sauce, divided

1 reduced-fat graham cracker piecrust (9" diameter)

8 tablespoons chopped pecans, divided

1 package (8 ounces) reduced-fat cream cheese

½ cup reduced-fat sour cream

2 tablespoons packed brown sugar

¾ cup unsweetened chunky applesauce

2 teaspoons vanilla extract

½ teaspoon ground cinnamon

1½ cups thawed light frozen whipped topping, divided

**SPREAD** ¼ cup of the caramel sauce over the piecrust and sprinkle with 6 tablespoons of the pecans. Set aside.

**BEAT** the cream cheese, sour cream, and brown sugar in a medium bowl with an electric mixer on medium-high speed for 2 minutes or until smooth. Add the applesauce, vanilla, and cinnamon; beat on low speed until combined.

**FOLD** ¾ cup of the whipped topping into the cream cheese mixture. Spread in the crust.

**CHILL** for at least 2 hours. Drizzle with the remaining 1 tablespoon caramel sauce and sprinkle with the remaining 2 tablespoons pecans. Spread with the remaining ¾ cup whipped topping.

Total time: 10 minutes + chilling time  ✻  Makes 8 servings

Per serving: Per serving: 333 calories, 6 g protein, 37 g carbohydrate, 19 g fat, 8 g saturated fat, 219 mg sodium, 2 g fiber

✻

Applesauce blends with cream cheese in this refrigerated pie. Delicious topped with caramel sauce and chopped pecans. To cut the sugars in this recipe, use sugar-free caramel sauce.

—Terry Bedwell, Terre Haute, Indiana

# Peanut Butter Pie

½ cup creamy peanut butter

4 ounces reduced-fat cream cheese

1 package (4-serving size) fat-free, sugar-free instant butterscotch pudding mix

1½ cups 2% or fat-free milk

2 cups thawed fat-free frozen whipped topping, divided

1 reduced-fat graham cracker piecrust (9" diameter)

**PLACE** the peanut butter and cream cheese in a small microwave-safe bowl. Microwave on medium for 1 minute, stirring once, until soft but not melted. Set aside.

**BEAT** the pudding mix and milk in a large bowl with an electric mixer on medium speed for 2 minutes or until well blended. Add the peanut butter mixture; beat until well blended. Gently stir in 1 cup of the whipped topping.

**SPREAD** the mixture in the crust. Garnish with the remaining 1 cup whipped topping.

**CHILL** for 2 hours or overnight until set.

-----

Total time: 10 minutes + chilling time ✳ Makes 8 servings

Per serving: 279 calories, 8 g protein, 28 g carbohydrate, 15 g fat, 4 g saturated fat, 271 mg sodium, 1 g fiber

I love this recipe because it has a little bit of all that is good in it. It will satisfy that urge for something sweet. I sometimes drizzle it with sugar-free chocolate syrup on top. **—Terry**

—Susan Francis, Brantford, Ontario

# Apple Crumble Pie

5  **cups peeled and thinly sliced apples**

2  **tablespoons sugar**

1  **tablespoon all-purpose flour**

2  **teaspoons ground cinnamon, divided**

1  **ready-made piecrust (9" diameter)**

½  **cup old-fashioned rolled oats, ground in a blender or food processor**

2  **tablespoons whole grain pastry flour**

¼  **cup packed brown sugar**

2  **tablespoons trans-free margarine, melted**

**PREHEAT** the oven to 350°F.

**COMBINE** the apples, sugar, all-purpose flour, and 1 teaspoon cinnamon in a large bowl. Place in the crust.

**COMBINE** the oats, pastry flour, brown sugar, and remaining 1 teaspoon cinnamon in a medium bowl. Add the margarine and stir until crumbs form. If needed, add some warm water to help crumbs adhere. Sprinkle evenly over the apples.

**BAKE** for 30 to 35 minutes or until the filling is bubbling and the topping is browned.

---

Total time: 1 hour  ✳  Makes 8 servings

Per serving: 207 calories, 2 g protein, 32 g carbohydrate, 8 g fat, 3 g saturated fat, 136 mg sodium, 2 g fiber

For the healthiest version of this recipe, opt for a frozen whole wheat crust and thaw as the package directs before using. Available at health food stores or in the natural food section of your market, these crusts have more fiber than traditional ones and are usually prepared with nonhydrogenated oil—an added benefit for weight loss.

—Diane Deems, Tulsa, Oklahoma

# Easy Chocolate Cream Pie

¾ cup sugar-free hot fudge topping

1 reduced-fat graham cracker piecrust (9" diameter)

1 package (4-serving size) fat-free, sugar-free instant chocolate pudding mix

1½ cups fat-free milk

1 container (8 ounces) light frozen whipped topping, thawed

**PLACE** the fudge topping in a microwave-safe bowl and microwave on medium for 2 minutes, stirring every 30 seconds, until soft. Spread half of the fudge on the crust. Set aside.

**WHISK** together the pudding mix and milk in a large bowl for 2 minutes. Let stand for 5 minutes to set.

**FOLD** half of the whipped topping into the pudding. Spread evenly over the crust. Dollop or spread the remaining whipped topping on the pie. Drizzle with the remaining fudge topping.

**PLACE** in the freezer to set for at least 1 hour.

Total time: 15 minutes + freezing time ✱ Makes 8 to 10 servings

Per serving: 247 calories, 3 g protein, 46 g carbohydrate, 7 g fat, 4 g saturated fat, 163 mg sodium, 1 g fiber

## NUTRITION NEWS TO USE

Overeating at work? There may be a reason—intellectual activities make people munch more. Students who performed a series of memory, attention, and vigilance tests ate 253 more calories than students who relaxed for the same amount of time, found researchers at Laval University in Quebec. The reason? Intellectual work causes larger fluctuations in blood sugar levels, and that can stir up the urge to nibble. To reduce your drive to eat when you're in thinking mode, try keeping a water bottle or a healthy snack nearby to help keep blood sugar steady while you work.

# Coconut Pie

1 cup Splenda sugar blend

¼ cup trans-free margarine, softened

4 large eggs

2 cups fat-free milk

1 cup unsweetened coconut

½ cup whole grain pastry flour

1 teaspoon vanilla or almond extract

**PREHEAT** the oven to 350°F. Coat a 9" pie plate with cooking spray.

**BEAT** the Splenda and margarine in a large bowl with an electric mixer on medium speed until well blended. Add the eggs, one at a time, beating well after each addition. Add the milk, coconut, flour, and vanilla and beat just until blended.

**BAKE** for 50 to 55 minutes or until set and a knife inserted in the center comes out clean. Cool on a rack for at least 1 hour.

Total time: 1 hour 5 minutes + cooling time  ✱  Makes 8 servings

Per serving: 203 calories, 7 g protein, 13 g carbohydrate, 14 g fat, 8 g saturated fat, 126 mg sodium, 2 g fiber

The flour from this recipe sinks to the bottom of the pan, creating its own crust, making this a super, easy, tasty treat for anyone.

—**Karrie**

# Warm Apple Cobbler

4 medium baking apples, peeled and thinly sliced

1 cup water

¼ cup fructose, Splenda, or other granular sugar substitute

2 tablespoons cornstarch or arrowroot

2 teaspoons ground cinnamon

1¼ cups whole wheat pastry flour

1 teaspoon baking powder

½ cup 1% buttermilk

4 tablespoons trans-free margarine, melted

1 tablespoon sugar

**PREHEAT** the oven to 350°F. Coat an 8" × 8" baking dish with cooking spray.

**COOK** the apples, water, fructose, cornstarch, and cinnamon in a large saucepan over medium heat for 10 minutes or until thickened. Pour into the prepared baking dish.

**STIR** together the flour and baking powder in a large bowl. Add the buttermilk, margarine, and sugar and stir with a fork until the flour mixture is moist and just holds together. Add additional buttermilk by tablespoons, if necessary.

**DROP** the dough by tablespoons on the apples, forming 8 biscuits.

**BAKE** for 20 minutes or until the biscuits are golden brown.

Total time: 50 minutes  ✱  Makes 8 servings

Per serving: 168 calories, 2 g protein, 28 g carbohydrate, 6 g fat, 2 g saturated fat, 147 mg sodium, 4 g fiber

293

Desserts

Using whole wheat pastry flour in baked goods allows you to get the health benefits of whole grains. Unlike traditional whole wheat flour, the pastry flour is ground much finer and works well in cakes, cookies, pies, tarts, and biscuits like those in this recipe.

# Fancy Fruit Tart

Crust

- **2 cups all-purpose or gluten-free flour**
- **1 teaspoon baking powder**
- **½ cup (1 stick) trans-free margarine, cut into small pieces**
- **¼ cup agave nectar**
- **1 large egg**
- **1 tablespoon milk**
- **1 teaspoon vanilla extract**

Filling

- **1 package (8 ounces) fat-free cream cheese, softened**
- **¼ cup agave nectar**
- **2 tablespoons trans-free margarine**
- **2 tablespoons milk**
- **1 tablespoon lemon juice**
- **3–4 cups sliced fruit or berries such as apricots, strawberries, and blueberries**

Glaze

- **½ cup all-fruit apricot spreadable fruit**

To Make the Crust:

**COMBINE** the flour and baking powder in a food processor. Add the margarine and pulse until crumbs form. Add the nectar, egg, milk, and vanilla, with the processor running, until the dough forms a ball. Form into a disk and wrap with plastic wrap. Chill for 3 hours.

**PREHEAT** the oven to 375°F.

**PRESS** the dough into a 12" pizza pan or a 10" tart pan. Prick all over with a fork. Bake the pizza pan for 8 to 10 minutes or until browned; bake the tart pan for 7 to 8 minutes. Cool completely on a rack.

To Make the Filling:

**BEAT** the cream cheese, nectar, margarine, milk, and lemon juice with an electric mixer on medium speed until blended. Spread on the crust. Arrange the fruit over the filling.

To Make the Glaze:

**PLACE** the spreadable fruit in a microwave-safe bowl. Microwave on high for 1 minute, stirring. Brush over the fruit.

---

Total time: 25 minutes + chilling time ✱ Makes 8 to 10 servings

Per serving: 414 calories, 9 g protein, 60 g carbohydrate, 15 g fat, 6 g saturated fat, 393 mg sodium, 2 g fiber

If you're using a pizza pan, create a "lip" around the edge of the pan to form sides.

# Peach and Blueberry Tart

1 large egg white, lightly beaten

2 tablespoons canola oil

1–3 tablespoons water, divided

¾ cup pecan halves

1 cup whole wheat pastry flour

2 teaspoons grated lemon zest

⅛ teaspoon salt

¾ cup all-fruit peach spreadable fruit

1½ tablespoons cornstarch

1¼ pounds firm ripe peaches, sliced

¾ cup blueberries

**PREHEAT** the oven to 375°F. Coat a 10" springform pan or fluted tart pan with removable bottom with cooking spray.

**WHISK** together the egg white, oil, and 1 tablespoon water in a measuring cup.

**GRIND** the pecans in a food processor until very fine. Add the flour, lemon zest, and salt. Process briefly to blend. With the machine running, slowly pour in the egg white mixture. Add 1 to 2 tablespoons water if needed, processing until the dough forms a ball.

**TURN** the dough onto a lightly floured surface and pat into a disk. Press into the bottom and ½" up the sides of the prepared pan. Refrigerate for 15 minutes.

**COMBINE** the spreadable fruit and cornstarch in a large bowl. Add the peaches and blueberries and toss gently. Spoon into the prepared crust. Bake for 1 hour 15 minutes or until the juices are bubbling. Cool in the pan on a rack.

Total time: 1 hour 30 minutes + chilling time  ✱  Makes 8 servings

Per serving: 248 calories, 3 g protein, 36 g carbohydrate, 11 g fat, 1 g saturated fat, 43 mg sodium, 3 g fiber

✱

If you prefer your peaches skinned, by all means go ahead and peel them. Instead of blanching, use a serrated peeler to make quick work of soft-skinned fruits. Look for one in your kitchen supply store.

# Rhubarb Crisp

⅓ cup + ½ c old-fashioned rolled oats, divided

⅔ cup chopped pecans

¼ cup packed brown sugar

3 tablespoons granulated sugar

3 tablespoons cold butter, cut into small pieces

1 teaspoon ground cinnamon

Rhubarb

2 pounds rhubarb, cut into ½" dice

¼ cup packed brown sugar

½ cup granulated sugar

3 tablespoons all-purpose flour

**PREHEAT** the oven to 375°F.

To make the crumbs:

**PLACE** ⅓ cup of the oats in a food processor and process until finely ground. Place in a mixing bowl with the pecans, brown sugar, granulated sugar, butter, cinnamon, and the remaining ½ cup oats. Mix with a pastry blender or your fingers until pea-size clumps form.

To make the rhubarb:

**STIR** together the rhubarb, brown sugar, granulated sugar, and flour in a 9" × 9" baking dish. Top with the oat mixture and bake for 20 to 25 minutes or until the rhubarb is bubbly.

---

Total time: 45 minutes  ✱  Makes 8 servings

Per serving: 293 calories, 3 g protein, 46 g carbohydrate, 13 g fat, 4 g saturated fat, 39 mg sodium, 4 g fiber

Sweet and sour rhubarb makes an extra-yummy crisp. Cook it in a baking dish as usual or turn it into company fare by using individual 6-ounce ramekins. If fresh rhubarb isn't available, use frozen and thaw it before assembling the crisp.

# Almond-Cherry Clafoutis

12 ounces large cherries, pitted, or frozen cherries, thawed and drained

4 tablespoons sugar, divided

3 tablespoons sliced almonds

3 tablespoons all-purpose flour

3 large eggs

1 large egg yolk

¾ cup milk

¼ teaspoon almond extract

Pinch of salt

4 teaspoons cognac or brandy (optional)

Confectioners' sugar

**PREHEAT** the oven to 375°F. Coat four 8-ounce ramekins or custard cups lightly with cooking spray. Toss the cherries with 2 tablespoons of the sugar in a medium bowl and divide among the ramekins.

**COMBINE** the almonds, flour, eggs, egg yolk, milk, almond extract, salt, and the remaining 2 tablespoons sugar in a food processor. Process for 30 seconds or until the almonds are ground and the mixture forms a smooth batter.

**EVENLY** divide the batter over the cherries. Top each serving with 1 teaspoon cognac and bake for 35 minutes or until puffed and brown. Let cool until warm (they will sink slightly). Sprinkle with confectioners' sugar before serving. Serve warm.

--------

Total time: 45 minutes + cooling time ✳ Makes 4 servings

Per serving: 244 calories, 9 g protein, 34 g carbohydrate, 9 g fat, 3 g saturated fat, 73 mg sodium, 3 g fiber

Clafoutis, pronounced kla-foo-TEE, is a classic French dessert featuring fresh fruit, often cherries, with a cakelike topping. Pears, apricots, or peaches work just as well. Traditionally served in a skillet, this recipe bakes the clafoutis in ramekins for individual servings.

## NUTRITION NEWS TO USE

Three tantalizing reasons to enjoy tart cherries such as Montmorency: They may help you stay slim, prevent inflammation linked with heart disease, and keep cholesterol under control. That's according to researchers at the University of Michigan who fed rats the equivalent of 1½ cups of tart cherries in addition to meals high in fat and cholesterol. The scientists are studying whether the antioxidant-rich fruit has the same effect on humans; previous research has found that sweet cherries may have similar benefits. For now, it can't hurt to add this fruit to your diet. If fresh isn't available, try stirring thawed frozen tart cherries into yogurt, mixing the dried variety with wild rice pilaf, or adding tart cherry juice to seltzer or tea.

# Grilled Peaches with Macaroons and Caramel Sauce

4 peaches, halved

4 coconut macaroons

¼ cup jarred caramel topping

**COAT** a grill rack with cooking spray. Preheat the grill.

**PLACE** the peaches, cut side down, on the rack and grill, turning once, for 10 minutes or until lightly browned and tender.

**ARRANGE** 2 peach halves on each of 4 dessert plates and crumble the macaroons into the cavities and over the tops. Drizzle with the caramel topping.

Total time: 15 minutes　✱　Makes 4 servings

Per serving: 209 calories, 2 g protein, 46 g carbohydrate, 4 g fat, 3 g saturated fat, 131 mg sodium, 3 g fiber

Grilling enhances the natural sugar found in summer-ripe fruit, and a drizzle of caramel makes it taste decadent.

## NUTRITION NEWS TO USE

For a hefty helping of disease-fighting antioxidants, sink your teeth into a juicy, portable peach, nectarine, or plum. Each stone fruit—so called because of the hard pit surrounding a seed—has potent antioxidants. According to scientists at Texas Agri Life Research, just one plum contains at least the same levels of phytonutrients and antioxidants as 1-plus cup of blueberries. Since stone fruits fit in the palm of your hand, it's easy to get your antioxidants on the run.

# "Baked" Apple Halves with Maple Cream

- 2 large apples, halved lengthwise and cored
- 4 teaspoons butter or trans-free margarine, cut into small pieces
- ½ cup orange juice
- 1 tablespoon apple cider vinegar
- ¼ cup evaporated milk
- 2 tablespoons maple syrup

**PLACE** a small mixing bowl in the refrigerator until needed.

**PLACE** the apples, skin side down, in a 4- to 6-quart slow cooker and dot with the butter. Mix the orange juice and vinegar and pour over top.

**COVER** and cook on low for 2 to 3 hours or until the apples are soft but still hold their shape. Remove to a plate. Pour the juice from the cooker into a small saucepan. Bring to a boil and boil for 3 to 4 minutes or until the liquid is thick and syrupy. Set aside.

**WHIP** the milk and maple syrup in the chilled bowl with an electric mixer on high speed for 3 to 5 minutes or until thickened.

**TOP** each apple half with 1½ tablespoons of maple cream and drizzle with 1 tablespoon reserved fruit syrup.

---

Total time: 3 hours 10 minutes ✳ Makes 4 servings

Per serving: 145 calories, 1 g protein, 27 g carbohydrate, 5 g fat, 2 g saturated fat, 51 mg sodium, 3 g fiber

✳

Bake the apples for up to a day ahead, cool, and store them in the refrigerator, covered. Great apples for this dish include Ida Reds, Jonathan, and Jonagold.

—Sally J. Meiresonne, Arvada, Colorado

# Inspired Kahlúa Pumpkin Pudding

1 can (14 ounces) fat-free sweetened condensed milk

½ cup fat-free egg substitute

¼ cup Splenda brown sugar blend

¼ cup Kahlúa or sugar-free coffee-flavored syrup

1 teaspoon pumpkin pie spice

1 teaspoon ground cinnamon

1 can (15 ounces) solid-pack pumpkin

**PREHEAT** the oven to 325°F. Coat a 1½-quart baking dish with cooking spray.

**STIR** together the condensed milk, egg substitute, Splenda, Kahlúa, pumpkin pie spice, and cinnamon in a large bowl until well blended. Add the pumpkin and stir until smooth.

**POUR** into the prepared baking dish. Bake for 40 to 45 minutes or until a knife inserted in the center comes out clean.

Total time: 1 hour ✱ Makes 8 servings

Per serving: 199 calories, 5 g protein, 41 g carbohydrate, 1 g fat, 0 g saturated fat, 63 mg sodium, 2 g fiber

This is a beloved family recipe I have made forever. My 'regular' version has eggs, brown sugar, corn syrup, and regular sweetened condensed milk. Everyone who tried my new version was clueless that I'd changed the recipe! Doubt I'll ever make my original version again. —**Sally**

—Patrice Hurd, Bemidji, Minnesota

# Cinnamon Cream Pavlovas

4 large egg whites

¼ teaspoon cream of tartar

Pinch of salt

½ cup sugar

2 teaspoons cornstarch

4 ounces reduced-fat cream cheese, softened

1 teaspoon ground cinnamon

1 package (4-serving size) fat-free, sugar-free instant white chocolate pudding mix

½ cup cold fat-free milk

1 container (8 ounces) light frozen whipped topping, thawed

3 ounces dark chocolate, melted

**PREHEAT** the oven to 250°F. Line a baking sheet with parchment paper.

**BEAT** the egg whites, cream of tartar, and salt in a large bowl with an electric mixer on high speed until foamy. Gradually add the sugar while beating until stiff, glossy peaks form. Fold in the cornstarch. Spoon the meringue into 8 rounds on the parchment, smoothing the tops evenly.

**BAKE** for 55 to 60 minutes or until the meringues are crisp but the centers are still soft. Turn off the oven and allow the meringues to stand in the oven for an additional 15 minutes. Remove from the oven and allow to cool completely on the sheet on a rack.

**BEAT** the cream cheese and cinnamon in a large bowl with an electric mixer on medium speed until smooth. Add the pudding mix and milk; beat on low speed until thoroughly blended. Fold in the whipped topping. Cover and refrigerate until serving.

**DRIZZLE** 8 dessert plates with some of the melted dark chocolate. Place 1 meringue on each plate. Evenly spoon the pudding onto the meringues. Lightly drizzle with the remaining melted chocolate.

Total time: 1 hour 10 minutes + cooling time ✳ Makes 8 servings

Per serving: 222 calories, 5 g protein, 32 g carbohydrate, 9 g fat, 7 g saturated fat, 90 mg sodium, 1 g fiber

303

Desserts

I try to implement interesting flavors and textures into my recipes, while cutting calories by using lighter ingredients wherever possible. This recipe is not only delicious and beautiful to look at, it's also deceptively light. Most important of all, though, it shows that 'light' doesn't have to be bland or boring.

—**Patrice**

# Pumpkin Soufflé

1  can (16 ounces) solid-pack pumpkin

1  cup fat-free egg substitute

½  cup Splenda or other granular sugar substitute

1  tablespoon pumpkin pie spice

½  teaspoon ground ginger

½  teaspoon ground cinnamon

½  cup finely chopped walnuts

   Sugar-free maple syrup

**PREHEAT** the oven to 375°F. Coat a 2½- to 3-quart baking dish with cooking spray.

**COMBINE** the pumpkin, egg substitute, Splenda, pumpkin pie spice, ginger, and cinnamon in a large bowl. Beat with an electric mixer on medium-high speed for 4 minutes or until blended.

**POUR** into the prepared baking dish. Sprinkle with the walnuts and bake for 20 minutes. Increase the temperature to 400°F. Bake for 5 minutes.

**REMOVE** to a rack and cool for 15 minutes. Serve topped with 1 to 2 tablespoons of the syrup.

Total time: 30 minutes + cooling time ✳ Makes 6 servings

Per serving: 133 calories, 4 g protein, 15 g carbohydrate, 8 g fat, 1 g saturated fat, 29 mg sodium, 4 g fiber

I have been a diabetic for 11 years. I lost 106 pounds in the past 3 years and am now off all medications. I make this in cold weather when I need a sweet and low-calorie treat.
**—Susan**

—Virginia Anthony, Blowing Rock, North Carolina

# Maple-Rum Strawberries with Vanilla Frozen Yogurt

- 4 **cups sliced strawberries**
- 4 **teaspoons maple syrup**
- 4 **teaspoons light rum or 2 teaspoons rum extract**
- ¼ **teaspoon pepper**
- 1 **pint low-fat vanilla frozen yogurt**
- 6 **mint sprigs (optional)**

**PLACE** the strawberries in a medium bowl. Add the maple syrup, rum, and pepper. Toss gently to blend well.

**PLACE** a scoop of the frozen yogurt in each of 6 goblets or dessert bowls. Divide the strawberries over the yogurt and garnish with mint.

---

Total time: 10 minutes ✱ Makes 6 servings

Per serving: 133 calories, 3 g protein, 26 g carbohydrate, 2 g fat, 1 g saturated fat, 45 mg sodium, 2 g fiber

✱

The unexpected combination of maple and rum complements the tart-sweet berries beautifully. Black pepper adds a surprise tingle of flavor to make the whole dessert extra special, but if pepper sounds too weird to you, just omit it.

**SUPERFOOD SPOTLIGHT: PERSIMMONS**

Ripening in orchards every fall: the sweet-tangy persimmon. Often compared to plums in taste and texture, persimmons are loaded with vitamins A and C, and one Hachiya persimmon—the most abundant variety in the United States—contains a whopping 6 grams of fiber, about one-fourth of your daily need.

**Try:** Eating a Hachiya persimmon when it's soft to the touch. Cut the fruit in half, and spoon right into your mouth. Persimmons also work well sliced thinly and tossed into a green salad.

**Buy:** A plump fruit with smooth, glossy skin and an orange-red tinge

# Creamy Orange Fruit Salad

- **2** packages (4-serving size) sugar-free orange gelatin
- **2** packages (4-serving size) fat-free instant vanilla pudding mix
- **3** cups boiling water
- **1** can (8 ounces) crushed pineapple, drained
- **1** can (11 ounces) mandarin oranges, drained and halved
- **1** container (8 ounces) light frozen whipped topping, thawed

**STIR** together the gelatin and pudding in a large heatproof bowl. Stir in the boiling water until the gelatin is dissolved. Chill for about 1 hour or until thick but not quite set.

**FOLD** in the pineapple, oranges, and whipped topping. Chill for at least 1 hour or until well set.

Total time: 10 minutes + chilling time ✳ Makes 8 servings

Per serving: 119 calories, 1 g protein, 23 g carbohydrate, 3 g fat, 3 g saturated fat, 53 mg sodium, 1 g fiber

The classic flavors of orange and vanilla cream come together in this fruit salad, which is the perfect finale to a rich meal.

**NUTRITION NEWS TO USE**
Not only are clementines portable and easy to peel, but two contain only 70 calories and a whopping 96% of your daily need for wrinkle-reducing vitamin C.

—Robin Crockett, Dover, New Hampshire

# Almond Egg Custard

3 cups fat-free milk

2 cups fat-free egg substitute

⅓ cup Splenda or other granular sugar substitute

½ teaspoon almond extract

6 tablespoons slivered almonds, toasted

1 teaspoon ground cinnamon

**PREHEAT** the oven to 350°F. Coat six 8-ounce custard cups with cooking spray. Place in a baking pan.

**COMBINE** the milk, egg substitute, Splenda, and almond extract in a blender. Pulse until well blended. Pour into the custard cups.

**TOP** each with 1 tablespoon of the almonds and a sprinkle of the cinnamon. Place the baking pan in the oven and pour boiling water around the custard cups until halfway up the cups.

**BAKE** for 30 to 35 minutes or until a knife inserted in the center comes out clean.

Total time: 50 minutes　✳　Makes 6 servings

Per serving: 143 calories, 7 g protein, 19 g carbohydrate, 4 g fat, 0 g saturated fat, 102 mg sodium, 1 g fiber

Pump up the fiber of this sweet, creamy dessert by serving it with fresh berries. A blend of raspberries, blueberries, and strawberries tossed in a touch of melted strawberry spreadable fruit will add great color and flavor.

# Coffee 'n' Cream Gelatin

½ cup 1% milk

2 envelopes (¼ ounce each) unflavored gelatin

1½ cups hot strong coffee

¼ cup Splenda sugar blend

1 container (8 ounces) light frozen whipped topping, thawed

**PLACE** the milk in a medium bowl and sprinkle with the gelatin. Let stand for 5 minutes to soften. Add the hot coffee and Splenda and stir to dissolve the gelatin. Pour into an 8" × 8" baking dish. Chill for 1 to 2 hours or until set.

**CUT** the gelatin into 1" squares. Layer the cubes with the whipped topping in 6 dessert dishes or parfait glasses.

Total time: 10 minutes + chilling time ✻ Makes 6 servings

Per serving: 125 calories, 1 g protein, 21 g carbohydrate, 4 g fat, 4 g saturated fat, 45 mg sodium, 0 g fiber

✻

Change up the flavor in these tasty coffee cubes by using your favorite flavored coffee, such as hazelnut, cinnamon spice, or French vanilla.

[ **SUPERFOOD SPOTLIGHT: PISTACHIOS** ]

It's no shell game—this tasty nut is proven to lower heart-disease risk. Pennsylvania State University researchers recently found that adults who got 20% of their calories from pistachios (that's about ½ cup for an 1,800-calorie diet) reduced LDL cholesterol by 12%.

**Buy:** In-shell, dye-free nuts—if stored in a chilled, airtight container, they'll remain fresh for up to a year.

**Try:** Crushing nuts to crust fish, sprinkling on salads, or tossing into a healthy trail mix

# Rich Chocolate Pudding

⅓ cup packed brown sugar

¼ cup unsweetened cocoa powder

3 tablespoons cornstarch

1 teaspoon instant espresso powder (optional)

⅛ teaspoon ground cinnamon

Pinch of salt

2 cups 1% milk, divided

1 large egg

2 ounces bittersweet chocolate chips

1½ teaspoons vanilla extract

**WHISK** together the sugar, cocoa, cornstarch, espresso powder, cinnamon, salt, and ½ cup of the milk in a medium saucepan. Pour the remaining milk into the pan while whisking. Bring to a simmer over medium-low heat. Simmer, whisking constantly, for 3 minutes or until slightly thickened.

**BEAT** the egg lightly in a small bowl. Whisk 1 cup of the hot milk mixture into the egg. Pour the egg mixture back into the pan. Cook over medium-low heat, stirring, for 2 minutes.

**REMOVE** the pan from the heat. Add the chocolate and vanilla. Whisk until smooth.

**POUR** into 4 serving dishes. Cover and chill for 2 hours or overnight.

Total time: 10 minutes + chilling time ✱ Makes 4 servings

Per serving: 250 calories, 8 g protein, 40 g carbohydrate, 9 g fat, 5 g saturated fat, 115 mg sodium, 3 g fiber

✱

You'd never guess this rich-tasting pudding is made from 1% milk. Cocoa powder has less fat and a higher concentration of antioxidants than regular chocolate; using a combo of the two is good for your heart and pleasing to your tastebuds.

# Cappuccino Cream Dessert

2 cups fat-free milk

1 package (4-serving size) fat-free, sugar-free instant vanilla pudding mix

2 teaspoons instant coffee powder

1 cup thawed light frozen whipped topping

⅛ teaspoon ground cinnamon

Raspberries (optional)

**WHISK** together the milk, pudding mix, and coffee in a large bowl for 2 minutes or until well blended.

**POUR** into four 6-ounce dessert dishes. Refrigerate for at least 1 hour.

**STIR** together the whipped topping and cinnamon in a small bowl. Top the puddings with the mixture and garnish with the raspberries.

-----

Total time: 10 minutes + chilling time  ✳  Makes 4 servings

Per serving: 89 calories, 4 g protein, 14 g carbohydrate, 2 g fat, 2 g saturated fat, 0 g fiber

Fat-free, sugar-free instant vanilla pudding is the perfect palette for quick, flavorful desserts. Here it's blended with instant coffee for a delicious cappuccino flavor. Change it up by replacing the coffee with almond extract for a nutty dessert or mint extract and a sprinkle of mini chocolate chips for mint chocolate chip pudding.

313

Desserts

## NUTRITION NEWS TO USE

Workout finished? Get milk. Research shows the white stuff is great for postworkout recovery—plus it can help you build metabolism-stoking muscle. Dairy drinkers in one study gained up to 63% more lean muscle after 12 weeks of weight training, compared with exercisers given a sports drink of equal calories. Rehydrating with low-fat or fat-free milk (even chocolate) provides an ideal mix of nutrients for repairing tiny muscle tears and replenishes electrolytes so you feel rejuvenated fast.

—Jay Davis, Knoxville, Tennessee

# Nutty Ice Cream Dessert

- **12 ounces soft-churned ice cream**
- **1 cup thawed fat-free frozen whipped topping**
- **¼ cup chunky peanut butter**
- **1 package (4-serving size) fat-free, sugar-free instant butterscotch pudding mix**
- **¾ cup Grape-Nuts cereal**

**BEAT** the ice cream, whipped topping, peanut butter, and pudding mix in a large bowl with an electric mixer on medium speed until well blended. Stir in the cereal. Pour into a 8" × 8" baking dish.

**COVER** and freeze for 1 hour or overnight.

Total time: 10 minutes + freezing time  ✶  Makes 4 servings

Per serving: 335 calories, 9 g protein, 49 g carbohydrate, 12 g fat, 4 g saturated fat, 3 g fiber

 The inspiration for this recipe was my kids! They love to cook, and it is just one of those really, really easy desserts that they can make. Serve in dishes or scooped into cones.

**—Jay**

# Tangerine Ice

8 tangerines
½ lime
Water
¼ teaspoon salt
3 tablespoons sugar

**SQUEEZE** the tangerines and lime into a measuring cup. Add enough water to equal 4 cups. Stir in the salt and sugar. Stir until the sugar dissolves.

**POUR** into a 9" × 9" metal pan (not nonstick). Cover with plastic wrap and freeze for 1 hour. Stir with a fork, breaking up the chunks. Cover and return to the freezer. Stir every 30 minutes for 2 hours or until the mixture is evenly icy and granular. Spoon into dessert bowls.

-------------

Total time: 3 hours 10 minutes ✳ Makes 4 servings

Per serving: 142 calories, 1 g protein, 34 g carbohydrate, 0 g fat, 0 g saturated fat, 148 mg sodium, 1 g fiber

Actual work time is brief, but because of the 3-hour freezing, this is definitely a make-ahead recipe.

## QUICK TIP: PICK YOUR CITRUS

You can make the ice with just about any kind of juice you like. Orange is good, and when clementines are at their peak, I almost always juice them for ice. If you're lucky enough to have Meyer lemons at your store, try one instead of a lime.

# Fruit "Sherbet"

2 cups fat-free or low-fat ricotta cheese

1 box (0.3 ounce) sugar-free strawberry gelatin

1 tablespoon vanilla extract

2 cups frozen mixed berries

**PLACE** the ricotta, gelatin, vanilla, and berries in a blender or food processor. Process until smooth. Spoon into 8 dessert bowls or glasses. Chill or freeze until ready to serve.

Total time: 5 minutes  ✱  Makes 8 servings

Per serving: 73 calories, 5 g protein, 9 g carbohydrate, 0 g fat, 0 g saturated fat, 72 mg sodium, 1 g fiber

**HEALTHY BAKING CHEAT SHEET**

### TO . . . BOOST FIBER

**Swap this** . . . All-purpose flour

**With one of these** . . . White whole wheat flour, Whole wheat pastry flour

**Tip:** Go gradual; replace just a quarter of the regular flour at first. If you like the taste and texture, up the whole wheat to half the total.

### TO . . . REDUCE SATURATED/TRANS FAT

**Swap this** . . . Butter or margarine

**With one of these** . . . Trans-free vegetable oil spread, Heart-healthy oil (canola, light olive, sunflower), Fruit puree

**Tip:** Butter adds richness and flavor, so leave in half and use a healthier substitute for the rest. A fruit puree helps keep baked goods tender and moist; substitute up to half of the amount of solid fat in a recipe. You may need to cut back on wet ingredients (such as milk) or increase dry ingredients to maintain consistency.

### TO . . . LOWER CHOLESTEROL

**Swap this** . . . Whole eggs

**With one of these** . . . Egg whites, Ground flaxseed and water, Liquid egg substitute

**Tip:** Reduce the number of whole eggs, rather than eliminate them. Two egg whites is equivalent to one whole egg. Another option: Replace one egg with 1 tablespoon ground flaxseed mixed in 3 tablespoons water.

### TO . . . ADD NUTRIENTS

**Swap this** . . . Refined white sugar

**With one of these** . . . Honey, Agave nectar, Brown rice syrup

**Tip:** Switching granulated sugar with a liquid sweetener can change consistency, so you may need to increase the dry ingredients and decrease other liquids. Because each substitute varies in sweetness, adjust accordingly.

# Fruit Freeze

1 can (15 ounces) peaches
  packed in juice
1 can (6 ounces) pineapple juice
1½ frozen bananas

**PLACE** the peaches with juice, pineapple juice, and bananas in a blender or food processor and pulse until well blended. Place the blender or food processor container in the freezer for 4 hours. Return the container to its base and whip the mixture. If not serving immediately, pour into a freezer container until ready to use.

------

Total time: 5 minutes + freezing time  ✱  Makes 8 servings

Per serving:  56 calories, 0 g protein, 14 g carbohydrate, 0 g fat, 0 g saturated fat, 5 mg sodium, 1 g fiber

✱

Similar to granita, this fat-free fruit dessert is the perfect ending to a spicy meal.

With a cornucopia of advantages that range from preventing heart disease to protecting gums and staving off urinary tract infections, the crimson cranberry is the epitome of a superfood. The sweet-tart fruit's health benefits come thanks in part to the proanthocyanidin antioxidants each berry is loaded with. Unfortunately, canned cranberry creations can be packed with high fructose corn syrup and calories that turn the power fruit into a nutritional flop. Try these fresh recipes instead.

**Cranberry relish:** In a food processor, pulse fresh cranberries, orange zest, orange juice, and unsweetened cranberry juice. Sweeten with maple syrup.

**Harvest rice:** Prepare brown rice with low-sodium broth; add cranberries as it simmers. Toss with scallions and walnuts.

**Tart baked apples:** Core apples and place in baking dish. Fill cavities with a mix of chopped fresh cranberries, walnuts, brown sugar, and cinnamon. Pour orange juice over apples, coating dish. Bake at 375°F until tender (15 to 20 minutes).

[ **CRANBERRIES: BAN THE CAN** ]

# Watermelon Granita

6 cups seedless watermelon
  chunks or balls
1 tablespoon lemon juice
1 tablespoon lime juice
½ cup ginger ale

**PUREE** the watermelon, lemon juice, and lime juice in a blender. Slowly pour into the ginger ale and mix.

**POUR** into an 8" × 8" metal pan (not nonstick). Cover with plastic wrap and freeze for 1 hour. Stir with a fork, breaking up the chunks. Cover and return to the freezer. Stir every 30 minutes for 2½ hours or until the mixture is evenly icy and granular. Spoon into dessert bowls.

---

Total time: 15 minutes + freezing time  ✻  Makes 4 servings

Per serving: 82 calories, 1 g protein, 21 g carbohydrate, 1 g fat, 0 g saturated fat, 5 mg sodium, 1 g fiber

✲

What's better than a slice of watermelon on a hot summer day? An icy granita that's bursting with natural sweetness but doesn't leave you with sticky fingers! Simple yet elegant granitas can be made with all sorts of fruits, juices, and herbs—even coffee—using the same basic technique of mixing, freezing, and breaking up the ice with a fork.

## NUTRITION NEWS TO USE

This sweet treat generally contains no fat or dairy—making it far less caloric than ice cream. Try ½ cup of strawberry or mango sorbet topped with 1 tablespoon of dark chocolate chips for a decadent, refreshing dessert that comes in at fewer than 200 calories.

# Watermelon with Lime and Ginger Syrup

¼ cup sugar

½ cup water

2 tablespoons lime juice

1 teaspoon grated fresh ginger

4 cups bite-size seedless watermelon cubes

**COMBINE** the sugar and water in a small saucepan and bring to a boil over medium-high heat. Cook, stirring, for 30 seconds or until the sugar dissolves. Remove from the heat. Place in a large bowl. Stir in the lime juice and ginger. Cool to room temperature.

**ADD** the watermelon and mix gently. Divide among 4 glasses or small dessert dishes.

---

Total time: 15 minutes ✻ Makes 4 servings

Per serving: 97 calories, 1 g protein, 25 g carbohydrate, 1 g fat, 0 g saturated fat, 3 mg sodium, 1 g fiber

Watermelon gets a zingy boost from fresh ginger. Garnish this refreshing dessert with thin slices of lime.

**QUICK TIP: STORE WATERMELON AT ROOM TEMPERATURE**

Leaving a whole watermelon on your kitchen counter for 5 days increases its lycopene and beta-carotene content by as much as 20 percent.

# Chocolate-Strawberry Ice Pops

1 cup thinly sliced strawberries

½ cup semisweet chocolate chips

1½ cups chocolate soy milk

**EVENLY** layer the strawberries, chocolate chips, and soy milk in 6 ice pop molds. (Note: There should be about ½" of space at the top of each mold to allow for expansion during freezing. Adjust the soy milk accordingly.) Insert handles or sticks into the molds.

**FREEZE** at least 4 hours.

Total time: 10 minutes + freezing time ✱ Makes 6 servings

Per serving: 151 calories, 3 g protein, 21 g carbohydrate, 6 g fat, 4 g saturated fat, 19 mg sodium, 1 g fiber

Think of these as frozen chocolate-covered strawberries on a stick—just as decadent but longer lasting. These pops are full of flavonoids and other health-promoting nutrients: a triple-whammy's worth from strawberries, chocolate, and soy. You can find molds at most kitchenware stores.

# Mixed Berry Ice Pops

⅔ cup blueberries

30 small mint leaves

1⅓ cups raspberries

1½ cups seltzer

2 tablespoons light floral honey, such as acacia

2 tablespoons lemon juice

**EVENLY** layer the blueberries, mint, and raspberries in 6 ice pop molds.

**STIR** together the seltzer, honey, and lemon juice gently in a measuring cup until the honey dissolves. Pour very slowly over the berries and mint. (Note: There should be about ½" of space at the top of each mold to allow for expansion during freezing. Adjust the liquid accordingly.) Insert handles or sticks into the molds.

**FREEZE** at least 4 hours.

---

Total time: 10 minutes + freezing time  ✳  Makes 6 servings

Per serving: 47 calories, 1 g protein, 12 g carbohydrate, 0 g fat, 0 g saturated fat, 1 mg sodium, 2 g fiber

✳

Most ice pops are just water and sugar with some artificial flavoring thrown in; even those made with juice sometimes contain high-fructose corn syrup! Our easy all-natural version captures the taste of fresh berries—and their nutrients as well.

# Menus for Special Times

**You don't have to stop** entertaining just because you're watching your weight. Actually, sharing these healthy delicious meals with family and friends is a great way to enjoy their company and introduce them to a new way of cooking. Whether you tell them they are weight-loss recipes or not, they will savor every bite. The key to success for any meal is a bit of advance planning. These menus will help you pull any party together no matter if it's a last-minute gathering or an elegant dinner party. Whether it's a Tex-Mex Fiesta, Super Bowl Supper, or Casual Birthday with Friends, no one but you will know you're watching your calories and portions.

✳

# Lazy Day Breakfast

Strawberry-Banana Pancakes, page 70

1 ounce extra-lean turkey sausage

1 cup fat-free milk

Per serving: 501 calories, 32 g protein, 53 g carbohydrate, 18 g fat, 9 g saturated fat, 463 mg sodium, 4 g fiber

✳

# Breakfast to Go

Breakfast Bowl-of-Oatmeal Cookies, page 60

Fat-free yogurt drink

1 apple

Per serving: 329 calories, 17 g protein, 60 g carbohydrate, 3 g fat, 1 g saturated fat, 165 mg sodium, 2 g fiber

# Holiday Brunch

Sweet Ricotta Cheese Crepes with Fruit, page 56

2 slices extra-lean turkey bacon

½–1 slice Pumpkin Zucchini Spice Bread, page 79

Coffee or tea

Per serving: 599 calories, 30 g protein, 68 g carbohydrate, 21 g fat, 5 g saturated fat, 441 mg sodium, 6 g fiber

# Sunday Lunch on the Patio

Pan-Seared Spicy Scallops Salad, page 106

1 small whole grain roll

Iced tea

½ cup lemon sorbet with ½ cup fresh blueberries

Per serving: 583 calories, 44 g protein, 108 g carbohydrate, 8 g fat, 1 g saturated fat, 935 mg sodium, 10 g fiber

✳

# Santa Fe Soup and Salad

Cajun Black Bean Soup, page 121

Jicama and Carrot Salad, page 94

Baked corn chips

Seltzer with lime

Per serving: 401 calories, 17 g protein, 79 g carbohydrate, 5 g fat, 1 g saturated fat, 1,170 mg sodium, 18 g fiber

✳

# Meatless Monday

Spinach Lasagna, page 186

Crudités with low-fat ranch dressing

Tangerine Ice, page 315

Per serving: 564 calories, 27 g protein, 81 g carbohydrate, 15 g fat, 5 g saturated fat, 1,554 mg sodium, 11 g fiber

# Tex-Mex Fiesta

Navajo Tacos, page 133

Iced herbal tea

Watermelon with Lime and Ginger
Syrup, page 321

Per serving: 567 calories, 26 g protein,
68 g carbohydrate, 22 g fat, 7 g
saturated fat, 1,090 mg sodium,
6 g fiber

# Easy Entertaining

Apple Crumble Pie, page 288

Savory Pot Roast, page 130

Caesar salad

Per serving: 698 calories, 51 g protein,
66 g carbohydrate, 25 g fat, 9 g
saturated fat, 1,270 mg sodium,
7 g fiber

✳

# Summer Grillin'

Grilled Steak with Cilantro Pesto, page 128

Delicious Coleslaw, page 92

Vegetable Ragout, page 225

Per serving: 559 calories, 37 g protein, 44 g carbohydrate, 27 g fat, 10 g saturated fat, 1,021 mg sodium, 7 g fiber

✳

# Super Bowl Supper

Do-It-Your-Way Red Salsa and Chips, page 232

Cereal-Nut Mix, page 237

White Chicken Chili, page 165

Chocolate Waffle Cookies, page 250

Per serving: 694 calories, 45 g protein, 65 g carbohydrate, 30 g fat, 9 g saturated fat, 874 mg sodium, 10 g fiber

# Saturday Night Movie

Dreamy Creamy Macaroni and Cheese, page 183

Mixed green salad with low-fat balsamic vinaigrette

Air-popped popcorn with Parmesan cheese

Per serving: 471 calories, 39 g protein, 40 g carbohydrate, 19 g fat, 10 g saturated fat, 1,117 mg sodium, 10 g fiber

# Halloween Gathering

Chicken Sausage Minestrone, page 112

Whole wheat breadsticks

Easy Red Velvet Cake, page 274

Per serving: 854 calories, 38 g protein, 116 g carbohydrate, 30 g fat, 2 g saturated fat, 1,210 mg sodium, 14 g fiber

✲

# Casual Birthday with Friends

Apple Sausage Penne, page 149

Salad greens with fat-free balsamic vinaigrette

Chocolate Buttermilk Cake, page 276

Per serving: 818 calories, 49 g protein, 92 g carbohydrate, 33 g fat, 13 g saturated fat, 1,377 mg sodium, 3 g fiber

✲

# Friday Night Fish

Pan-Seared Tilapia, page 170

½ cup whole grain couscous

Steamed green beans

Easy Chocolate Cream Pie, page 291

Per serving: 615 calories, 44 g protein, 80 g carbohydrate, 17 g fat, 9 g saturated fat, 533 mg sodium, 9 g fiber

# Calorie & Nutrient Counter

**There's no better** way to upset your weight-loss goals than to not have the right foods to eat on hand. But with the sheer number of foods available in the average market, making the best choices isn't always as easy as it would seem. That's why we've gathered all the nutrition facts you need to consider in the following list of common foods. Use this handy chart as your guide to determine which of your favorite fresh fruits and vegetables offer the most fiber, learn which cuts of meat are leaner than others, and make sure you're not overloading on too much sodium or saturated fat in your cheese choices.

You can also use this chart to get a grasp on exactly what you're eating so you can find out where the bulk of your calories comes from. Then you can make simple substitutions that shave off calories without sacrificing taste or satisfaction. For example, consider trading a handful of pretzels for 3 cups of air-popped popcorn sprinkled with 1 tablespoon of grated Parmesan cheese—you'll save about 115 calories and enjoy loads more flavor while tripling your portion size. Need some more motivation? Just remember that when you're guessing how many calories you can eat, being off by just 100 calories a day can keep you 6 to 10 pounds overweight.

# ✳ BEANS AND LEGUMES

| FOOD ITEM | SERVING SIZE | CALORIES | PROTEIN (G) |
|---|---|---|---|
| Baked beans | ⅓ c | 126 | 5 |
| Baked beans, vegetarian | ⅓ c | 79 | 4 |
| Bean sprouts (mung beans) | ½ c | 13 | 1 |
| Black beans, cooked with salt | ½ c | 114 | 8 |
| Black-eyed peas (cowpeas), cooked with salt | ½ c | 99 | 7 |
| Butter beans (lima), cooked with salt | ½ c | 105 | 6 |
| Cannellini beans, cooked without salt | ½ c | 100 | 6 |
| Chickpeas (garbanzo beans), cooked with salt | ½ c | 134 | 7 |
| Edamame (immature green soybeans), frozen, prepared | ½ c | 95 | 8 |
| Edamame, out of shell, cooked without salt | ½ c | 100 | 10 |
| Falafel, cooked | 2¼-patty | 57 | 2 |
| French beans, cooked with salt | ½ c | 114 | 6 |
| Hummus | ⅛ c | 54 | 1 |
| Kidney beans, red, cooked with salt | ½ c | 112 | 8 |
| Lentils, brown, cooked with salt | ½ c | 115 | 9 |
| Navy beans, cooked with salt | ½ c | 127 | 7 |
| Pinto beans, cooked with salt | ½ c | 122 | 8 |
| Refried beans, canned | ½ c | 118 | 7 |
| Refried beans, fat-free | ½ c | 130 | 6 |
| Refried beans, vegetarian | ½ c | 100 | 6 |
| Soybeans, dry-roasted, salted | ¼ c | 194 | 17 |
| White beans, small, cooked with salt | ½ c | 127 | 8 |

| CARB (G) | FIBER (G) | SUGAR (G) | FAT (G) | SAT FAT (G) | SODIUM (MG) |
|---|---|---|---|---|---|
| 18 | 5 | 0 | 4 | 2 | 352 |
| 18 | 3 | 7 | 1 | 0 | 288 |
| 3 | 1 | 2 | 0 | 0 | 6 |
| 20 | 8 | 0 | 1 | 0 | 204 |
| 18 | 6 | 3 | 0.5 | 0 | 205 |
| 20 | 5 | 1 | 0 | 0 | 215 |
| 17 | 5 | 1 | 1 | 0 | 40 |
| 22 | 6 | 4 | 2 | 0 | 199 |
| 8 | 4 | 2 | 4 | 0 | 5 |
| 9 | 1 | 2 | 2.5 | 0 | 70 |
| 5 | 0 | 0 | 3 | 0 | 50 |
| 21 | 8 | 0 | 1 | 0 | 214 |
| 6 | 1 | 0 | 3 | 0 | 74 |
| 20 | 7 | 0 | 0 | 0 | 211 |
| 20 | 8 | 2 | 0 | 0 | 236 |
| 24 | 10 | 0 | 1 | 0 | 216 |
| 22 | 8 | 0 | 1 | 0 | 203 |
| 20 | 7 | 0 | 2 | 1 | 379 |
| 18 | 6 | 1 | 0 | 0 | 580 |
| 17 | 6 | 2 | 1 | 0 | 560 |
| 14 | 4 | 0 | 9 | 1 | 70 |
| 23 | 9 | 0 | 1 | 0 | 213 |

(continued)

# ✳ CHEESE

| FOOD ITEM | SERVING SIZE | CALORIES | PROTEIN (G) |
|---|---|---|---|
| American, pasteurized process, fat-free | 1-in cube | 24 | 4 |
| American, pasteurized process, low-fat | 1-in cube | 32 | 4 |
| American cheese food | 1 oz | 93 | 6 |
| American cheese food, low-fat | 1-in cube | 32 | 4 |
| Blue, crumbled | 1 Tbsp | 30 | 2 |
| Brie | 1-in cube | 57 | 4 |
| Cheddar | 1-in cube | 69 | 4 |
| Cheddar, fat-free | 1-in cube | 40 | 8 |
| Cheddar, low-fat | 1-in cube | 30 | 4 |
| Cottage cheese, low-fat 1% | 4 oz | 81 | 14 |
| Cottage cheese, fat-free, large curd, dry | ½ c | 96 | 20 |
| Cottage cheese, low-fat 2% | ¼ c | 51 | 8 |
| Cream cheese | 2 Tbsp | 101 | 2 |
| Cream cheese, fat-free | 2 Tbsp | 28 | 4 |
| Cream cheese, low-fat | 2 Tbsp | 69 | 3 |
| Feta | 1-in cube | 45 | 2 |
| Monterey Jack, fat-free | 1-in cube | 40 | 8 |
| Monterey Jack, low-fat | 1-in cube | 53 | 5 |
| Mozzarella, fat-free, shredded | ¼ oz | 42 | 9 |
| Mozzarella, low-sodium | 1-in cube | 50 | 5 |
| Mozzarella, part-skim, low moisture | 1 oz | 86 | 7 |
| Mozzarella, string | 1 (1 oz) | 80 | 8 |
| Muenster | 1-in cube | 66 | 4 |
| Muenster, low-fat | 1-in cube | 49 | 4 |
| Parmesan, grated | 2 Tbsp | 43 | 4 |
| Parmesan, hard | 1-in cube | 40 | 4 |

| CARB (G) | FIBER (G) | SUGAR (G) | FAT (G) | SAT FAT (G) | SODIUM (MG) |
|---|---|---|---|---|---|
| 2 | 0 | 2 | 0 | 0 | 244 |
| 1 | 0 | 0 | 1 | 1 | 257 |
| 2 | 0 | 2 | 7 | 4 | 452 |
| 1 | 0 | 0 | 1 | 1 | 257 |
| 0 | 0 | 0 | 2.5 | 1.5 | 118 |
| 0 | 0 | 0 | 5 | 3 | 107 |
| 0 | 0 | 0 | 6 | 4 | 106 |
| 1 | 0 | 1 | 0 | 0 | 220 |
| 0 | 0 | 0 | 1 | 1 | 106 |
| 3 | 0 | 3 | 1 | 1 | 459 |
| 2 | 0 | 2 | 0 | 0 | 15 |
| 2 | 0 | 0 | 1 | 1 | 229 |
| 1 | 0 | 0 | 10 | 6 | 86 |
| 2 | 0 | 0 | 0 | 0 | 158 |
| 2 | 0 | 0 | 5 | 3 | 89 |
| 1 | 0 | 1 | 4 | 3 | 190 |
| 1 | 0 | 1 | 0 | 0 | 220 |
| 0 | 0 | 0 | 4 | 2 | 96 |
| 1 | 1 | 0 | 0 | 0 | 210 |
| 1 | 0 | 0 | 3 | 2 | 3 |
| 1 | 0 | 0 | 6 | 4 | 150 |
| 1 | 0 | 0 | 6 | 3 | 240 |
| 0 | 0 | 0 | 5 | 3 | 113 |
| 1 | 0 | 1 | 3 | 2 | 108 |
| 0 | 0 | 0 | 3 | 2 | 153 |
| 0 | 0 | 0 | 3 | 2 | 165 |

(continued)

## ✳ CHEESE (cont.)

| FOOD ITEM | SERVING SIZE | CALORIES | PROTEIN (G) |
| --- | --- | --- | --- |
| Provolone | 1-in cube | 60 | 4 |
| Ricotta | ¼ c | 107 | 7 |
| Ricotta, low-fat | ¼ c | 85 | 7 |
| Swiss | 1-in cube | 57 | 4 |
| Swiss, low-fat | 1-in cube | 27 | 4 |
| Swiss, low-fat, singles | 1 slice | 50 | 8 |

## ✳ OTHER DAIRY

| FOOD ITEM | SERVING SIZE | CALORIES | PROTEIN (G) |
| --- | --- | --- | --- |
| Sour cream | 1 Tbsp | 31 | 0 |
| Yogurt, banana, low-fat | 4 oz | 120 | 5 |
| Yogurt, blueberry–French vanilla, low-fat | 4 oz | 120 | 5 |
| Yogurt, coffee, fat-free | 4 oz | 103 | 6 |
| Yogurt, plain, fat-free | 4 oz | 63 | 6 |
| Yogurt, plain, low-fat | 4 oz | 71 | 6 |
| Yogurt, plain, whole milk | 4 oz | 69 | 4 |
| Yogurt, strawberry, fat-free, Breyer's | 4 oz | 62 | 4 |
| Yogurt, strawberry, low-fat, Breyer's | 4 oz | 109 | 4 |
| Yogurt, vanilla, low-fat | 4 oz | 96 | 6 |

Calorie &
Nutrient Counter

| CARB (G) | FIBER (G) | SUGAR (G) | FAT (G) | SAT FAT (G) | SODIUM (MG) |
|---|---|---|---|---|---|
| 0 | 0 | 0 | 5 | 3 | 149 |
| 2 | 0 | 0 | 8 | 5 | 52 |
| 3 | 0 | 0 | 5 | 3 | 77 |
| 1 | 0 | 0 | 4 | 3 | 29 |
| 1 | 0 | 0 | 1 | 1 | 39 |
| 1 | 0 | 0 | 1 | 1 | 73 |

| CARB (G) | FIBER (G) | SUGAR (G) | FAT (G) | SAT FAT (G) | SODIUM (MG) |
|---|---|---|---|---|---|
| 1 | 0 | 0 | 3 | 2 | 8 |
| 21 | 0 | 18 | 2 | 2 | 60 |
| 24 | 0 | 21 | 1 | 0 | 70 |
| 20 | 0 | 20 | 0 | 0 | 78 |
| 9 | 0 | 9 | 0 | 0 | 87 |
| 8 | 0 | 8 | 2 | 1 | 79 |
| 5 | 0 | 5 | 4 | 2 | 52 |
| 11 | 0 | 9 | 0 | 0 | 51 |
| 21 | 0 | 20 | 1 | 1 | 59 |
| 16 | 0 | 16 | 1 | 1 | 75 |

(continued)

# ✳ EGGS

| FOOD ITEM | SERVING SIZE | CALORIES | PROTEIN (G) |
|---|---|---|---|
| Egg, hard-cooked | 1 large | 78 | 6 |
| Egg, poached | 1 large | 71 | 6 |
| Egg, scrambled | 1 large | 102 | 7 |
| Egg white, cooked | 1 large | 17 | 4 |
| Egg white, Egg Beaters | ¼ c | 30 | 6 |

# ✳ FATS AND OILS

| FOOD ITEM | SERVING SIZE | CALORIES | PROTEIN (G) |
|---|---|---|---|
| Butter, with salt | 1 tsp | 34 | 0 |
| Butter, without salt | 1 tsp | 34 | 0 |
| Butter-margarine blend, stick, without salt | 1 tsp | 33 | 0 |
| Flaxseed oil | 1 tsp | 40 | 0 |
| Margarine, hard, corn and soybean oils | 1 tsp | 33 | 0 |
| Margarine, hard, corn oil | 1 tsp | 34 | 0 |
| Margarine, hard, soybean oil | 1 tsp | 34 | 0 |
| Margarine, regular, with salt | 1 tsp | 34 | 0 |
| Margarine, regular, without salt | 1 tsp | 34 | 0 |
| Oil, canola | 1 tsp | 40 | 0 |
| Oil, olive | 1 tsp | 40 | 0 |
| Oil, safflower | 1 tsp | 40 | 0 |
| Oil, sesame | 1 tsp | 40 | 0 |
| Oil, walnut | 1 tsp | 40 | 0 |

| CARB (G) | FIBER (G) | SUGAR (G) | FAT (G) | SAT FAT (G) | SODIUM (MG) |
|---|---|---|---|---|---|
| 1 | 0 | 1 | 5 | 2 | 62 |
| 0 | 0 | 0 | 5 | 2 | 147 |
| 1 | 0 | 1 | 7 | 2 | 171 |
| 0 | 0 | 0 | 0 | 0 | 55 |
| 1 | 0 | 0 | 0 | 0 | 115 |

| CARB (G) | FIBER (G) | SUGAR (G) | FAT (G) | SAT FAT (G) | SODIUM (MG) |
|---|---|---|---|---|---|
| 0 | 0 | 0 | 4 | 2 | 27 |
| 0 | 0 | 0 | 4 | 2 | 1 |
| 0 | 0 | 0 | 4 | 1 | 1 |
| 0 | 0 | 0 | 5 | 0 | 0 |
| 0 | 0 | 0 | 4 | 1 | 30 |
| 0 | 0 | 0 | 4 | 1 | 44 |
| 0 | 0 | 0 | 4 | 1 | 44 |
| 0 | 0 | 0 | 4 | 1 | 44 |
| 0 | 0 | 0 | 4 | 1 | 0 |
| 0 | 0 | 0 | 5 | 0 | 0 |
| 0 | 0 | 0 | 5 | 1 | 0 |
| 0 | 0 | 0 | 5 | 0 | 0 |
| 0 | 0 | 0 | 5 | 1 | 0 |
| 0 | 0 | 0 | 5 | 0 | 0 |

(continued)

# ✳ FISH

| FOOD ITEM | SERVING SIZE | CALORIES | PROTEIN (G) |
|---|---|---|---|
| Cod, Atlantic, baked | 3 oz | 89 | 19 |
| Flounder, baked | 3 oz | 99 | 21 |
| Grouper, baked | 3 oz | 100 | 21 |
| Halibut, Atlantic and Pacific, baked | 3 oz | 119 | 23 |
| Mahi mahi, baked | 3 oz | 93 | 20 |
| Salmon, Alaskan chinook, smoked, canned | 3 oz | 128 | 20 |
| Salmon, pink, canned, drained | 3 oz | 116 | 20 |
| Swordfish, baked | 3 oz | 132 | 22 |
| Tilapia, baked or broiled | 3 oz | 109 | 22 |
| Tuna, bluefin, baked | 3 oz | 156 | 25 |
| Tuna, StarKist Chunk Light, canned in water, drained | 2 oz | 70 | 15 |
| Tuna, white, canned in water, drained | 3 oz | 109 | 20 |
| Tuna, yellowfin, baked | 3 oz | 118 | 25 |

# ✳ FRUIT

| FOOD ITEM | SERVING SIZE | CALORIES | PROTEIN (G) |
|---|---|---|---|
| Apple | 1 medium (2¾-in diam) | 72 | 0 |
| Apricot | 1 | 17 | 0 |
| Avocado | ¼ c | 58 | 1 |
| Banana | 1 large (8 in) | 121 | 1 |
| Blackberries | 1 c | 62 | 2 |
| Blueberries | ½ c | 42 | 1 |
| Cantaloupe, wedged | ⅛ medium | 23 | 1 |
| Cranberries | 1 c | 44 | 0 |
| Grapefruit, pink, red, white | ½ medium | 41 | 1 |

| CARB (G) | FIBER (G) | SUGAR (G) | FAT (G) | SAT FAT (G) | SODIUM (MG) |
|---|---|---|---|---|---|
| 0 | 0 | 0 | 1 | 0 | 66 |
| 0 | 0 | 0 | 1 | 0 | 89 |
| 0 | 0 | 0 | 1 | 0 | 45 |
| 0 | 0 | 0 | 3 | 0 | 59 |
| 0 | 0 | 0 | 1 | 0 | 96 |
| 1 | 0 | 0 | 5 | n/a | n/a |
| 0 | 0 | 0 | 4 | 1 | 339 |
| 0 | 0 | 0 | 4 | 1 | 98 |
| 0 | 0 | 0 | 2 | 1 | 48 |
| 0 | 0 | 0 | 5 | 1 | 42 |
| 0 | 0 | 0 | 0 | 0 | 230 |
| 0 | 0 | 0 | 3 | 1 | 320 |
| 0 | 0 | 0 | 1 | 0 | 40 |

| CARB (G) | FIBER (G) | SUGAR (G) | FAT (G) | SAT FAT (G) | SODIUM (MG) |
|---|---|---|---|---|---|
| 19 | 3 | 14 | 0 | 0 | 1 |
| 4 | 1 | 3 | 0 | 0 | 0 |
| 3 | 2 | 0 | 5 | 1 | 3 |
| 31 | 4 | 17 | 0 | 0 | 1 |
| 14 | 8 | 7 | 1 | 0 | 1 |
| 11 | 2 | 7 | 0 | 0 | 1 |
| 6 | 1 | 5 | 0 | 0 | 11 |
| 12 | 4 | 4 | 0 | 0 | 2 |
| 10 | 1 | 9 | 0 | 0 | 0 |

(continued)

## ❋ FRUIT (cont.)

| FOOD ITEM | SERVING SIZE | CALORIES | PROTEIN (G) |
|---|---|---|---|
| Grapes, green or red | ½ c | 52 | 1 |
| Lemon | 1 medium (2⅛ in) | 17 | 1 |
| Nectarine | 1 medium (2¾ in) | 69 | 2 |
| Orange | 1 large (3¹/₁₆ in) | 86 | 2 |
| Peach | 1 medium | 58 | 1 |
| Pear | ½ medium | 52 | 0 |
| Pineapple | ¼ | 57 | 1 |
| Plum | 1 (2⅛ in) | 30 | 0 |
| Raspberries, red | ¾ c | 48 | 1 |
| Strawberry | 1 medium | 4 | 0 |
| Watermelon, sliced | 1 wedge (¹/₁₆ of melon) | 86 | 2 |

## ❋ GRAINS AND RICES

| FOOD ITEM | SERVING SIZE | CALORIES | PROTEIN (G) |
|---|---|---|---|
| Couscous, cooked | ⅓ c | 59 | 2 |
| Oat bran, cooked | ⅓ c | 29 | 2 |
| Oats, rolled, dry | 2 Tbsp | 37 | 1 |
| Quinoa, dry | 2 Tbsp | 79 | 3 |
| Rice, brown, long-grain, cooked | ¼ c | 54 | 1 |
| Rice, brown, medium-grain, cooked | ¼ c | 55 | 1 |
| Rice, brown, short-grain, dry | 1½ Tbsp | 66 | 1 |
| Rice, whole grain, brown, Uncle Ben's 10-minute, dry | ¼ c | 170 | 1 |

| CARB (G) | FIBER (G) | SUGAR (G) | FAT (G) | SAT FAT (G) | SODIUM (MG) |
|---|---|---|---|---|---|
| 14 | 1 | 12 | 0 | 0 | 2 |
| 5 | 2 | 1 | 0 | 0 | 1 |
| 16 | 3 | 12 | 1 | 0 | 0 |
| 22 | 4 | 17 | 0 | 0 | 0 |
| 14 | 2 | 13 | 0 | 0 | 0 |
| 14 | 3 | 9 | 0 | 0 | 1 |
| 15 | 2 | 11 | 0 | 0 | 1 |
| 8 | 1 | 7 | 0 | 0 | 0 |
| 11 | 6 | 4 | 1 | 0 | 1 |
| 1 | 0 | 1 | 0 | 0 | 2 |
| 22 | 1 | 18 | 0 | 0 | 3 |

| CARB (G) | FIBER (G) | SUGAR (G) | FAT (G) | SAT FAT (G) | SODIUM (MG) |
|---|---|---|---|---|---|
| 12 | 1 | 0 | 0 | 0 | 3 |
| 8 | 2 | n/a | 1 | 0 | 1 |
| 7 | 1 | 0 | 1 | 0 | 0 |
| 15 | 1 | n/a | 1 | 0 | 4 |
| 11 | 1 | 0 | 0 | 0 | 2 |
| 11 | 1 | n/a | 0 | 0 | 0 |
| 15 | 1 | 0 | 1 | 0 | 2 |
| 35 | 2 | 0 | 1.5 | 0 | 0 |

(continued)

## ❋ GRAINS AND RICES (cont.)

| FOOD ITEM | SERVING SIZE | CALORIES | PROTEIN (G) |
|---|---|---|---|
| Rice, white, long-grain, cooked | ¼ c | 51 | 1 |
| Rice, wild, cooked | ⅓ c | 55 | 2 |

## ❋ MEATS

| FOOD ITEM | SERVING SIZE | CALORIES | PROTEIN (G) |
|---|---|---|---|
| **BEEF** | | | |
| Bottom round, all lean, roasted, boneless | 3 oz | 144 | 24 |
| Filet mignon, lean, broiled | 3 oz | 164 | 24 |
| Flank steak, lean, braised | 3 oz | 201 | 24 |
| Ground patty, 10% fat, raw | 4 oz | 199 | 23 |
| Ground, extra lean, raw (5% fat) | 4 oz | 155 | 24 |
| Hot dog, beef, fat-free | 1 frank | 62 | 7 |
| Roast beef, lunchmeat, medium-rare | 1 oz | 30 | 6 |
| Steak, top sirloin, lean, broiled | 3 oz | 160 | 26 |
| **PORK** | | | |
| Bacon, medium slice, cooked | 1 slice | 43 | 3 |
| Canadian bacon, grilled | 1 slice | 43 | 6 |
| Chop, center lean, with bone, braised | 3 oz | 172 | 25 |
| Chop, sirloin, lean, with bone, braised | 1 chop | 142 | 19 |
| Ground, cooked | 3 oz | 252 | 22 |
| Ham, low-sodium, 96% fat-free, roasted, boneless | 1 oz | 47 | 6 |
| Hot dog, pork | 1 frank | 204 | 10 |
| Ribs, country-style, lean, braised | 3 oz | 199 | 22 |

| CARB (G) | FIBER (G) | SUGAR (G) | FAT (G) | SAT FAT (G) | SODIUM (MG) |
|---|---|---|---|---|---|
| 11 | 0 | 0 | 0 | 0 | 0 |
| 12 | 1 | 0 | 0 | 0 | 2 |

| CARB (G) | FIBER (G) | SUGAR (G) | FAT (G) | SAT FAT (G) | SODIUM (MG) |
|---|---|---|---|---|---|
| 0 | 0 | 0 | 5 | 2 | 32 |
| 0 | 0 | 0 | 7 | 3 | 50 |
| 0 | 0 | 0 | 11 | 5 | 61 |
| 0 | 0 | 0 | 11 | 5 | 75 |
| 0 | 0 | 0 | 6 | 3 | 75 |
| 3 | 0 | 0 | 1 | 0 | 455 |
| 1 | 0 | 1 | 1 | 1 | 235 |
| 0 | 0 | 0 | 6 | 2 | 54 |
| 0 | 0 | 0 | 3 | 1 | 185 |
| 0 | 0 | 0 | 2 | 1 | 363 |
| 0 | 0 | 0 | 7 | 3 | 53 |
| 0 | 0 | 0 | 6 | 2 | 38 |
| 0 | 0 | 0 | 18 | 7 | 62 |
| 0 | 0 | 0 | 2 | 1 | 275 |
| 0 | 0 | 0 | 18 | 7 | 620 |
| 0 | 0 | 0 | 12 | 4 | 54 |

(continued)

## ✳ MEATS (cont.)

| FOOD ITEM | SERVING SIZE | CALORIES | PROTEIN (G) |
| --- | --- | --- | --- |
| Sausage, pork, cooked | 1 oz (1 each) | 82 | 4 |
| Tenderloin, roasted, lean | 3 oz | 139 | 24 |
| **VEAL** | | | |
| Breast, braised, boneless, lean | 3 oz | 185 | 26 |
| Ground, broiled | 3 oz | 146 | 21 |
| Loin, roasted, lean | 3 oz | 149 | 22 |

## ✳ NUTS, SEEDS, AND BUTTERS

| FOOD ITEM | SERVING SIZE | CALORIES | PROTEIN (G) |
| --- | --- | --- | --- |
| Almond butter, plain, with salt | 1 Tbsp | 101 | 2 |
| Almonds, dry-roasted, with salt | ½ oz (11 nuts) | 85 | 3 |
| Almonds, natural, sliced | ½ oz | 82 | 3 |
| Brazil nuts, dried | 1 nut | 33 | 1 |
| Brazil nuts, dried | ½ oz (3 nuts) | 93 | 2 |
| Cashew butter, plain, with salt | 1 Tbsp | 94 | 3 |
| Cashew nuts, dry-roasted, with salt | ½ oz | 81 | 2 |
| Cashew nuts, raw | ½ oz | 78 | 3 |
| Flaxseed, ground | 1 Tbsp | 37 | 1 |
| Macadamia nuts, dry-roasted, with salt | ½ oz (5–6 nuts) | 101 | 1 |
| Mixed nuts, dry-roasted, with peanuts, with salt | ½ oz | 84 | 2 |
| Peanut butter, creamy, with salt | 1 Tbsp | 94 | 4 |
| Peanut butter, with salt, reduced-fat | 1 Tbsp | 83 | 4 |
| Peanut butter, crunchy, with salt | 1 Tbsp | 95 | 4 |
| Peanut butter, natural | 1 Tbsp | 100 | 4 |

| CARB (G) | FIBER (G) | SUGAR (G) | FAT (G) | SAT FAT (G) | SODIUM (MG) |
|---|---|---|---|---|---|
| 0 | 0 | 0 | 7.5 | 3 | 200 |
| 0 | 0 | 0 | 4 | 1 | 48 |

| CARB (G) | FIBER (G) | SUGAR (G) | FAT (G) | SAT FAT (G) | SODIUM (MG) |
|---|---|---|---|---|---|
| 0 | n/a | n/a | 8 | 3 | 58 |
| 0 | 0 | 0 | 6 | 3 | 71 |
| 0 | 0 | 0 | 6 | 2 | 82 |

| CARB (G) | FIBER (G) | SUGAR (G) | FAT (G) | SAT FAT (G) | SODIUM (MG) |
|---|---|---|---|---|---|
| 3 | 1 | 1 | 9 | 1 | 72 |
| 3 | 2 | 1 | 7 | 1 | 48 |
| 3 | 2 | 1 | 7 | 1 | 0 |
| 1 | 0 | 0 | 3 | 1 | 0 |
| 2 | 1 | 0 | 9 | 2 | 0 |
| 4 | 0 | 1 | 8 | 2 | 98 |
| 5 | 0 | 1 | 7 | 1 | 91 |
| 4 | 1 | 1 | 6 | 1 | 2 |
| 2 | 2 | 0 | 3 | 0 | 2 |
| 2 | 1 | 1 | 11 | 2 | 38 |
| 4 | 1 | 1 | 7 | 1 | 95 |
| 3 | 1 | 1 | 8 | 2 | 73 |
| 6 | 1 | 1 | 5 | 1 | 86 |
| 3 | 1 | 1 | 8 | 1 | 78 |
| 4 | 1 | 1 | 8 | 1 | 60 |

(continued)

## ✱ NUTS, SEEDS, AND BUTTERS (cont.)

| FOOD ITEM | SERVING SIZE | CALORIES | PROTEIN (G) |
|---|---|---|---|
| Peanuts, dry-roasted, with salt | ½ oz | 83 | 3 |
| Peanuts, shelled, cooked, with salt | 1 Tbsp | 36 | 2 |
| Pecans, dried, chopped | ⅛ c | 94 | 1 |
| Pecans, dried, halved | ⅛ c | 86 | 1 |
| Pecans, dry-roasted, with salt | ½ oz | 101 | 1 |
| Pistachios, dry-roasted, with salt | ½ oz | 81 | 3 |
| Walnuts, dried, black | 1 Tbsp | 48 | 2 |
| Walnuts, English, ground | ⅛ c | 65 | 2 |
| Walnuts, dried, halved | ½ oz | 93 | 2 |

## ✱ PASTA

| FOOD ITEM | SERVING SIZE | CALORIES | PROTEIN (G) |
|---|---|---|---|
| Angel hair, whole wheat, dry | 1 oz | 106 | 4 |
| Bow ties, semolina, dry | 1 oz | 103 | 4 |
| Fettuccine (tagliatelle), semolina, dry | 1 oz | 102 | 4 |
| Fettuccine (tagliatelle), spinach, dry | 1 oz | 98 | 4 |
| Lasagna, semolina, dry | 1 oz | 102 | 4 |
| Linguine, semolina, dry | 1 oz | 102 | 4 |

| CARB (G) | FIBER (G) | SUGAR (G) | FAT (G) | SAT FAT (G) | SODIUM (MG) |
|---|---|---|---|---|---|
| 3 | 1 | 1 | 7 | 1 | 115 |
| 2 | 1 | 0 | 2.5 | 0.5 | 84 |
| 2 | 1 | 1 | 10 | 0 | 0 |
| 2 | 1 | 1 | 9 | 1 | 0 |
| 2 | 1 | 1 | 11 | 1 | 54 |
| 4 | 2 | 1 | 7 | 1 | 57 |
| 1 | 1 | 0 | 5 | 0 | 0 |
| 1 | 1 | 0 | 7 | 1 | 0 |
| 2 | 1 | 0 | 9 | 0 | 0 |

| CARB (G) | FIBER (G) | SUGAR (G) | FAT (G) | SAT FAT (G) | SODIUM (MG) |
|---|---|---|---|---|---|
| 21 | 3 | 1 | 1 | 0 | 5 |
| 21 | 1 | 1 | 0 | 0 | 1 |
| 21 | 1 | 1 | 1 | 0 | 2 |
| 20 | 1 | 1 | 1 | 0 | 9 |
| 21 | 1 | 1 | 1 | 0 | 1 |
| 21 | 1 | 1 | 1 | 0 | 2 |

(continued)

# PASTA (cont.)

| FOOD ITEM | SERVING SIZE | CALORIES | PROTEIN (G) |
|---|---|---|---|
| Penne, semolina, dry | 1 oz | 106 | 4 |
| Penne, whole wheat, dry | 1 oz | 106 | 4 |
| Spaghetti, whole wheat, dry | 1 oz | 99 | 4 |

*Note: For most pasta shapes, 1 ounce of dry pasta makes approximately ½ cup cooked.

# POULTRY

| FOOD ITEM | SERVING SIZE | CALORIES | PROTEIN (G) |
|---|---|---|---|
| CHICKEN | | | |
| Chicken, breast, boneless, without skin, stewed | ½ breast | 143 | |
| Chicken, drumstick, without skin, roasted | ½ drumstick | 76 | 12 |
| Chicken, thigh, boneless, without skin, roasted | 1 thigh | 109 | 13 |
| Chicken frankfurter | 1 frank | 116 | 6 |
| Chicken lunchmeat, deli | 1 oz | 23 | 5 |
| TURKEY | | | |
| Turkey, breast, with skin, roasted | 1 lb | 150 | |
| Turkey, dark meat, with skin, roasted | 1 lb | | |
| Turkey, ground, cooked | 3 oz | 145 | 17 |
| Turkey, light meat, with skin, roasted | 1 lb | 134 | 19 |
| Turkey frankfurter | 1 | 102 | 6 |
| Turkey sausage, smoked, hot | 1 oz | 44 | 4 |

| CARB (G) | FIBER (G) | SUGAR (G) | FAT (G) | SAT FAT (G) | SODIUM (MG) |
|---|---|---|---|---|---|
| 22 | 1 | 1 | 0.5 | 0 | 3 |
| 21 | 3 | 1 | 1 | 0 | 5 |
| 21 | 4 | 1 | 0.5 | 0 | 2 |

| CARB (G) | FIBER (G) | SUGAR (G) | FAT (G) | SAT FAT (G) | SODIUM (MG) |
|---|---|---|---|---|---|
| 0 | 0 | 0 | 3 | 1 | 77 |
| 0 | 0 | 0 | 2 | 1 | 42 |
| 0 | 0 | 0 | 6 | 2 | 46 |
| 3 | 0 | 0 | 9 | 2 | 616 |
| 0 | 0 | 0 | 0 | 0 | 210 |
| 0 | 0 | 0 | 3 | 1 | 52 |
| 0 | 0 | 0 | 12 | 4 | 79 |
| 0 | 0 | 0 | 8 | 2 | 66 |
| 0 | 0 | 0 | 6 | 2 | 43 |
| 1 | 0 | 0 | 8 | 3 | 642 |
| 1 | 0 | 1 | 2 | 1 | 260 |

(continued)

## ❋ SEAFOOD

| FOOD ITEM | SERVING SIZE | CALORIES | PROTEIN (G) |
|---|---|---|---|
| Crab, Alaskan, king crab, steamed | 3 oz | 82 | 16 |
| Crab, baked or broiled | 3 oz | 117 | 16 |
| Crab, imitation (surimi) | 3 oz | 81 | 6 |
| Crab, sautéed | 3 oz | 117 | 16 |
| Lobster, Northern steamed | 3 oz | 83 | 17 |
| Shrimp, cooked | 3 oz | 84 | 17 |
| Shrimp, steamed | 1 large | 5 | 1 |

## ❋ VEGETABLES

| FOOD ITEM | SERVING SIZE | CALORIES | PROTEIN (G) |
|---|---|---|---|
| Alfalfa sprouts | ½ c | 4 | 1 |
| Artichoke | 1 medium | 60 | 4 |
| Asparagus, cooked | 8 spears | 26 | 3 |
| Bell pepper, chopped | 1 c | 30 | 1 |
| Bell pepper, boiled | 1 c | 38 | 1 |
| Broccoli, chopped, boiled | 1 c | 55 | 4 |
| Broccoli, florets, fresh | 1 c | 20 | 2 |
| Brussels sprouts, raw | 1 c | 38 | 3 |
| Cabbage, raw | 1 medium leaf | 6 | 0 |
| Carrot | 1 medium | 25 | 1 |
| Carrot, baby | 1 medium | 4 | 0 |
| Cauliflower | ¼ medium head | 36 | 3 |
| Celery | 1 medium stalk | 6 | 0 |
| Celery, chopped | 1 c | 16 | 1 |

| CARB (G) | FIBER (G) | SUGAR (G) | FAT (G) | SAT FAT (G) | SODIUM (MG) |
|---|---|---|---|---|---|
| 0 | 0 | 0 | 1 | 0 | 911 |
| 0 | 0 | n/a | 5.5 | 1 | 270 |
| 13 | 0 | 5 | 0 | 0 | 715 |
| 0 | 0 | 0 | 5 | 1 | 270 |
| 1 | 0 | 0 | 1 | 0 | 323 |
| 0 | 0 | 0 | 1 | 0 | 190 |
| 0 | 0 | 0 | 0 | 0 | 12 |

| CARB (G) | FIBER (G) | SUGAR (G) | FAT (G) | SAT FAT (G) | SODIUM (MG) |
|---|---|---|---|---|---|
| 0 | 0 | 0 | 0 | 0 | 1 |
| 13 | 7 | 1 | 0 | 0 | 397 |
| 5 | 2 | 2 | 0 | 0 | 17 |
| 7 | 3 | 4 | 0 | 0 | 4 |
| 9 | 2 | 3 | 0 | 0 | 3 |
| 11 | 5 | 2 | 1 | 0 | 64 |
| 4 | 2 | 0 | 0 | 0 | 19 |
| 8 | 3 | 2 | 0 | 0 | 22 |
| 1 | 1 | 1 | 0 | 0 | 4 |
| 6 | 2 | 3 | 0 | 0 | 42 |
| 1 | 0 | 0 | 0 | 0 | 8 |
| 8 | 4 | 4 | 0 | 0 | 43 |
| 1 | 1 | 1 | 0 | 0 | 32 |
| 3 | 2 | 2 | 0 | 0 | 81 |

(continued)

# ✱ VEGETABLES (cont.)

| FOOD ITEM | SERVING SIZE | CALORIES | PROTEIN (G) |
|---|---|---|---|
| Cherry tomatoes, red | 1 c | 27 | 1 |
| Corn, sweet white or yellow | ½ c | 66 | 2 |
| Corn, sweet white or yellow | 1 large ear | 123 | 5 |
| Cucumber with peel, raw | 1 (8¼ in) | 45 | 2 |
| Garlic | 1 clove | 4 | 0 |
| Green beans, snap, raw | 1 c | 34 | 2 |
| Green beans, with almonds, frozen, Green Giant | 1 c | 91 | 3 |
| Lettuce, iceberg | 5 large leaves | 10 | 1 |
| Lettuce, romaine | 4 leaves | 19 | 1 |
| Mushrooms, brown Italian | 5 | 27 | 3 |
| Onion, green (scallions), tops and bulbs, chopped | ½ c | 16 | 1 |
| Onion, red or yellow | 1 medium | 44 | 1 |
| Peas, green, raw | ½ c | 59 | 4 |
| Peas, snow, whole, raw | ½ c | 13 | 1 |
| Potato, baked, with skin, without salt | 1 medium | 161 | 4 |
| Sauerkraut, canned, low-sodium | 1 c | 31 | 1 |
| Spinach | 3 oz | 20 | 2 |
| Spinach, cooked, with salt | 1 c | 41 | 5 |
| Spinach, cooked, without salt | 1 c | 41 | 5 |
| Squash, summer | 1 medium | 31 | 2 |
| Sweet potato, baked, with skin, without salt | 1 small | 54 | 1 |
| Tomato, red | 1 medium | 22 | 1 |
| Zucchini, with skin, raw | 1 medium | 31 | 2 |

| CARB (G) | FIBER (G) | SUGAR (G) | FAT (G) | SAT FAT (G) | SODIUM (MG) |
|---|---|---|---|---|---|
| 6 | 2 | 4 | 0 | 0 | 7 |
| 15 | 2 | 2 | 1 | 0 | 12 |
| 27 | 4 | 5 | 2 | 0 | 21 |
| 11 | 2 | 5 | 0 | 0 | 6 |
| 1 | 0 | 0 | 0 | 0 | 1 |
| 8 | 4 | 2 | 0 | 0 | 7 |
| 8 | 3 | 3 | 4.5 | 0 | 144 |
| 2 | 1 | 1 | 0 | 0 | 8 |
| 4 | 2 | 1 | 0 | 0 | 9 |
| 4 | 1 | 2 | 0 | 0 | 6 |
| 4 | 1 | 1 | 0 | 0 | 8 |
| 10 | 2 | 5 | 0 | 0 | 4 |
| 10 | 4 | 4 | 0 | 0 | 4 |
| 2 | 1 | 1 | 0 | 0 | 1 |
| 37 | 4 | 2 | 0 | 0 | 17 |
| 6 | 4 | 3 | 0 | 0 | 437 |
| 3 | 2 | 0 | 0 | 0 | 67 |
| 7 | 4 | 1 | 0 | 0 | 551 |
| 7 | 4 | 1 | 0 | 0 | 126 |
| 7 | 2 | 4 | 0 | 0 | 4 |
| 12 | 2 | 4 | 0 | 0 | 22 |
| 5 | 1 | 3 | 0 | 0 | 0 |
| 7 | 2 | 3 | 0 | 0 | 20 |

Calorie &
Nutrient Counter

# Photo Credits

Recipe photography ©Kate Sears/Sublime Management
Food styling by Alison Attenborough
Prop styling by Pamela Duncan Silver

**With the following exceptions:**

Page 3 (left to right): ©Photodisc, ©Veer, ©Photodisc,
   ©Mitch Mandel/Rodale Images(2)
Page 12: ©Dave Bradley Photography/Getty Images
Page 26 (left to right): ©Photo Alto, ©Alamy, ©Kate Sears,
   ©Mitch Mandel/Rodale Images
Page 27: ©Steve Gorton/Dorling Kindersley/Getty Images
Page 36: ©Kana Okada
Page 44: ©Yunhee Kim
Page 45: ©Mitch Mandel/Rodale Images & Thomas MacDonald
Page 48: ©Hector Sanchez
Page 50: ©Ted Morrison
Page 84: ©Shay Peretz
Page 124: ©Shay Peretz
Page 194: ©Anna Knott
Page 226: ©Melanie Grizzel
Page 266: ©Brian Smith

# Index

Underscored page references indicate boxed text or sidebars. **Boldfaced** page references indicate photographs.

# B

# M

# Conversion Chart

These equivalents have been slightly rounded to make measuring easier.

### VOLUME MEASUREMENTS

| U.S. | IMPERIAL | METRIC |
|------|----------|--------|
| ¼ tsp | – | 1 ml |
| ½ tsp | – | 2 ml |
| 1 tsp | – | 5 ml |
| 1 Tbsp | – | 15 ml |
| 2 Tbsp (1 oz) | 1 fl oz | 30 ml |
| ¼ cup (2 oz) | 2 fl oz | 60 ml |
| ⅓ cup (3 oz) | 3 fl oz | 80 ml |
| ½ cup (4 oz) | 4 fl oz | 120 ml |
| ⅔ cup (5 oz) | 5 fl oz | 160 ml |
| ¾ cup (6 oz) | 6 fl oz | 180 ml |
| 1 cup (8 oz) | 8 fl oz | 240 ml |

### WEIGHT MEASUREMENTS

| U.S. | METRIC |
|------|--------|
| 1 oz | 30 g |
| 2 oz | 60 g |
| 4 oz (¼ lb) | 115 g |
| 5 oz (⅓ lb) | 145 g |
| 6 oz | 170 g |
| 7 oz | 200 g |
| 8 oz (½ lb) | 230 g |
| 10 oz | 285 g |
| 12 oz (¾ lb) | 340 g |
| 14 oz | 400 g |
| 16 oz (1 lb) | 455 g |
| 2.2 lb | 1 kg |

### LENGTH MEASUREMENTS

| U.S. | METRIC |
|------|--------|
| ¼" | 0.6 cm |
| ½" | 1.25 cm |
| 1" | 2.5 cm |
| 2" | 5 cm |
| 4" | 11 cm |
| 6" | 15 cm |
| 8" | 20 cm |
| 10" | 25 cm |
| 12" (1') | 30 cm |
| 2.2 lb 1kg | |

### PAN SIZES

| U.S. | METRIC |
|------|--------|
| 8" cake pan | 20 × 4 cm sandwich or cake tin |
| 9" cake pan | 23 × 3.5 cm sandwich or cake tin |
| 11" × 7" baking pan | 28 × 18 cm baking tin |
| 13" × 9" baking pan | 32.5 × 23 cm baking tin |
| 15" × 10" baking pan | 38 × 25.5 cm baking tin (Swiss roll tin) |
| 1½ qt baking dish | 1.5 liter baking dish |
| 2 qt baking dish | 2 liter baking dish |
| 2 qt rectangular baking dish | 30 × 19 cm baking dish |
| 9" pie plate | 22 × 4 or 23 × 4 cm pie plate |
| 7" or 8" springform pan | 18 or 20 cm springform or loose-bottom cake tin |
| 9" × 5" loaf pan | 23 × 13 cm or 2 lb narrow loaf tin or pâté tin |

### TEMPERATURES

| FAHRENHEIT | CENTIGRADE | GAS |
|------------|------------|-----|
| 140° | 60° | – |
| 160° | 70° | – |
| 180° | 80° | – |
| 225° | 105° | ¼ |
| 250° | 120° | ½ |
| 275° | 135° | 1 |
| 300° | 150° | 2 |
| 325° | 160° | 3 |
| 350° | 180° | 4 |
| 375° | 190° | 5 |
| 400° | 200° | 6 |
| 425° | 220° | 7 |
| 450° | 230° | 8 |
| 475° | 245° | 9 |
| 500° | 260° | – |